Collins

# Perfect SCIENCE ASSESSMENTS 9

Register online to get access to Analytics, Reports and Remedial

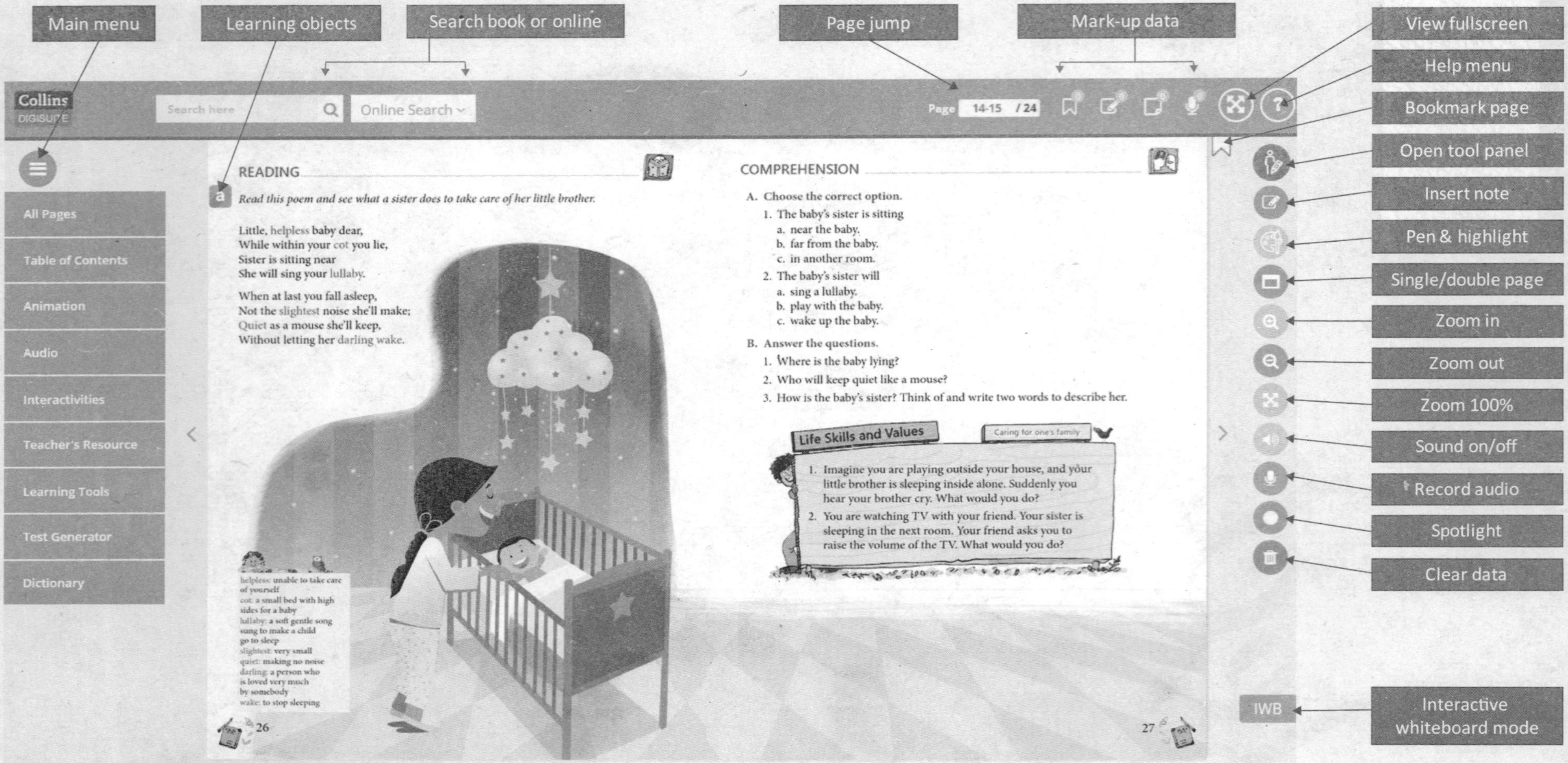


| Student + Teacher | | Teacher-only | |
|---|---|---|---|
| a animations | ia activities | g games | lp lesson plans | tn teacher's notes |
| ilt instructor-led tutorials | w worksheets | v videos | w worksheets | ak answer keys |
| | audio | | | |

# PREFACE

***Collins Perfect Science Assessments*** is a comprehensive science self-assessment series for classes 6 to 10, for schools across all boards. This series adheres to the guidelines of the *National Education Policy* (NEP) 2020 in which self-assessment is stated as one of the tools for transforming the culture of assessment. This series follows a holistic approach and promotes active engagement with learning. It aims to make the students move away from rote learning; and hence, elevate the status of the student from a passive learner to an active learner and facilitate learner autonomy, higher cognitive abilities and metacognitive engagement. A smooth transition of questions from easy, average to difficult would enable better understanding of concepts, self-analysis and hence excellence in any competitive exam.

The workbooks can also be used by teachers for review and assessments in an academic year, if they want to, as each assessment paper has a variety of questions.

## KEY FEATURES

Each book contains the following features.

**Part 1 (Multiple Choice Questions)**

**Pre-Test** Questions to assess pre-existing knowledge and identify misconceptions

**Keywords** Definitions of important terms giving an overview of concepts in a chapter

**Concept Map** Summary of a chapter in the form of a graphic organizer for quick revision

**Self-Assessments** One or two carefully graded, differentiated and topic-specific, self-assessment papers per chapter with 25 questions per assessment paper

Questions tagged with three difficulty levels: Easy 🙂, Average 😐 or Difficult 🙁

**Part 2 (Subjective Type Questions)**

**Self-Assessment** One chapter-wise assessment paper containing only short answer and long answer (+ picture-based) type questions

**PISA-based Questions** Sample questions (for Grades 9 and 10) based on the Organisation for Economic Co-operation and Development's (OECD's) Programme for International Student Assessment (PISA) science framework

**End of the book**

**General Tips** Suggested tools and techniques that can be used to ease the process of learning

**Quick Tips** Suggested strategies for effective learning and acing exams

**Answer Keys** Answers to all the questions for easy self-evaluation

**Hints for Difficult Questions** Supporting texts to help in answering difficult questions

**Sample OMR Answer Sheets** Answer sheets in the form of an OMR sheet for students to mark the answers

**Online Version**

Subscription-based online version of the assessment papers in Part 1 is available where students can try the assessment online via digital OMR sheets and have access to analytics, reports and remedial.

We would like to take this opportunity to thank all the teachers who reviewed the workbooks and provided their feedback, which helped us in improving the quality of the content.

Feedback, invaluable comments and suggestions from users are welcome.

Authors

# Key Features

***Collins Perfect Science Assessments*** series is aligned with the *National Education Policy* (NEP) 2020. The key features have been designed to provide students with a comprehensive understanding of the fundamental concepts and their applications, to reinforce critical thinking and problem-solving skills; and thus, move away from rote learning. Each book consists of two main parts.

## PART 1
### MULTIPLE CHOICE QUESTIONS

**PRE-TEST**

**Choose the correct option.**

1. What would happen if a piece of coal is hammered?
   A. Flattens.
   B. Breaks into pieces.
   C. Does not break.

Assess your pre-existing knowledge and identify misconceptions

**KEYWORDS**

**Evaporation:** The process of conversion of a liqu

**Latent heat of vaporization:** The heat energy re state at boiling point under the standard atm

**Latent heat of fusion:** The heat energy required melting point under the standard atmospheric p

Overview the concepts of a chapter with the definitions of important terms

**Concept Map**

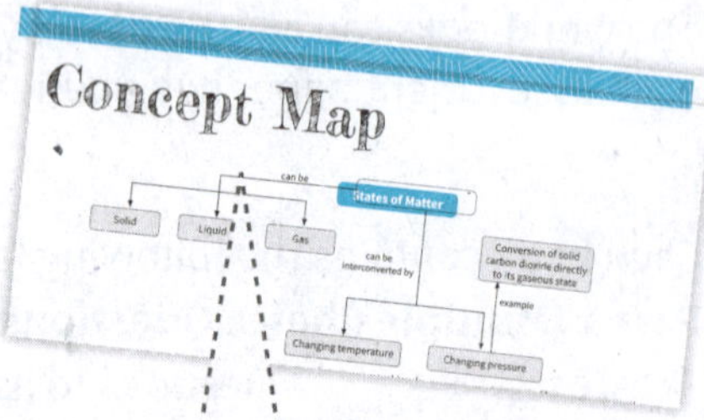

Summarize and revise quickly with the help of the graphic organizer summary

Chapter 1 Matter in Our Surroundings

**SELF-ASSESSMENT 1**

Chapter 1 Matter in Our Surroundings

**SELF-ASSESSMENT 2**

**Choose the correct option.**

1. Which of the following is due to evaporation?
   A. Cooling of a surface
   B. Boiling of surface particles
   C. Moderate temperature of a surface
   D. Melting of surface particles
2. Which of the following changes in the state of matter takes place during the evaporation process?
   A. Liquid to solid
   B. Liquid to gas
   C. Solid to gas
   D. Gas to solid
5. Which of the following is obtained by cooling a gas of low density at a low temperature?
   A. Bose-Einstein condensate
   B. Plasma particle
   C. Dry ice
   D. Camphor
6. Which of the following uses plasma?
   A. LED bulb
   B. Fluorescent tube
   C. Halogen tube
   D. Incandescent bulb

Pick the right (or best) option from the distracters!

Easy questions are tagged with this smiley!

Average questions are tagged with this smiley!

Difficult questions are tagged with this smiley!

# PART 2

## SUBJECTIVE TYPE QUESTIONS

Chapter 2 Is Matter Around Us Pure?

SELF-ASSESSMENT 3

A. Short Answer Type Questions

1. Give reasons for the following questions.

- Assess your reasoning, detailing, explaining, describing or schematic representation skills.
- Think and plan how you can organize and structure your answer.

2. Answer the following questions in brief.

i. How is smoke different from fog?

ii. What is th...

iii. Name an... ...ture.

PISA-based Questions

Chapter Matter in Our Surroundings

Choose the correct option.

1. Concentrated Dettol solution is diluted ten times and used to disinfect various surfaces. Which of the following is used as a solvent to dilute Dettol?

A. Water B. Kerosene

- In classes 9 and 10, Life Skills questions, PISA-based questions as per PISA science framework included for extended learning.

# AT THE END OF THE BOOK

**General Tips**

Use these tools and techniques to ease the process of your learning

**Quick Tips**

Apply these strategies for effective learning and ace your exams

**Answer Keys**

Compare your marked answers with this and find the areas where you need an extra effort

**Hints for Difficult Questions**

Take help from the supporting texts and find answers to difficult questions

**Collins Perfect Science Assessments 9**

CHAPTER 2

SAMPLE OMR ANSWER SHEET

*IMPORTANT: PLEASE FILL IN NAME, SCHOOL CODE, CLASS, SECTION & ROLL NO. CORRECTLY*

| PERSONAL DETAILS |
|---|
| 1. STUDENT NAME (IN ENGLISH CAPITAL LETTERS ONLY) |

| MARK YOUR ANSWERS | | |
|---|---|---|
| 1. Ⓐ Ⓑ Ⓒ Ⓓ | | 26. Ⓐ Ⓑ Ⓒ Ⓓ |
| 2. Ⓐ Ⓑ Ⓒ Ⓓ | | 27. Ⓐ Ⓑ Ⓒ Ⓓ |

Mark your answer in this and measure your progress

# Contents

# PART 1

## MULTIPLE CHOICE QUESTIONS

Chapter 1

# Matter in Our Surroundings

## PRE-TEST

**Choose the correct option.**

1. What would happen if a piece of coal is hammered?
   A. It flattens.
   B. It breaks into pieces.
   C. It does not break.
   D. It changes into a thin wire.

2. Which of the following is a good conductor of electricity?
   A. A piece of coal
   B. Sulphur cake
   C. Copper wire
   D. A piece of chalk

3. Which of the following can be drawn into a thin wire?
   A. Aluminium B. Zinc
   C. Mercury D. Lead

4. Identify the odd one out from the following.
   A. Iron B. Copper
   C. Aluminium D. Mercury

5. Which of the following is a poor conductor of heat?
   A. Carbon B. Aluminium
   C. Magnesium D. Iron

## KEYWORDS

**Evaporation:** The process of conversion of a liquid into its vapour or gaseous state

**Latent heat of vaporization:** The heat energy required to change a liquid into its gaseous state at its boiling point under the standard atmospheric pressure

**Latent heat of fusion:** The heat energy required to change a solid into its liquid form at its melting point under the standard atmospheric pressure

**Sublimation:** The process through which a solid substance directly changes into its gaseous state without the intermediate liquid state

# Concept Map

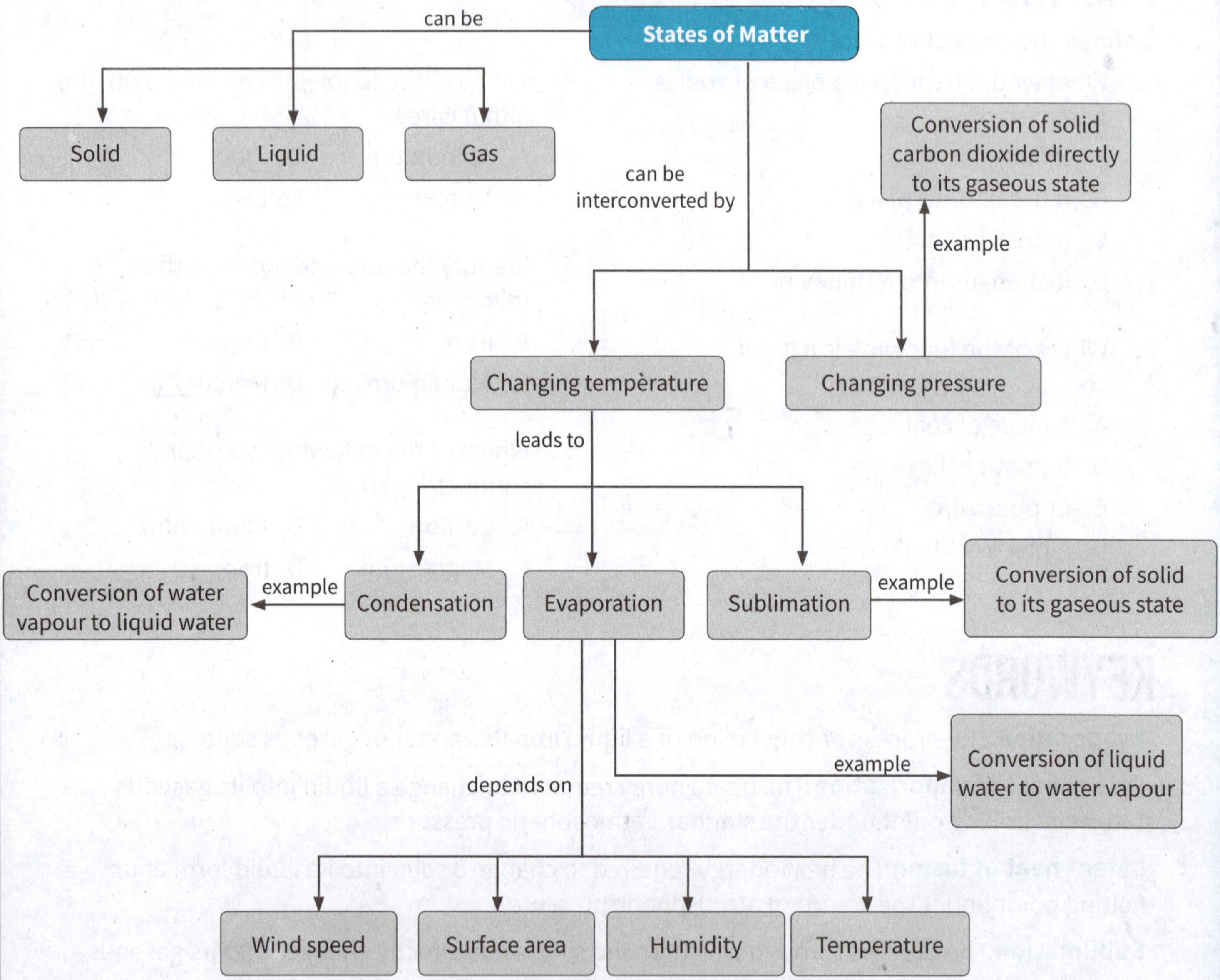
States of Matter
can be
Solid
Liquid
Gas
can be interconverted by
Conversion of solid carbon dioxide directly to its gaseous state
example
Changing temperature
Changing pressure
leads to
Conversion of water vapour to liquid water
example
Condensation
Evaporation
Sublimation
example
Conversion of solid to its gaseous state
example
Conversion of liquid water to water vapour
depends on
Wind speed
Surface area
Humidity
Temperature

# SELF-ASSESSMENT 1

**Choose the correct option.**

1. Which of the following is due to evaporation?
   A. Cooling of a surface
   B. Boiling of surface particles
   C. Solidification of a liquid
   D. Melting of surface particles

2. Which of the following changes in the state of matter takes place during the evaporation process?
   A. Liquid to solid
   B. Liquid to gas
   C. Solid to gas
   D. Gas to solid

3. Which of the following phenomena occurs when water is sprinkled on the hot roof of a building?
   A. Vaporization
   B. Fusion
   C. Condensation
   D. Sublimation

4. Which of the following is also known as the fourth state of matter?
   A. Solid
   B. Liquid
   C. Gas
   D. Plasma

5. Which of the following is obtained by cooling a gas of low density to a low temperature?
   A. Bose–Einstein condensate
   B. Plasma particle
   C. Dry ice
   D. Camphor

6. Which of the following uses plasma?
   A. LED bulb
   B. Fluorescent tube
   C. Halogen tube
   D. Incandescent bulb

7. Which of the following gases is present in a fluorescent bulb?
   A. Helium
   B. Oxygen
   C. Carbon monoxide
   D. Nitrogen

8. Which of the following increases the rate of diffusion?
   A. Increase in temperature
   B. Decrease in temperature
   C. Decrease in kinetic energy
   D. Increase in potential energy

9. Identify the correct pair from the following.
   A. Hot food—Smell diffuses when kept open
   B. Hot food—No diffusion of smell when kept open
   C. Cold food—No diffusion of smell when kept open
   D. Cold food—Faster diffusion of smell when kept open

10. Which of the following properties is observed when a swimmer cuts through the surface of water?
   A. Particles of water are tightly packed.
   B. Forces of attraction between the particles of liquid water are not very strong.
   C. Swimmer diffuses into water.
   D. Particles of liquid water are rigid.

11. When 2 mℓ of Dettol is dissolved in 1000 mℓ of water, we can still smell it. Which of the following properties is indicated by this?
   A. Particles of matter are very small.
   B. Particles of matter are fixed.
   C. Particles of matter do not have space between them.
   D. Particles of matter repel each other.

12. Two drops of red ink are mixed in a glass of cold water and a glass of hot water, respectively. Which of the following statements is correct?
   A. Ink diffuses faster in cold water.
   B. Ink diffuses faster in hot water.
   C. It diffuses after the water reaches room temperature.
   D. Ink diffuses neither in cold water nor in hot water.

13. Which of the following helps aquatic organisms to survive in water?
   A. Diluted chemicals in water
   B. Dissolved oxygen and carbon dioxide in water
   C. Dissolved potassium permanganate in water
   D. Dissolved soil particles in water

14. Which of the following compressed gases is used in the hospitals?
   A. Compressed natural gas
   B. Compressed petroleum gas
   C. Compressed oxygen gas
   D. Compressed argon gas

15. **Statement I:** Gases generally have lower densities than liquids and solids.
   **Statement II:** Ice floats on water.
   A. Statement I is correct and statement II is incorrect.
   B. Statement I is incorrect and statement II is correct.
   C. Both statements I and II are correct.
   D. Both statements I and II are incorrect.

16. Which of the following characteristics of a gas makes it hit the walls of the container it is stored in?
   A. High potential energy of the particles
   B. Direction of movement of the particles
   C. Compressibility of the particles
   D. Random movement of the particles

17. Which of the following breaks the force of attraction between solid particles?
   A. Increase in kinetic energy
   B. Increase in potential energy
   C. Increased compressibility
   D. Increased rigidity

18. Which of the following is equal to 100 °C?

A. 273 K
B. 373 K
C. 473 K
D. 173 K

19. What can be inferred from the following equation?

$$\text{Solid state} \underset{\text{Cool}}{\overset{\text{Heat}}{\rightleftarrows}} \text{Liquid state} \underset{\text{Cool}}{\overset{\text{Heat}}{\rightleftarrows}} \text{Gaseous state}$$

A. The state of matter can be changed by changing temperature.
B. Latent heat of fusion is released while changing the state of matter.
C. Sublimation of gas to solid is not possible.
D. Compression of liquid to solid is not possible.

20. Which of the following converts a substance from its liquid state into its solid state?

A. Low temperature
B. High temperature
C. Evaporation
D. Crystallisation

21. Which of the following has more energy?

A. Water at 100 °C
B. Water vapour at 100 °C
C. Ice at 0 °C
D. Water at 62 °C

22. Which of the following processes can be observed when a plugged conical flask containing camphor is heated?

A. Sublimation
B. Evaporation
C. Condensation
D. Boiling

23. Which of the following is also called dry ice?

A. Liquid carbon dioxide
B. Gaseous carbon dioxide
C. Solid carbon dioxide
D. Carbon dioxide in plasma state

24. Clothes dry faster on a ___________.

A. windy day
B. cold day
C. snowy day
D. rainy day

25. Which of the following factors influences the rate of evaporation?

A. Temperature
B. Exposed surface area
C. Humidity
D. All of these

# SELF-ASSESSMENT 2

**Choose the correct option.**

26. Which of the following states of matter consists of super energetic and excited particles?
    A. Solid B. Liquid
    C. Gas D. Plasma

27. Which of the following uses the fourth state of matter?
    A. Neon signboard
    B. LED acrylic signboard
    C. 3D LED with aluminium casing signboard
    D. PVC signboard

28. Which of the following is the result of diffusion?
    A. Smelling a burning incense stick
    B. Stretching of rubber band
    C. Powdering a piece of chalk
    D. Hammering an iron nail

29. Which of the following increases with the increase in the temperature of a particle?
    A. Kinetic energy
    B. Potential energy
    C. Rate of condensation
    D. Rate of crystallisation

30. Which of the following solid materials can be compressed?
    A. A sponge bar B. An iron bar
    C. A wooden bar D. A steel bar

31. Which of the following retains the same shape when poured or transferred into containers of different shapes?
    A. Solid
    B. Liquid
    C. Gas
    D. Semi-liquid

32. Which of the following will have more latent heat of vaporization?
    A. Solidifying ice cubes
    B. Steam
    C. Condensing water vapour
    D. Melting of ice

33. Which of the following will dry faster?
    A. Folded wet cloth
    B. Partially folded wet cloth
    C. Partially spread wet cloth
    D. Spread wet cloth

34. Which of the following processes causes the formation of water droplets on the outer surface of a bottle containing ice-cold juice?
    A. Evaporation
    B. Condensation
    C. Sublimation
    D. Solidification

35. Water stored in an earthen pot remains cool during summer. Why?
   - A. The energy absorbed during evaporation is regained by water.
   - B. The earthen pot absorbs humidity from its surroundings.
   - C. The earthen pot allows air to cool the water stored in it.
   - D. Water condenses in an earthen pot.

36. Which of the following will give your skin a cooling effect?
   - A. Petroleum jelly
   - B. Coconut oil
   - C. Olive oil
   - D. Perfume

37. Which of the following is correct about drinking tea?
   - A. It is easier to drink hot tea from a saucer.
   - B. It is easier to drink hot tea from silverware.
   - C. It tastes better when served in a plastic mug.
   - D. It cools faster when sipped from a steel tumbler.

38. Which of the following is best-suited for summer season?
   - A. Tight woollen clothing
   - B. Loose cotton clothing
   - C. Loose polyester clothing
   - D. Tight silk clothing

39. The temperature of a city was recorded to be 32 °C . What will be its value on the kelvin scale?
   - A. 305 K
   - B. 241 K
   - C. 337 K
   - D. 9 K

40. Which of the following characteristics is responsible for a gas filling in a whole container it is stored in?
   - A. Negligible force of attraction between the gas particles
   - B. Strong force of attraction between the gas particles
   - C. Less space between the gas particles
   - D. Lower energy of the gas particles

41. Which of the following will be observed if equal volumes of a liquid and a gas are filled in the containers of the same size and shape?
   - A. Gas will occupy more space.
   - B. Liquid will occupy more space.
   - C. Both gas and liquid will occupy same space.
   - D. Gas will occupy half the space compared to liquid.

42. Which of the following has a higher rate of diffusion?
   - A. Sugar crystals
   - B. Sugar solution
   - C. Sugar cube
   - D. Powdered sugar

43. Which of the following will take the shape of the jar to which it is poured in?
   - A. Sugar
   - B. Salt
   - C. Pulses
   - D. Milk

44. If 25 g of sugar, orange juice, salt and steam are stored in containers of the same volume, which would occupy more space?
   - A. Salt
   - B. Sugar
   - C. Steam
   - D. Orange juice

45. Which of the following makes a rubber band change its shape?
   A. Cold temperature
   B. High pressure
   C. High force
   D. Both high force and high pressure

46. When force is applied, a solid breaks down into pieces ____________.
   A. but does not change its particle arrangement
   B. and changes its shape
   C. and loses its rigidity
   D. and melts

47. Which of the following involves diffusion?
   A. Movement of particles from higher to lower concentration
   B. Movement of particles from lower to higher concentration
   C. Movement of particles across equal concentration
   D. Loss of energy by particles on cooling

48. Which of the following is used by aquatic plants for photosynthesis?
   A. Oxygen dissolved in water
   B. Carbon dioxide dissolved in water
   C. Algae growing on the surface of water
   D. Microorganisms suspended in water

49. Which of the following has a fixed shape?
   A. Potassium permanganate solution
   B. Crystals of potassium permanganate
   C. Vapours of potassium permanganate
   D. Supersaturated solution of potassium permanganate

50. Which of the following would take place when a sugar cube is dropped into a glass of water?
   A. Intermixing of sugar and water
   B. Solidification of water
   C. Sublimation of sugar cube
   D. Deposition of water

Chapter 2

# Is Matter Around Us Pure?

## PRE-TEST

**Choose the correct option.**

1. Solution in which no more solute can be dissolved at a given temperature is called __________ solution.
   A. unsaturated  B. colloidal
   C. saturated  D. condensed

2. Cream is separated from milk by the process of __________.
   A. condensation  B. centrifugation
   C. sedimentation  D. evaporation

3. Which of the following substances is added to water to increase the rate of sedimentation?
   A. Salt  B. Sugar
   C. Alum  D. Soap

4. Which of the following separation techniques is not used in agriculture?
   A. Threshing
   B. Sieving
   C. Crystallisation
   D. Winnowing

5. Which of the following substances is not considered to be pure?
   A. Copper sulphate
   B. Diamond
   C. Glucose
   D. Milk

## KEYWORDS

**Aerosol:** Colloidal suspension dispersed in air

**Alloy:** A combination of a metal with one or more metals or non-metals

**Boiling point:** The temperature at which a boiling liquid turns into vapour

**Centrifugation:** A technique which uses centrifugal force to separate the particles in a solution

**Chromatography:** A technique used for the separation of substances from a solution through a medium

**Colloid:** A mixture of particles of one substance uniformly suspended in another substance

**Compound:** A substance composed of two or more separate elements

**Dispersed phase:** The particles that are dispersed in a colloidal solution

**Dispersion medium:** The medium in which the colloidal particles are dispersed

**Distillation:** The process of purifying a liquid by heating and then cooling it

**Emulsion:** A fine dispersion of minute droplets of liquid

**Evaporation:** The process of conversion of liquid into gas

**Filtration:** The process of separation of suspended solids from liquids

**Fractional distillation:** Method used to separate a mixture of two or more miscible liquids having a temperature difference of less than 25 K

**Heterogeneous mixtures:** Mixtures containing physically distinct components and having non-uniform compositions

**Homogeneous mixtures:** Mixtures having a uniform composition throughout

**Immiscible:** Incapable of being mixed to form a homogeneous substance

**Melting point:** The temperature at which a solid starts melting

**Mixture:** Combination of two or more chemically different components in any proportion such that all the components retain their properties and can be separated by simple physical methods

**Saturated solution:** Solution containing the maximum concentration of a solute dissolved in a solvent

**Sieving:** The process of separation of a mixture based on its size

**Sol:** A colloid in which the solid particles are suspended in a liquid

**Solubility:** The ability of a given solute to dissolve in a given solvent

**Solute:** Substance that gets dissolved in a solvent to form a solution

**Solution:** Homogeneous mixture of two or more substances

**Solvent:** Substance in which a solute is dissolved

**Sublimation:** Direct conversion of a solid into gas without the intermediate liquid phase

**Suspension:** Larger solute particles that are dispersed or settled down in the solvent

**Tyndall effect:** The scattering of light as a light beam passes through a colloid

# Concept Map

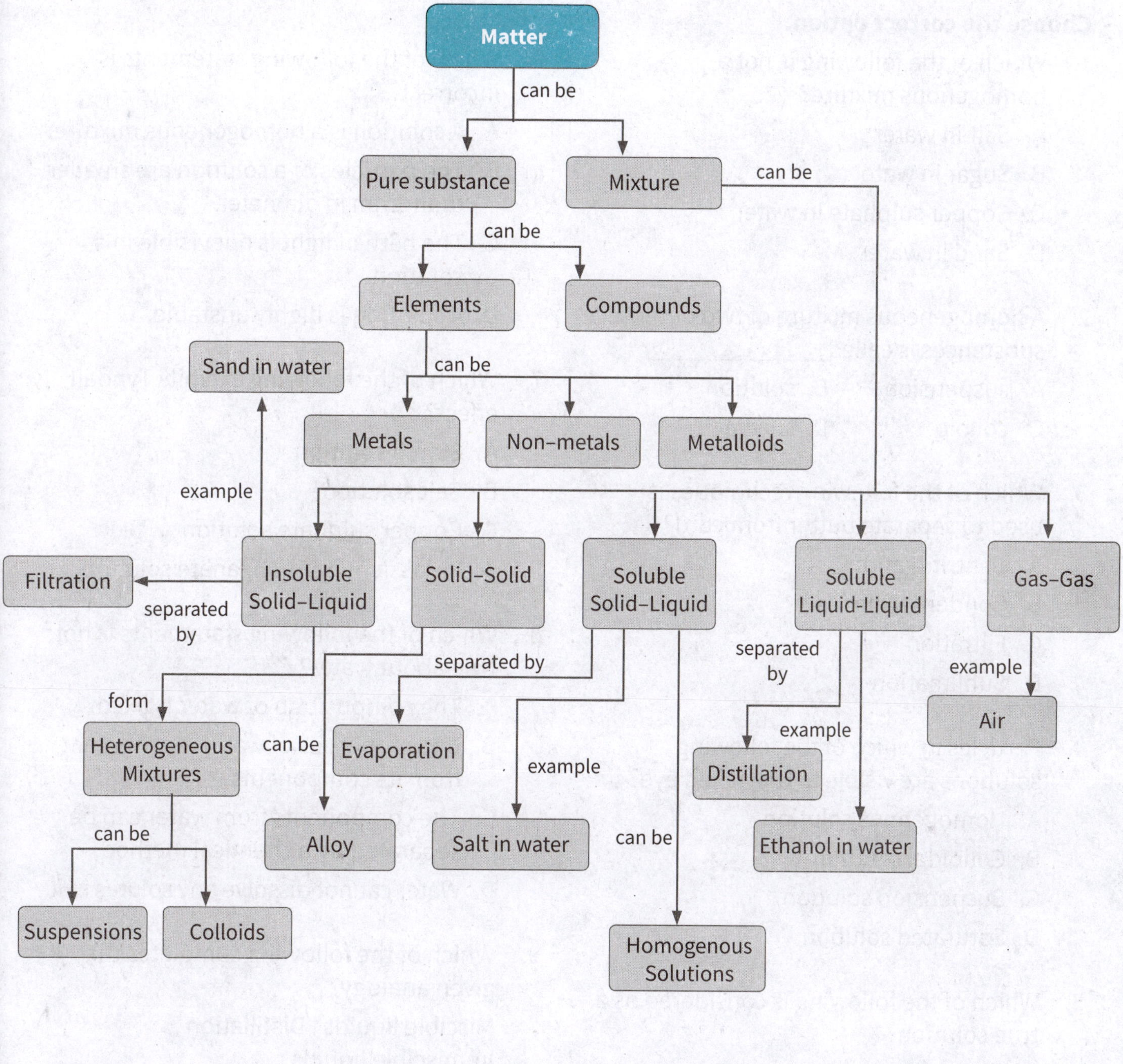

Matter
can be
Pure substance
Mixture
can be
can be
Elements
Compounds
can be
Metals
Non-metals
Metalloids
Sand in water
example
Filtration
separated by
Insoluble Solid-Liquid
Solid-Solid
Soluble Solid-Liquid
Soluble Liquid-Liquid
Gas-Gas
separated by
separated by
example
Air
form
Heterogeneous Mixtures
can be
Evaporation
example
example
Distillation
Alloy
Salt in water
can be
Ethanol in water
can be
Suspensions
Colloids
Homogenous Solutions

# SELF-ASSESSMENT 1

**Choose the correct option.**

1. Which of the following is not a homogenous mixture?
   A. Salt in water
   B. Sugar in water
   C. Copper sulphate in water
   D. Sand in water

2. A homogeneous mixture of two or more substances is called ______________.
   A. suspension B. solution
   C. colloid D. solvent

3. Which of the following techniques is used to separate butter from curd?
   A. Centrifugation
   B. Condensation
   C. Filtration
   D. Sublimation

4. Particles in which of the following solutions are visible to the naked eye?
   A. Homogenous solution
   B. Colloidal solution
   C. Suspension solution
   D. Saturated solution

5. Which of the following is considered as a true solution?
   A. Blood
   B. Milk
   C. Sugar solution
   D. Chalk powder in water

6. Which of the following statements is incorrect?
   A. A solution is a homogeneous mixture.
   B. The particles of a solution are smaller than 1 nm in diameter.
   C. The path of light is not visible in a solution.
   D. A solution is highly unstable.

7. Which of the following exhibits Tyndall effect?
   A. Starch solution
   B. Salt solution
   C. Copper sulphate solution
   D. Potassium permanganate solution

8. Which of the following statements is not true about water?
   A. The composition of water is fixed.
   B. The properties of water are different from its components.
   C. The components from water can be separated by a chemical method.
   D. Water cannot dissolve any solutes in it.

9. Which of the following completes the given analogy?
   Miscible liquids : Distillation ::
   Immiscible liquids : ______________
   A. Filtration
   B. Crystallisation
   C. Chromatography
   D. Separation funnel

10. Which of the following scrap metals cannot be separated by magnetic separation?
    A. Chromium
    B. Iron
    C. Nickel
    D. Steel

11. Identify the correct composition of a filtration tank in a water purification system.
    A. Water, fine sand, gravel and coarse gravel
    B. Water, clay, gravel and boulders
    C. Water, fine sand, gravel and mud
    D. Water, clay, gravel and sand

12. Which of the following elements will melt at 303 K?
    A. Gold and Silver
    B. Argon and Neon
    C. Mercury and Bromine
    D. Gallium and Caesium

13. Which of the following substances can be obtained by the crystallisation technique?
    A. Pure copper sulphate crystals
    B. Pure butter
    C. Camphor
    D. Pure ethanol

14. Which of the following gases cannot be separated from air by fractional distillation?
    A. Oxygen
    B. Hydrogen
    C. Nitrogen
    D. Argon

15. The technique in which denser particles are forced to the bottom while lighter particles stay at the top during the rapid spinning of a liquid mixture is called ___________.
    A. centrifugation
    B. fractional distillation
    C. evaporation
    D. crystallisation

16. A heterogeneous mixture containing the solute particles suspended throughout the solvent that can be seen with the naked eye is called a ___________.
    A. colloidal solution
    B. supersaturated solution
    C. solid sol
    D. suspension

17. Concentration of a solution can be defined as ___________.
    A. the amount of solute present per unit volume or per unit mass of the solution
    B. the amount of solution present per unit volume or per unit mass of the solvent
    C. the amount of solvent present per unit volume or per unit mass of the solute
    D. the amount of solution present per unit volume or per unit mass of the solute

18. Which of the following techniques can be used to separate crystals of alum from an impure sample?
    A. Distillation
    B. Sublimation
    C. Crystallisation
    D. Centrifugation

19. A solution contains 38 g of common salt dissolved in 280 g of water. Calculate the concentration in terms of mass by mass percentage of the solution.

A. 10.5% B. 11.9%

C. 12.2% D. 9.9%

20. Peter dissolved 15 g of sugar in 100 mℓ of water taken in a beaker and heated the solution until it was reduced to half. How many grams of sugar can be recovered from the resulting solution?

A. 0 g B. 5 g

C. 10 g D. 15 g

21. **Statement I:** Weight of a mixture is equal to the sum of the weights of their components.

**Statement II:** Energy is given out when a mixture is being prepared.

A. Statement I is correct and statement II is incorrect.

B. Statement II is correct and statement I is incorrect.

C. Both statements I and II are correct.

D. Both statements I and II are incorrect.

22. **Statement I:** Alcohol can be separated from a mixture of alcohol and water by a separating funnel.

**Statement II:** Salt can be recovered from an aqueous salt solution by the process of evaporation.

A. Statement I is correct and statement II is incorrect.

B. Statement II is correct and statement I is incorrect.

C. Both statements I and II are correct.

D. Both statements I and II are incorrect.

23. A mixture contains three constituents P, Q and R. The constituent P is a yellow-coloured solid element which dissolves in liquid R. The constituent Q is a blue-coloured salt which is insoluble in liquid R but dissolves easily in another liquid S. Identify Q and S.

A. Q—Sulphur; S—Carbon disulphide

B. Q—Copper sulphate; S—Water

C. Q—Sulphur; S—Water

D. Q—Copper sulphate; S—Carbon disulphide

24. Three components P, Q and R are to be separated from a mixture. Components P and R are soluble in water. Substance R sublimates on heating. In what sequence can these components be separated?

A. Sublimation, filtration, dissolution, crystallisation

B. Dissolution, filtration, sublimation, crystallisation

C. Filtration, sublimation, crystallisation, dissolution

D. Sublimation, dissolution, filtration, crystallisation

25. Match the following.

| Column I | Column II |
|---|---|
| a. Sublimation | i. Separation of benzene and aniline |
| b. Distillation | ii. Separation of iron and sand |
| c. Separating funnel | iii. Separation of iodine and sand |
| d. Magnetic separation | iv. Separation of water and carbon tetrachloride |

A. a→i; b→ii; c→iii; d→iv

B. a→iii; b→i; c→iv; d→ii

C. a→iv; b→iii; c→ii; d→i

D. a→i; b→ii; c→iv; d→iii

# SELF-ASSESSMENT 2

**Choose the correct option.**

26. Which of the following processes is used to extract salt from seawater?
    A. Condensation
    B. Evaporation
    C. Sublimation
    D. Precipitation

27. Which of the following is not a heterogeneous mixture?
    A. Cereals in milk
    B. Ice in soda
    C. Rainwater
    D. Orange juice with pulp

28. Identify the composition of the tincture of iodine.
    A. Iodine in water
    B. Iodine in alcohol
    C. Iodine in acetone
    D. Iodine in benzene

29. Mixture of sand in water is an example of a ______________.
    A. true solution
    B. colloidal solution
    C. suspension
    D. solvent

30. Hydrogen sulphide gas has a smell of ______________.
    A. rotten vegetables
    B. fresh lemons
    C. rotten eggs
    D. fresh flowers

31. Which of the following processes is used to separate insoluble solids from a liquid?
    A. Decantation
    B. Filtration
    C. Evaporation
    D. Crystallisation

32. Sodium chloride (48 g) is dissolved in 100 mℓ of water at 124°C. What will be the concentration of the resultant solution at this temperature?
    A. 100%
    B. 50%
    C. 48%
    D. 24%

33. What happens when iron filings and sulphur powder are heated in a china dish to a very high temperature?
    A. There will be no change in the substances.
    B. A mixture of iron and sulphur is obtained.
    C. Iron sulphide, a yellow powder, is formed.
    D. Black-coloured ferrous sulphide is formed.

34. Identify the odd one out.
    A. Growth of a plant
    B. Rusting of iron
    C. Freezing of water
    D. Burning of a candle

35. Which of the following completes the given analogy?

Liquid dispersed in gas : Cloud :: ________________ : Butter

A. Liquid dispersed in solid
B. Solid dispersed in solid
C. Gas dispersed in solid
D. Solid dispersed in liquid

36. What is the correct increasing order of the boiling points of following gases in liquid air?

A. Nitrogen, oxygen, argon
B. Nitrogen, argon, oxygen
C. Argon, oxygen, nitrogen
D. Oxygen, argon, nitrogen

37. Which of the following non-metals is used to kill germs during purification of water?

A. Iodine
B. Chlorine
C. Bromine
D. Hydrogen

38. Identify the incorrect pair with respect to colloids.

A. Fog—Aerosol
B. Shaving cream—Foam
C. Mud—Sol
D. Pumice—Solid sol

39. Which of the following mixtures can be separated using a separating funnel?

A. Kerosene oil and water
B. Ink and water
C. Milk and fat
D. Sand and water

40. Naphthalene balls kept in a container reduce in size over a period of time. Why?

A. Because of evaporation
B. Because of sublimation
C. Because of crystallisation
D. Because of condensation

41. Tincture of iodine is a solution of ________________.

A. alcohol in iodine
B. iodine in alcohol
C. water in iodine
D. iodine in water

42. Which of the following statements is not true with respect to a compound?

A. It is composed of two or more elements.
B. It is a pure substance.
C. It cannot be separated into constituents by physical means.
D. The components of a compound can be mixed in any proportion by mass.

43. Which of the following techniques can be used to separate a mixture of water and acetone?

A. Distillation
B. Fractional distillation
C. Vaporization
D. Sublimation

44. A solution contains 6.5 $cm^3$ of alcohol mixed with 175 $cm^3$ of water. Find the concentration of the solution.

A. 2.15% B. 2.95%
C. 3.08% D. 3.58%

45. Which of the following statements is incorrect?
   A. Centrifugation method can be used to separate butter from cream.
   B. Coloured component of blue ink can be separated by evaporation.
   C. Chromatography can be used to detect drugs in blood.
   D. Camphor can be separated from salt by crystallisation.

46. **Statement I:** In a compound, elements combine in definite proportion.
   **Statement II:** Element is always a metal.
   A. Statement I is correct and statement II is incorrect.
   B. Statement II is correct and statement I is incorrect.
   C. Both statements I and II are correct.
   D. Both statements I and II are incorrect.

47. **Statement I:** Both suspension and colloidal solution can scatter light and make its path visible.
   **Statement II:** In a suspension, the particles can be seen by a naked eye, whereas in a colloidal solution, they cannot be seen.
   A. Statement I is correct and statement II is incorrect.
   B. Statement II is correct and statement I is incorrect.
   C. Both statements I and II are correct.
   D. Both statements I and II are incorrect.

48. Tincture of iodine is a mixture of two components X and Y. The component Y has a property that its solid form can be converted directly into vapours on heating by the process of sublimation. What could component Y be?
   A. Iodine
   B. Alcohol
   C. Water
   D. Butane

49. Two different processes X and Y can be observed when a candle burns. Which of the following statements is correct about the processes X and Y?
   A. Process X is a physical change.
   B. Process Y is a chemical change.
   C. Both process X and process Y are chemical changes.
   D. Process X is a chemical change and process Y is a physical change.

50. **Statement I:** Mixtures are always the combinations of more than one type of pure form of matter.
   **Statement II:** We can separate the components of all mixtures by filtration.
   A. Statement I is correct and statement II is incorrect.
   B. Statement II is correct and statement I is incorrect.
   C. Both statements I and II are correct.
   D. Both statements I and II are incorrect.

Chapter 3

# Atoms and Molecules

## PRE-TEST

**Choose the correct option.**

1. How many elements are present in the Modern Periodic Table?
   A. 100 B. 94
   C. 80 D. 118
2. Which of the following is the molecular formula of common salt?
   A. NaCl B. $NaNH_2$
   C. $NH_3$ D. HCOONa
3. What is the ratio of the number of atoms of hydrogen and oxygen in a molecule of water?
   A. 1 : 8
   B. 8 : 1
   C. 1 : 2
   D. 2 : 1
4. Which of the following is a symbolic representation of a compound?
   A. Chemical equation
   B. Chemical formula
   C. Valency
   D. Ionic equation
5. The hydrogen element in a Periodic Table is represented as shown below. What does the number in the image indicate?

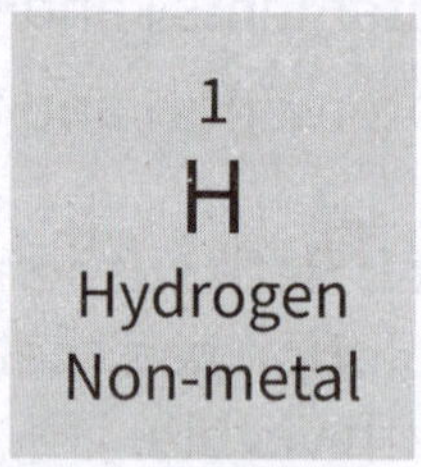


   A. Atomic number B. Serial number
   C. Atomic mass D. Isotope number

## KEYWORDS

**Anion:** Negatively charged ion formed by the gain of electrons by an atom

**Atom:** The smallest particle of an element that takes part in a chemical change

**Atomic mass:** The numerical indication of the number of times an atom of an element is heavier than 1/12th of the mass of a carbon-12 atom

**Atomicity:** The number of atoms present in a molecule of an element or a compound

**Avogadro's constant or Avogadro's number:** The number of particles present in one mole of an atom, ions or molecules

**Binary compound:** A substance composed of exactly two different elements that cannot be simplified further by any chemical means

**Cation:** Positively charged ion formed by the loss of electron from an atom

**Formula unit mass:** The sum of the atomic masses of all the atoms in a formula unit

**Gram atomic mass:** Atomic mass of an element expressed in grams

**Ion:** An electrically charged atom or group of atoms

**Law of conservation of mass:** Mass can neither be created nor destroyed in a chemical reaction

**Law of constant proportion:** In a chemical substance, the elements are always present in definite proportions by mass

**Mole:** A collection of $6.022 \times 10^{23}$ particles present in any substance

**Molecular mass:** The number of times a molecule of a compound is heavier than the $1/12^{th}$ of the mass of a carbon-12 atom

**Molecule:** The smallest particle of an element or compound that shows all the properties of that substance and is capable of independent existence

**Symbol:** Abbreviation used for the name of an element

**Valency:** The combining capacity of an element

# Concept Map

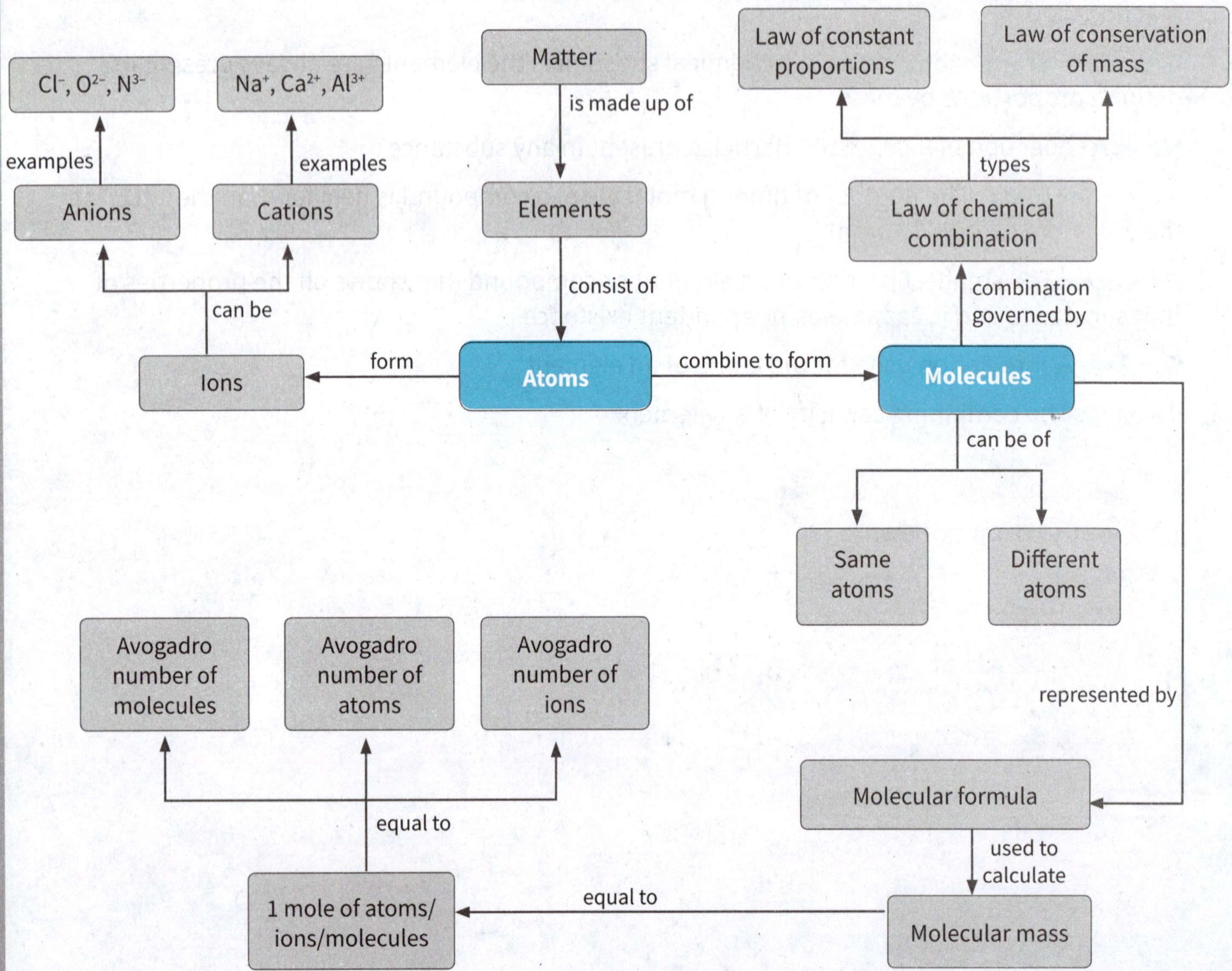
Cl⁻, O²⁻, N³⁻
Na⁺, Ca²⁺, Al³⁺
Matter
is made up of
Law of constant proportions
Law of conservation of mass
examples
examples
types
Anions
Cations
Elements
Law of chemical combination
consist of
combination governed by
can be
form
Ions
Atoms
combine to form
Molecules
can be of
Same atoms
Different atoms
Avogadro number of molecules
Avogadro number of atoms
Avogadro number of ions
represented by
Molecular formula
equal to
used to calculate
1 mole of atoms/ ions/molecules
equal to
Molecular mass

# SELF-ASSESSMENT 1

**Choose the correct option.**

1. Who laid the foundation of chemical sciences?
   A. Democritus
   B. Leucippus
   C. Antoine L. Lavoisier
   D. Joseph L. Proust

2. Which of the following terms defines the combining capacity of an element?
   A. Valency
   B. Radical
   C. Anion
   D. Cation

3. How many atoms of oxygen does an ozone molecule contain?
   A. One
   B. Two
   C. Three
   D. Four

4. Which of the following is used as a standard reference for measuring atomic masses?
   A. H-1
   B. C-12
   C. O-16
   D. C-14

5. What is the valency of a noble gas?
   A. Zero B. One
   C. Two D. Three

6. How many atoms of hydrogen are present in one mole of methane?
   A. $4 \times 6.023 \times 10^{23}$
   B. $2 \times 6.023 \times 10^{23}$
   C. $6.023 \times 10^{23}$
   D. $8 \times 6.023 \times 10^{23}$

7. Calculate the number of moles for 288 g of oxygen atoms.
   A. 28 B. 20
   C. 88 D. 18

8. Calculate the molecular mass of $H_2SO_4$.
   A. 100 g $mol^{-1}$ B. 98 g $mol^{-1}$
   C. 102 g $mol^{-1}$ D. 89 g $mol^{-1}$

9. Which of the following is the molecular formula of ammonium sulphate.
   A. $2NH_4SO_4$ B. $(NH_4)_2SO_4$
   C. $(NH_4)_6SO_2$ D. $NH_4SO_4$

10. Which of the following is not a postulate of Dalton's atomic theory?
    A. All matter is made of very tiny particles called atoms.
    B. Atoms are made up of electrons, protons and neutrons.
    C. Atoms of a given element are identical in mass and chemical properties.
    D. Atoms of different elements have different masses and chemical properties.

11. Which of these elements is represented by the symbol 'W' in the Periodic Table?

A. Tungsten  B. Tin
C. Mercury  D. Antimony

12. Calculate the molecular mass of $C_8H_9NO_2$ (paracetamol).

A. 132 g $mol^{-1}$  B. 334 g $mol^{-1}$
C. 151 g $mol^{-1}$  D. 340 g $mol^{-1}$

13. How many moles of oxygen molecules are present in 12 g of oxygen gas?

A. 0.375 mole
B. 1.37 mole
C. 3.75 mole
D. 0.137 mole

14. What does the symbol C–12 stand for?

A. A carbon atom weighs 12 grams.
B. A carbon atom weighs 12 amu.
C. There are 12 carbon atoms in a substance.
D. The melting point of carbon is 12 °C.

15. Which of the following pair of compounds have the same molecular mass?

A. Calcium chloride, potassium carbonate
B. Calcium oxide, hydrochloric acid
C. Carbon monoxide, ammonia
D. Carbon dioxide, nitrous oxide

16. Calculate the molecular mass of $CCl_4$ molecule.

A. 153.81 $gmol^{-1}$
B. 90.03 $gmol^{-1}$
C. 36.46 $gmol^{-1}$
D. 292.24 $gmol^{-1}$

17. What is the ratio by mass of carbon and oxygen in carbon dioxide?

A. 14 : 3  B. 1 : 14
C. 1 : 8  D. 3 : 8

18. Which of the following relative sizes is incorrectly matched?

A. $10^{-10}$ m—Atom of hydrogen
B. $10^{-9}$ m—Molecule of water
C. $10^{-8}$ m—Molecule of haemoglobin
D. $10^{-4}$ m—Ant

19. Which of the following triplets of elements have atomic weights 32, 35.5 and 40 respectively?

A. Sulphur, Chlorine, Calcium
B. Oxygen, Sodium, Magnesium
C. Hydrogen, Carbon, Nitrogen
D. Magnesium, Nitrogen, Chlorine

20. Identify the odd one out based on the atomicity and nature of the following elements.

A. Sodium  B. Copper
C. Argon  D. Aluminium

21. **Statement I:** One mole of copper contains the same number of atoms as one mole of tin.

**Statement II:** One mole of an element would weigh the same as one mole of its isotope.

A. Statement I is correct and statement II is incorrect.
B. Statement II is correct and statement I is incorrect.
C. Both statements I and II are correct.
D. Both statements I and II are incorrect.

22. Match the following.

| Column A | Column B |
|---|---|
| a. Sodium oxide | i. $AlCl_3$ |
| b. Aluminium chloride | ii. $Mg(OH)_2$ |
| c. Sodium sulphide | iii. $Na_2O$ |
| d. Magnesium hydroxide | iv. $Na_2S$ |

A. a→i; b→ii; c→iii; d→iv
B. a→iii; b→i; c→iv; d→ii
C. a→ii; b→i; c→iv; d→iii
D. a→iv; b→i; c→ii; d→iii

23. **Statement I:** 1/16th of the mass of an atom of naturally occurring oxygen is the universally accepted unit of standard reference for measuring the atomic mass.
**Statement II:** The relative atomic masses of all elements have been found with respect to an atom of Carbon-12.
A. Statement I is correct and statement II is incorrect.
B. Statement II is correct and statement I is incorrect.
C. Both statements I and II are correct.
D. Both statements I and II are incorrect.

24. Which of the following laws is supported by the data given below?
A sample of water molecule, irrespective of its source, contains 88.90% of oxygen and 11.10% of hydrogen by mass.
A. Law of conservation of mass
B. Law of definite proportion
C. Law of multiple proportion
D. Avogadro's law

25. In compound X, 7 g nitrogen combines with 8 g oxygen. In compound Y, 7 g nitrogen combines with 16 g oxygen. Which of the following laws is followed?
A. Law of constant proportion
B. Law of multiple proportion
C. Law of reciprocal proportion
D. Dalton's law of partial pressure

# SELF-ASSESSMENT 2

**Choose the correct option.**

26. Who coined the term 'atom'?
   A. Leucippus
   B. Democritus
   C. Lavoisier
   D. Proust

27. What is a group of atoms carrying a charge called?
   A. Diatomic ion
   B. Monoatomic ion
   C. Polyatomic ion
   D. Triatomic ion

28. The number of atoms constituting a molecule is called its ____________.
   A. valency
   B. atomicity
   C. atomic factor
   D. molecularity

29. What is the accepted unit for the representation of atomic mass and molecular mass of a substance?
   A. amu  B. g
   C. kg  D. g $mol^{-1}$

30. Which of these elements has the same gram atomic and gram molecular mass?
   A. Hydrogen  B. Nitrogen
   C. Oxygen  D. Argon

31. Which of these is the chemical formula of zinc phosphate?
   A. $Zn(PO_4)_3$
   B. $Zn_2PO_4$
   C. $Zn_3(PO_4)_2$
   D. $ZnPO_4$

32. Which of the following completes the given analogy?
   Chlorine : Cl :: Cobalt : ____________.
   A. CO  B. Co
   C. C  D. Ca

33. Which of these statements is incorrect?
   A. Atoms are made up of electrons, protons and neutrons.
   B. Atoms are very tiny particles.
   C. Nucleus of an atom is made up of protons and neutrons.
   D. Atoms of different elements have the same chemical properties.

34. What is the full form of IUPAC?
   A. International Union of Pure and Applied Chemistry
   B. International Union Power of Applied Chemistry
   C. Internal Union of Pure Applied Chemistry
   D. International Universal Pure and Applied Chemistry

35. What is the correct representation of the relation between Avogadro's number and the number of particles and moles?

A. $n = N/N_o$

B. $n = N_o/N$

C. $n = N \times N_o$

D. $n = N + N_o$

36. Identify the molecular mass of ammonium sulphate $[(NH_4)_2SO_4]$.

A. 132 g $mol^{-1}$

B. 334 g $mol^{-1}$

C. 135 g $mol^{-1}$

D. 340 g $mol^{-1}$

37. What is the mole value of 25 g of water?

A. 1.11 mole

B. 1.38 mole

C. 13 mole

D. 0.11 mole

38. Identify the cation and anion in sodium chloride.

A. Sodium is cation and chlorine is anion

B. Sodium is anion and chlorine is cation

C. Sodium and chlorine are both anions

D. Sodium and chlorine are both cations

39. Which of these symbols is correctly matched?

A. Chlorine—Ch

B. Carbon—Ca

C. Calcium—Cl

D. Potassium—K

40. Element 'M' is divalent and element 'N' is tetravalent. The compound formed by these two elements will be ________.

A. $M_4N_2$

B. $M_2N_4$

C. $NM_2$

D. $N_4M_2$

41. Which of the following substances contains the largest number of particles?

A. 8 g of $CH_4$

B. 4.4 g of $CO_2$

C. 34.2 g of $C_{12}H_{22}O_{11}$

D. 2 g of $H_2$

42. How many molecules are present in 1 gram of hydrogen?

A. $6.032 \times 10^{23}$

B. $3.011 \times 10^{23}$

C. $1.505 \times 10^{23}$

D. $0.752 \times 10^{23}$

43. If the valency of Mg is 2 and the valency of Cl is 1, the formula of magnesium chloride will be ___________.

A. $Mg_2Cl$

B. 2MgCl

C. $MgCl_2$

D. $(MgCl)_2$

44. Calculate the number of moles for $12.044 \times 10^{23}$ helium atoms.

A. 1 mole

B. 2 mole

C. 3 mole

D. 4 mole

45. What is the percentage of oxygen in a molecule of water?

A. 98.88 % B. 22.22 %

C. 11.11 % D. 88.89 %

46. **Statement I:** The symbols for all the elements are derived from their Latin names.

**Statement II:** The symbols for all the elements always begin with a capital letter.

A. Statement I is correct and statement II is incorrect.

B. Statement II is correct and statement I is incorrect.

C. Both statements I and II are correct.

D. Both statements I and II are incorrect.

47. What is the formula for the phosphate of a metal X, if the formula for the chloride of that metal is $XCl_3$?

A. $XPO_4$ B. $X_2PO_4$

C. $X_3PO_4$ D. $X_2(PO_4)_3$

48. Which of these is the correct arrangement of compounds in an increasing order of their molecular weights?

A. $H_2O > H_2S > CO_2 > SO_2$

B. $H_2O > CO_2 > H_2S > SO_2$

C. $H_2O < H_2S < CO_2 < SO_2$

D. $H_2S > H_2O > CO_2 > SO_2$

49. Match the following.

| | Column A | | Column B |
|---|---|---|---|
| a. | $Al_2(SO_4)_3$ | i. | Sodium bicarbonate |
| b. | $K_2SO_4$ | ii. | Copper nitrate |
| c. | $NaHCO_3$ | iii. | Aluminium sulphate |
| d. | $Cu(NO_3)_2$ | iv. | Potassium sulphate |

A. a→iii; b→iv; c→i; d→ii

B. a→iii; b→i; c→iv; d→ii

C. a→ii; b→i; c→iv; d→iii

D. a→iv; b→i; c→ii; d→iii

50. **Statement I:** Atomic theory proposed by Maharishi Kanad was the turning point in the study of matter.

**Statement II:** Pakudha Katyayama elaborated this doctrine and said that these particles normally exist in a combined form.

A. Statement I is correct and statement II is incorrect.

B. Statement II is correct and statement I is incorrect.

C. Both statements I and II are correct.

D. Both statements I and II are incorrect.

Chapter 4

# Structure of the Atom

## PRE-TEST

**Choose the correct option.**

1. Which of the following would happen if you comb your hair and bring it near tiny pieces of paper?
   A. Paper pieces will stick to the comb.
   B. Paper pieces will move away from the comb.
   C. No change is observed.
   D. The comb moves away from the pieces of paper.

2. Who among the following stated that an atom will be stable and less reactive if the atomic shells are complete?
   A. Rutherford
   B. Niels Bohr
   C. J Chadwick
   D. J J Thomson

3. Identify the atom which does not contain neutrons in it.
   A. Helium B. Oxygen
   C. Carbon D. Hydrogen

4. Which of the following properties of an element would differ from their isotopes?
   A. Chemical property
   B. Physical property
   C. Electronic configuration
   D. Number of protons

5. Which of the following scientists was the first to propose a model for the structure of an atom?
   A. E. Rutherford B. Niels Bohr
   C. J.J. Thomson D. J. Chadwick

## KEYWORDS

**Atomic number:** The total number of protons present in the nucleus of an atom

**Isobars:** Atoms of different elements with different atomic numbers and same mass number

**Isotopes:** Atoms of the same element that have the same atomic number but different mass numbers

**Mass number:** The sum of the total number of protons and neutrons present in the nucleus of an atom

**Neutrons:** Subatomic particles with no charge but with a mass nearly equal to that of a proton

**Valency:** The combining capacity of an element

# Concept Map

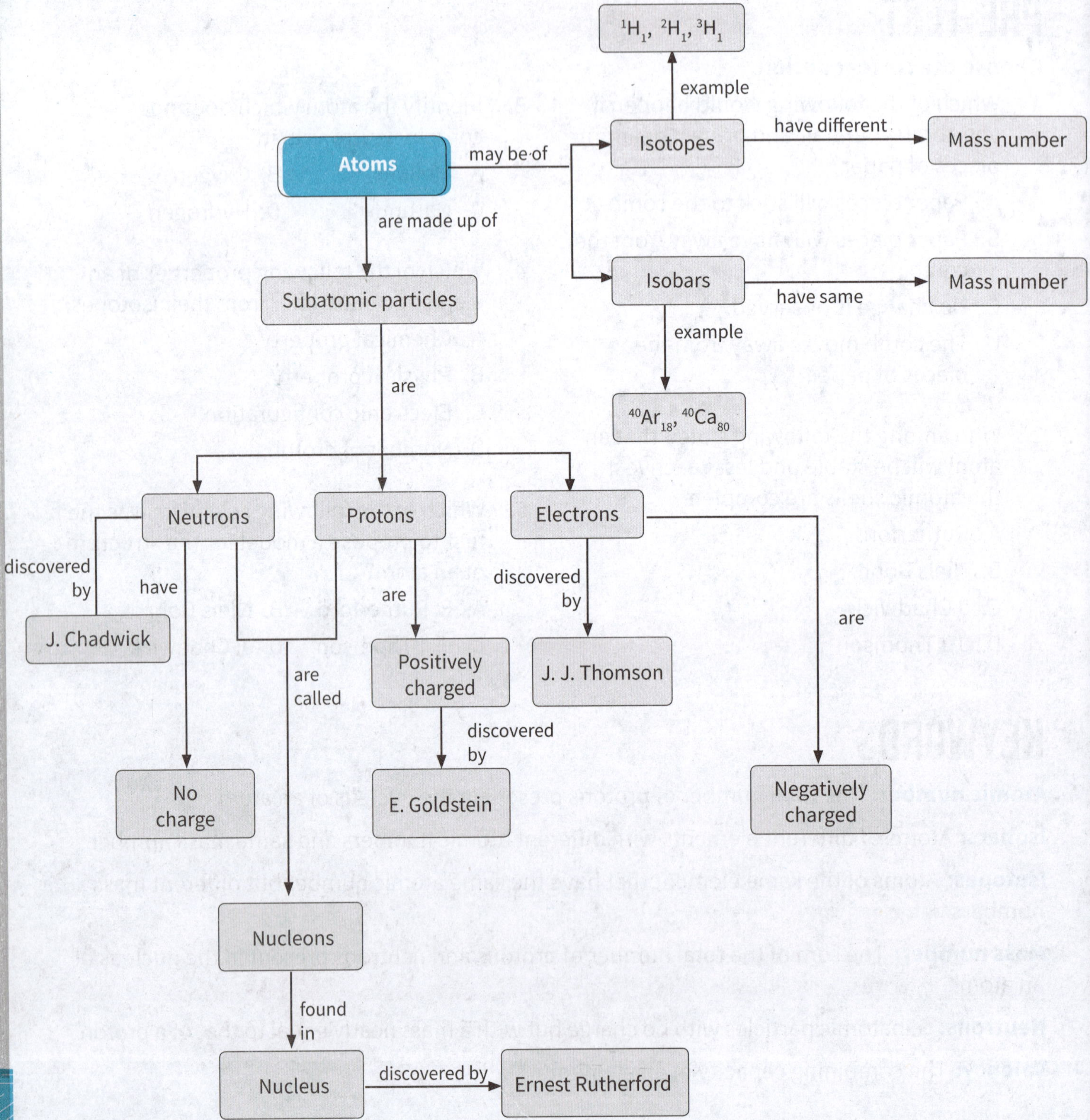

Atoms
may be of
Isotopes
example
$^{1}H_{1}$, $^{2}H_{1}$, $^{3}H_{1}$
have different
Mass number
Isobars
have same
Mass number
example
$^{40}Ar_{18}$, $^{40}Ca_{80}$
are made up of
Subatomic particles
are
Neutrons
Protons
Electrons
discovered by
J. Chadwick
have
No charge
are called
Nucleons
found in
Nucleus
discovered by
Ernest Rutherford
are
Positively charged
discovered by
E. Goldstein
discovered by
J. J. Thomson
are
Negatively charged

# SELF-ASSESSMENT 1

**Choose the correct option.**

1. Who among the following was the first to identify electrons?
   A. E. Goldstein
   B. J. J. Thomson
   C. Ernest Rutherford
   D. Dalton

2. Identify the incorrect pair from the following.
   A. Nucleus—Positive sphere
   B. Neutrons—Neutral charge
   C. Electrons—Positive charge
   D. α-particle—Helium ions

3. Which of the following shells is represented by n = 4?
   A. N
   B. M
   C. K
   D. L

4. Which of the following is a postulate of Bohr's atomic model?
   A. The revolving electrons lose energy and fall into the nucleus of an atom.
   B. Electrons revolve in discrete orbits inside an atom.
   C. The positively charged centre of an atom contains only protons.
   D. The mass of an atom is the total number of protons and neutrons.

5. The valency of an atom of an element is_______________.
   A. its mass number
   B. its nucleon number
   C. the mass of that atom
   D. definite combining capacity

6. Identify the correct statement related to protons.
   A. In an atom, the number of protons and electrons are equal.
   B. They revolve around the nucleus in an atom.
   C. They are negatively charged.
   D. The do not contribute to the mass of an atom.

7. Which of the following was not used by Rutherford in his model of atom?
   A. Helium ions
   B. Gold foil
   C. β particles
   D. Deflection and reflection of particles

8. The maximum number of electrons present in a M-shell is represented by the following formula.
   A. $2 \times 1^2$
   B. $2 \times 3^2$
   C. $2 \times 2^2$
   D. $2 \times 4^2$

9. Identify the element based on the atomic structure given below.

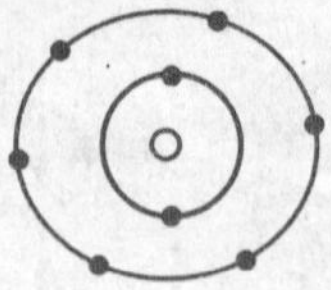

A. Oxygen
B. Nitrogen
C. Neon
D. Sodium

10. What is the maximum number of electrons that can be accommodated in the outermost orbit of aluminium atom?

A. 8
B. 2
C. 3
D. 4

11. Identify the correct order of energy shells occupied by sodium starting from the nucleus.

A. K-2, L-8, M-7
B. K-2, L-8, M-8
C. K-2, L-8, M-2
D. K-2, L-8, M-1

12. Identify the element that contains only seven electrons in its M-shell.

A. Chlorine
B. Argon
C. Sulphur
D. Silicon

13. Which of the following elements contains half-filled M- shell?

A. Aluminium
B. Silicon
C. Phosphorus
D. Sulphur

14. Which of the following has the same atomic number but different mass number?

(i) Protium
(ii) Deuterium
(iii) Carbon
(iv) Chlorine

A. (i) and (ii) only
B. (ii), (iii) and (iv)
C. (i) and (iii) only
D. (i), (ii), (iii) and (iv)

15. The isotope of an element 'X' has atomic number one (1) and neutron number two (2). Identify the isotope

A. Hydrogen
B. Protium
C. Deuterium
D. Tritium

16. Which of the following isotopic elements is used in the treatment of cancer?

A. Carbon B. Chorine
C. Cobalt D. Iodine

17. Identify the average atomic mass of chlorine given that the isotopes of chlorine are $_{17}Cl^{35}$ and $_{17}Cl^{37}$.

A. 37 u B. 35.5 u
C. 35 u D. 72 u

18. Isobars of different elements contain __________.

A. same mass number but different atomic numbers
B. same mass number and same atomic number
C. different mass numbers and different atomic numbers
D. same atomic number and different mass numbers

19. According to Chadwick, the mass of an electron is_____.

A. 1/2000 times the mass of H-atom

B. 1/1000 times the mass of H-atom

C. 1 unit

D. 2 units

20. Which of the following is the maximum number of electrons that can be accommodated in the M-shell of the first 20 elements in the periodic table?

A. 2 B. 8

C. 4 D. 6

21. Identify the element that has a valency equal to that of electrons in the filled K-shell.

A. Beryllium B. Oxygen

C. Magnesium D. All of these

22. **Assertion (A):** The atomic number of an element can be identified by its electron number.

**Reason (R):** The number of protons is equal to the number of electrons in an atom.

A. A is true but R is false.

B. Both A and R are false.

C. Both A and R are true.

D. A is false but R is true.

23. Which of the following is the mass number of phosphorus if its atomic number is 15 and the number of neutrons is 16?

A. 31 u

B. 1 u

C. 30 u

D. 32 u

24. Which of the following is not an isobar of $^{40}K$?

(i) $^{23}Na$

(ii) $^{23}Mg$

(iii) $^{40}S$

A. (i) and (iii)

B. (ii) and (iii)

C. (i) and (ii)

D. (i), (ii) and (iii)

25. An isotope of which of the following elements is used in the treatment of goitre?

A. Iodine

B. Chlorine

C. Fluorine

D. Silicon

# SELF-ASSESSMENT 2

**Choose the correct option.**

26. Which of the following models of an atom is compared to a 'watermelon'?
    A. Bohr's Model
    B. Thomson's Model
    C. Rutherford's Model
    D. Dalton's Model

27. Identify the correct statement related to 'electrons'.
    A. They are positively charged.
    B. They do not have any charge.
    C. They are negatively charged.
    D. The mass of an electron is more than the mass of a proton.

28. Identify the letter that represents the third shell or orbit in an atom.
    A. M  B. K
    C. N  D. L

29. Isotopes are the elements that contain___________.
    A. same mass number but different atomic numbers
    B. same mass number and same atomic number
    C. different mass numbers and different atomic numbers
    D. same atomic number but different mass numbers

30. Which of the following statements is true about the representation of an atom $_{10}X^{20}$?
    A. The number of neutrons is double the number of protons.
    B. The number of protons and neutrons is the same.
    C. The number of protons and neutrons together is thirty.
    D. The number of neutrons is half the number of protons.

31. Which of the following is not a postulate of 'Thomson's atomic model'?
    A. Electrons are distributed in different shells with discrete energy around the nucleus.
    B. The atoms are stable.
    C. The discrete orbits are called energy levels.
    D. While revolving in discrete orbits the electrons do not radiate energy.

32. Identify the correct pair from the following.
    A. Nucleus—Chadwick
    B. Neutrons—Rutherford
    C. Electrons—Thomson
    D. Protons—Niels Bohr

33. Which of the following features did the Rutherford's α-particle scattering experiment fail to explain?
   A. The arrangement of electrons in the orbit.
   B. The size of the nucleus.
   C. The positively charged centre of an atom.
   D. The movement of electrons in well-defined orbits.

34. Identify the incorrect statement related to Rutherford's α-particles.
   A. α-particles are doubly charged helium ions.
   B. Most of the fast moving α-particles were passed straight through the gold foil.
   C. α-particles are much heavier than protons.
   D. Most of the α-particles were deflected back.

35. Which of the following gives the maximum number of electrons present in a shell around a nucleus?
   A. $2n^8$ B. $2n^2$
   C. 2n D. $2n^4$

36. What is the maximum number of electrons that can be accommodated in the outermost orbit?
   A. 32 B. 2
   C. 8 D. 18

37. Identify the correct order of energy shells starting from the nucleus.
   A. M < L < N < K B. N < M < L < K
   C. L < M < K < N D. K < L < M < N

38. Identify the element that contains only one electron in its K-shell.
   A. Helium
   B. Hydrogen
   C. Fluorine
   D. Chlorine

39. Identify the atomic number of the element 'X' that contains 7 electrons in its M-shell or third orbit.
   A. 7
   B. 8
   C. 18
   D. 17

40. Identify the element that has the atomic structure as given below.

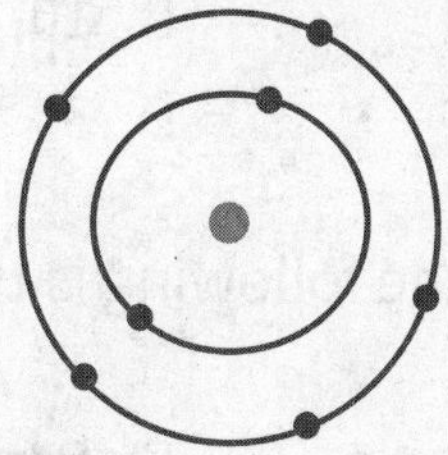

   A. Beryllium
   B. Lithium
   C. Oxygen
   D. Nitrogen

41. Identify the electronic configuration of an atom that contains 13 protons and 27 nucleons.
   A. 2, 8, 17 B. 2, 8, 3
   C. 8, 3, 2 D. 17, 8, 2

42. Identify the correct depiction of an atom 'A' that contains 9 protons and 10 neutrons.
   A. ${}^{9}_{19}A$ B. ${}^{19}_{9}A$
   C. ${}^{10}_{9}A$ D. ${}^{9}_{10}A$

43. Identify the element that contains seven (7) electrons in its outermost orbit.

(i) $_{7}N$

(ii) $_{17}Cl$

A. (i)

B. (ii)

C. Both (i) and (ii)

D. Neither (i) nor (ii)

44. Identify the number of protons present in the nucleus of an atom from the electronic structure given below.

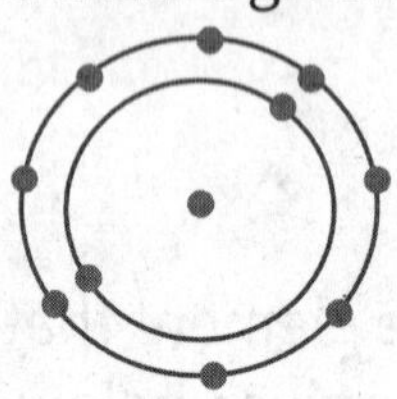

A. 11 B. 10

C. 5 D. 3

45. Which of the following is the other name of $^{2}_{1}H$?

A. Tritium B. Protium

C. Uranium D. Deuterium

46. **Assertion (A):** The atomic number of an element can be identified by its proton number.

**Reason (R):** The atomic number is the total number of protons of an atom.

A. A is true but R is false.

B. Both A and R are false.

C. Both A and R are true.

D. A is false but R is true.

47. Identify the nucleon number in the image given below.

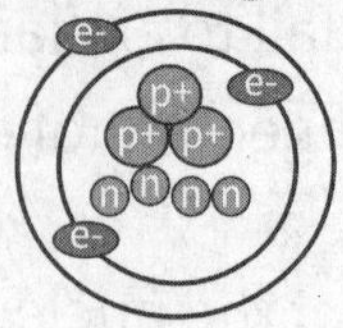


A. 3

B. 10

C. 7

D. 4

48. Which of the following elements has a valency of '4'?

A. Boron

B. Beryllium

C. Lithium

D. Carbon

49. Identify the valency of an element with Z = 18.

A. 3

B. 2

C. 0

D. 4

50. The representation of an element is $_{15}X^{31}$. Identify the element and the number of electrons that a single atom of this element contains?

A. Silicon; 31 electrons

B. Palladium; 46 electrons

C. Sulphur; 16 electrons

D. Phosphorus; 15 electrons

Chapter 5

# The Fundamental Unit of Life

## PRE-TEST

**Choose the correct option.**

1. Which of the following conveys the meaning of a cell in Latin?
   A. Bricks B. Boxes
   C. Little room D. Spheres
2. Simple, compound and electron are different types of ________________.
   A. stethoscopes B. microscopes
   C. rain gauge D. thermometers
3. Which of the following cells is also known as primitive cells?
   A. Bacteria B. Button mushroom
   C. Sea sponge D. Starfish
4. Identify the odd one from the following.
   A. Cell wall
   B. Centrioles
   C. Golgi apparatus
   D. Mitochondria
5. Which of the following cells is found in both animals and plants?
   A. Ovum
   B. Bone cell
   C. Neuron
   D. Smooth muscle cell

## KEYWORDS

**Black reaction:** A staining technique used to stain nerve or other cell structures using silver nitrate solution

**Cisterns:** The stacks of Golgi apparatus that are arranged parallel to each other

**Endocytosis:** The process of engulfing food materials by a living cell through its folded cell membrane

**Hypertonic solution:** A solution or medium in which the cell is immersed has a lower concentration of water than the cell

**Hypotonic solution:** A solution or medium in which the cell is immersed has a higher concentration of water than the cell

**Isotonic solution:** A solution or medium in which the cell is immersed has the same concentration of water as the cell

**Osmosis:** A special case of diffusion in which the movement of water molecules take place from a region of higher water concentration to a region of lower water concentration through a selectively permeable membrane

**Plasmolysis:** The phenomenon in which the protoplasm of a plant cell or a bacterium shrinks away from the cell wall due to the loss of water after being placed in a hypertonic solution

# Concept Map

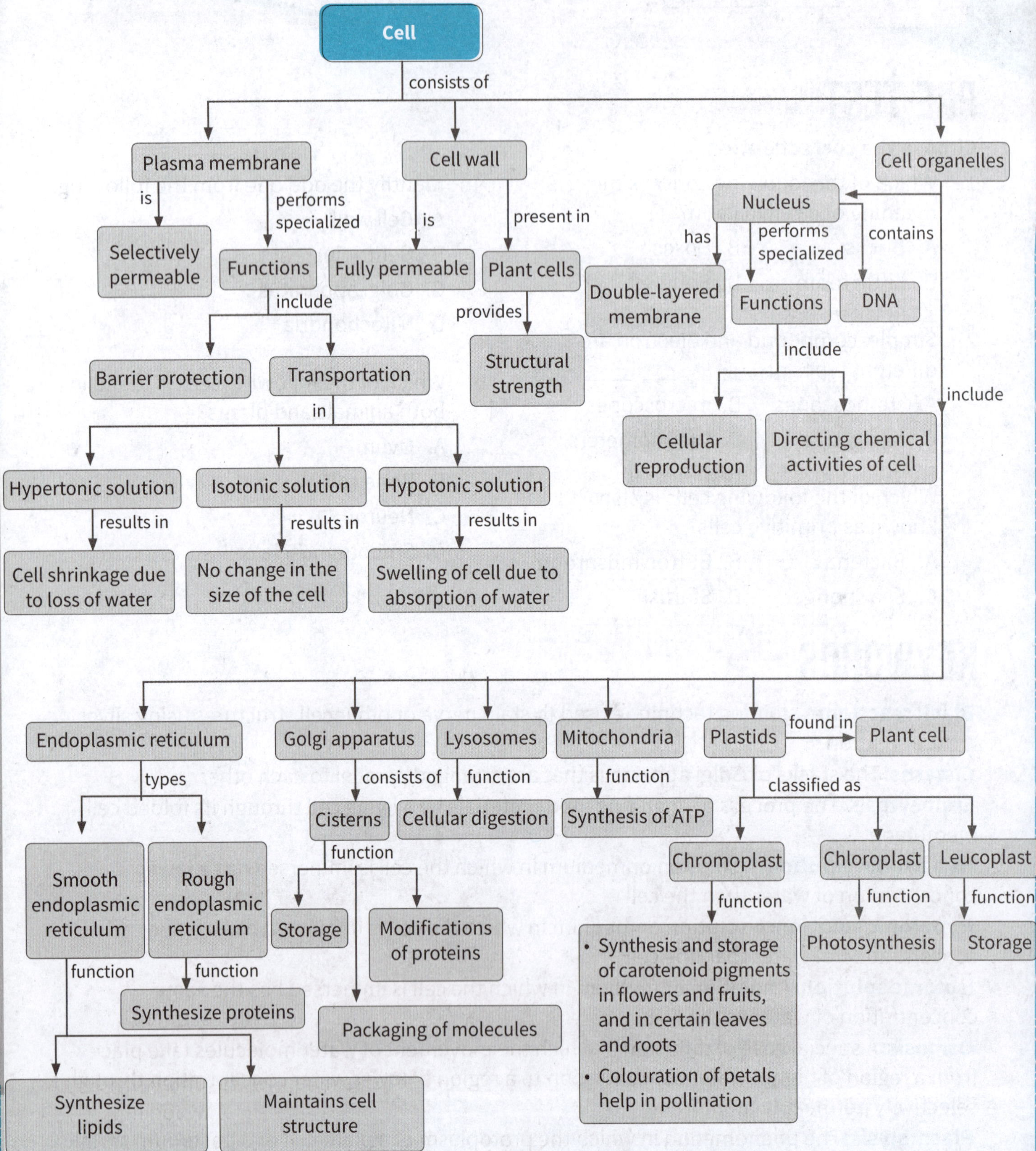
Cell
consists of
Plasma membrane
is
Selectively permeable
performs specialized
Functions
include
Barrier protection
Transportation
in
Hypertonic solution
results in
Cell shrinkage due to loss of water
Isotonic solution
results in
No change in the size of the cell
Hypotonic solution
results in
Swelling of cell due to absorption of water
Cell wall
is
Fully permeable
present in
Plant cells
provides
Structural strength
Cell organelles
Nucleus
has
Double-layered membrane
performs specialized
Functions
include
Cellular reproduction
Directing chemical activities of cell
contains
DNA
include
Endoplasmic reticulum
types
Smooth endoplasmic reticulum
function
Synthesize lipids
Maintains cell structure
Rough endoplasmic reticulum
function
Synthesize proteins
Golgi apparatus
consists of
Cisterns
function
Storage
Modifications of proteins
Packaging of molecules
Lysosomes
function
Cellular digestion
Mitochondria
function
Synthesis of ATP
Plastids
found in
Plant cell
classified as
Chromoplast
function
• Synthesis and storage of carotenoid pigments in flowers and fruits, and in certain leaves and roots
• Colouration of petals help in pollination
Chloroplast
function
Photosynthesis
Leucoplast
function
Storage

# Chapter 5 The Fundamental Unit of Life

## SELF-ASSESSMENT 1

**Choose the correct option.**

1. Which of the following processes refers to the staining of an individual nerve cell structure?
   A. Gram staining
   B. Negative staining
   C. Black reaction
   D. Blue reaction

2. In which of the following organisms, a single cell constitutes the whole organism?
   A. *Chlamydomonas*
   B. Button mushroom
   C. Sea sponge
   D. Starfish

3. Who discovered the nucleus in a cell?
   A. Robert Brown
   B. Leeuwenhoek
   C. Purkinje
   D. Schleiden

4. Which of the following was observed by Leeuwenhoek with his improvised microscope?
   A. Cork cell
   B. Water droplet
   C. Piece of cloth
   D. A drop of blood

5. Which of the following moves across the selectively permeable membrane during osmosis?
   A. Solvent
   B. Water molecules
   C. Cell organelle
   D. Protoplasm

6. In which of the following solutions will an onion cell swell by absorbing water?
   A. Hypotonic sugar solution
   B. Isotonic salt solution
   C. Isotonic sugar solution
   D. Hypertonic salt solution

7. A cell will neither swell nor shrink in a/an ___________ solution.
   A. hypotonic
   B. isotonic
   C. hypertonic
   D. brine

8. Which of the following is the correct pair with respect to the food consumption by an *Amoeba*?
   A. *Amoeba*—Plasmolysis
   B. *Amoeba*—Ingestion
   C. *Amoeba*—Endocytosis
   D. *Amoeba*—Ejection

9. Which of the following is correct about the plasma membrane?
   A. It is selectively permeable.
   B. It is completely permeable.
   C. It is composed of cellulose.
   D. It provides a rigid structure to the cell.

10. Which of the following helps aquatic organisms to survive in water?
    A. Diluted chemicals in water
    B. Diffused oxygen and carbon dioxide in water
    C. Diffused potassium permanganate in water
    D. Dissolved food particles in water

11. Which of the following happens during plasmolysis?
    A. Cell membrane swells and pushes itself towards the cell wall.
    B. Cell membrane and cell wall remain in the same position.
    C. Cell membrane shrinks away from the cell wall.
    D. The cell wall pushes itself towards the cell membrane.

12. **Assertion (A):** The cell is the basic unit of life.

    **Reason (R):** The cell theory states that all plants and animals are composed of cells.
    A. A is true and R is false.
    B. A is false and R is true.
    C. Both A and R are true.
    D. Both A and R are false.

13. Which of the following is the correct reason for darker appearance of some regions upon staining of a cell?
    A. Composition of the cell
    B. Concentration of the cell
    C. Type of stain used
    D. Type of microscope used

14. Arrange the following steps in the correct sequence for observing cheek cells under a microscope.
    (i) Add a drop of methylene blue solution on to the smear.
    (ii) Scrap the inner cheek gently with an ice cream stick.
    (iii) Mount the cells on the glass slide with a drop of water.
    (iv) Observe the slide under the microscope.
    A. (i), (ii), (iii), (iv)
    B. (ii), (iii), (i), (iv)
    C. (ii), (i), (iii), (iv)
    D. (i), (iv), (iii), (i)

15. Which of the following organelles in a bacterium contains chlorophyll?
    A. Plastid
    B. Membranous vesicle
    C. Vacuole
    D. Chloroplast

16. Which of the following structures stains less when compared to the others?
    A. Cytoplasm
    B. Nucleus
    C. Mitochondria
    D. Golgi body

17. **Assertion (A):** Viruses do not show the characteristics of life until they enter a host.

**Reason (R):** Viruses have thick cell wall.

A. A is true and R is false.

B. A is false and R is true.

C. Both A and R are true.

D. Both A and R are false.

18. Which of the following organisms contains more than one chromosome?

A. *Paramoecium*

B. Bacteria

C. *Chlamydomonas*

D. *Hydrilla*

19. Which of the following cell organelles will be found on the rough endoplasmic reticulum?

A. Ribosome B. Centriole

C. Mitochondria D. Lysosome

20. In which of the following cell organelles protein synthesis takes place?

A. Golgi bodies B. Ribosomes

C. Lysosomes D. Centrioles

21. Which of the following structures stores, modifies and packages materials or substances that are synthesized in the cell?

A. Golgi apparatus

B. Smooth endoplasmic reticulum

C. Vacuoles

D. Ribosomes

22. Identify the correct pair among the following.

A. Ribosome—Lipid molecules

B. Lysosome—Waste disposal

C. Golgi apparatus—Cell membrane

D. Mitochondria—Storage house

23. Leucoplasts store starch, oil and granules of proteins. The colour of a leucoplast is __________.

A. green

B. red

C. white

D. yellow

24. Which of the following pair of structures is similar in their external appearances?

A. Mitochondria and plastid

B. Nucleus and mitochondria

C. Vacuole and nucleus

D. Lysosome and ribosome

25. Which of the following are the components of a plasma membrane?

A. Lipids and proteins

B. Cellulose

C. Lipids and cellulose

D. Starch and lipids

# SELF-ASSESSMENT 2

**Choose the correct option.**

26. Which of the following cell organelles does not contain a double membrane?
    A. Chloroplast B. Mitochondria
    C. Nucleus D. Lysosome

27. Which of the following cell organelles matches the functions of an organelle described below?
    (i) Protects the DNA from chemical reactions of the cytoplasm
    (ii) Selectively allows certain substances in and out of the nucleus
    (iii) Controls the biochemical reactions of the cell
    A. Nucleus
    B. Mitochondria
    C. Endoplasmic reticulum
    D. Vacuole

28. Which of the following is true about eukaryotic animal cells?
    A. They are bound by a cell wall.
    B. They have a shell membrane.
    C. They are bound by a cell membrane.
    D. They have a basement membrane.

29. Which of the following organelles is also known as the storehouse of oils and protein granules?
    A. Leucoplast
    B. Golgi apparatus
    C. Chloroplast
    D. Vacuole

30. Which of the following is referred to as the energy currency of a cell?
    A. ATP B. DNA
    C. RNA D. RER

31. The functional segments of DNA are ____________.
    A. genes B. cells
    C. cisterns D. ATPs

32. If a cell lacks ribosomes, it will not be able to ____________.
    A. synthesize DNA
    B. synthesize proteins
    C. respire
    D. digest the ingested food

33. Which of the following organelles occupies most of the cell volume in a green plant cell?
    A. Vacuole
    B. Cytoplasm
    C. Both vacuole and cytoplasm
    D. Chloroplast

34. In which of the following types of organisms, the compartmentalization of cytoplasm is observed?
    A. Eukaryotes
    B. Viruses
    C. Prokaryotes
    D. Cyanobacteria

35. Which among the following does not adhere to cell theory?
    A. Bacteria  B. Animals
    C. Plants  D. Viruses

36. Proteins move across the plasma membrane through _____________.
    A. endocytosis
    B. diffusion
    C. membrane biogenesis
    D. exocytosis

37. Which of the following are commonly known as suicide bags?
    A. Ribosomes  B. Lysosomes
    C. Mitochondria  D. Golgi apparatus

38. Which of the cell organelles is absent in plant cells?
    A. Mitochondria  B. Chloroplasts
    C. Vacuoles  D. Lysosomes

39. Which of the following is known as waste bags in mature plant cells?
    A. Vacuoles
    B. Mitochondria
    C. Golgi apparatus
    D. Ribosomes

40. The chromosomes are composed of only nucleic acids in __________.
    A. eukaryotes  B. prokaryotes
    C. viruses  D. fungi

41. The drugs are detoxified in the liver of vertebrates by ______________.
    A. Golgi apparatus
    B. smooth endoplasmic reticulum
    C. ribosomes
    D. mitochondria

42. **Assertion (A):** Mitochondria are referred to as powerhouses of the cell.

    **Reason (R):** Mitochondria perform metabolic reactions and release ATP, the energy required for the function of cells.
    A. Both A and R are true and R is the correct explanation of A.
    B. Both A and R are true but R is not correct explanation of A.
    C. A is true but R is false.
    D. R is true but A is false.

43. Identify the correct set by reading the statements given below.
    (i) It is also referred to as a non-pigmented plastid.
    (ii) It contains yellow or orange-coloured pigment.
    (iii) It contains the chlorophyll in plant cells.
    A. (i) Nucleus; (ii) Leucoplast; (iii) Chloroplast
    B. (i) Leucoplast; (ii) Chromoplast; (iii) Chloroplast
    C. (i) Lysosome; (ii) Ribosomes; (iii) Leucoplast
    D. (i) Leucoplast; (ii) Mitochondria; (iii) Leucoplast

44. **Statement I:** Some cell organelles have their own DNA.

    **Statement II:** The mitochondrial DNA helps in the manufacturing of proteins.
    A. Statement I is correct and statement II is incorrect.
    B. Statement II is correct and statement I is incorrect.
    C. Both statements are correct.
    D. Both statements are incorrect.

45. Match the following and choose the correct option.

| Column I | | Column II | |
|---|---|---|---|
| a. | Golgi apparatus | i. | Skeletal support to the cell |
| b. | Endoplasmic reticulum | ii. | Hydrolytic degradation of the substances |
| c. | Lysosomes | iii. | Synthesize lysosomes |

A. a→i; b→ii; c→iii
B. a→iii; b→ii; c→i
C. a→ii; b→iii; c→i
D. a→iii; b→i; c→ii

46. The organelles that contain DNA, RNA and ribosomes are ________.
A. plastids
B. lysosomes
C. mitochondria
D. plastids and mitochondria

47. The nuclear materials are separated from the cytoplasm by the layers formed from ____________.
A. lipids
B. cellulose
C. protein
D. lipids and proteins

48. A cytoplasmic framework for biochemical processes is provided by ___________.
A. endoplasmic reticulum
B. mitochondria
C. vacuole
D. nuclear membrane

49. Which of the following helps in building a cell membrane?
A. Carbohydrates
B. Lipids
C. Vitamins
D. Minerals

50. The cell organelle that can increase its size along with the cell is __________.
A. endoplasmic reticulum
B. mitochondria
C. vacuole
D. nucleus

Chapter 6

# Tissues

## PRE-TEST

**Choose the correct option.**

1. Which of the following is a unicellular organism?
   A. *Amoeba* B. Plant
   C. Ant D. Cat

2. Which of the following cells undergo contraction and relaxation?
   A. Nerve cell B. Muscle cell
   C. Heart cell D. Blood cell

3. Which of the following organ systems in humans helps in the movement of hormones throughout the body?
   A. Nervous system
   B. Circulatory system
   C. Respiratory system
   D. Excretory system

4. Which of the following completes the given analogy?
   Egg : Cell :: ____________ : Tissue
   A. RBC
   B. Platelet
   C. Blood
   D. WBC

5. Which of the following cells contain chloroplasts?
   A. Skin cells
   B. Plant cells
   C. Blood cells
   D. Nerve cells

## KEYWORDS

**Adipose connective tissue:** Animal tissues filled with fat globules for the storage of fats and acts as insulator

**Aerenchyma:** Parenchyma found in plant cells with large air spaces to give buoyancy

**Animal tissues:** A group of connected cells that have a similar function within an animal

**Apical meristems:** Plant tissues present at the growing tip of the stem and roots

**Areolar connective tissue:** Animal tissue that is found beneath the epithelium, surrounding the blood vessels, nerve bundles, muscles and organs

**Blood:** A fluid connective tissue that transports oxygen and nutrients to the cells and carries away carbon dioxide and other waste products in animals

**Bone:** A connective tissue found in animals with hard matrix, composed of calcium and phosphorus

**Cardiac muscles:** Cylindrical, branched and uninucleate involuntary muscle tissues found in animals (also called heart muscles)

**Cartilage:** A connective tissue found in animals with a solid matrix composed of proteins and sugars

**Chlorenchyma:** Parenchyma with chlorophyll found in plants which aids in photosynthesis

**Collenchyma:** Plant tissues that are thickened at the corners, have very little intercellular space and provide mechanical support

**Companion cells:** A specialized parenchyma cell found within the phloem of a flowering plant, located adjacent to sieve elements

**Guard cells:** Plant cells that guard the stomata (kidney shaped in dicots and dumbbell shaped in monocots)

**Histology:** The study of tissues

**Intercalary meristems:** Meristematic tissues present at internodes of leaves

**Lateral meristems:** Meristematic tissues present at the lateral side of stems and roots

**Meristems:** Plant tissues having the power of cell division (also called meristematic tissues)

**Muscular tissues:** Animal tissues with special contractile proteins that are responsible for movements of the body

**Parenchyma:** Plant tissues that are loosely packed, having large intracellular space and providing support to the plants

**Permanent tissues:** Plant tissues that have completed growth and are incapable of any meristematic activity

**Phloem:** Living tissue in vascular plants that consists of sieve tubes, companion cells, phloem parenchyma and phloem fibres

**Sclerenchyma:** Plant tissues that are thickened due to lignin, having no intercellular space and that makes the plant hard and stiff.

**Sieve elements:** Long and narrow phloem cells that are connected together to form the sieve tube

**Sieve tubes:** Specialized phloem cells composed of sieve element cells and companion cells

**Simple permanent tissues:** Plant tissues that are made of one type of cell

**Striated muscles:** Skeletal muscles or voluntary muscles with cylindrical, unbranched, striated and multinucleated tissues

**Tracheids:** Elongated cells in the xylem of vascular plants that transport water and mineral salts, and lack perforated plates

**Unicellular organisms:** Organisms in which a single cell performs all the basic life functions

**Unstriated muscles:** Smooth or involuntary muscles with spindle-shaped, non-striated and involuntary muscle tissues

**Vessels:** Tubular structures in the xylem of vascular plants that conduct water and minerals and has perforation plates

**Xylem:** Plant cells with thick cell wall consisting of tracheids, vessels, xylem parenchyma and xylem fibres

# Concept Map

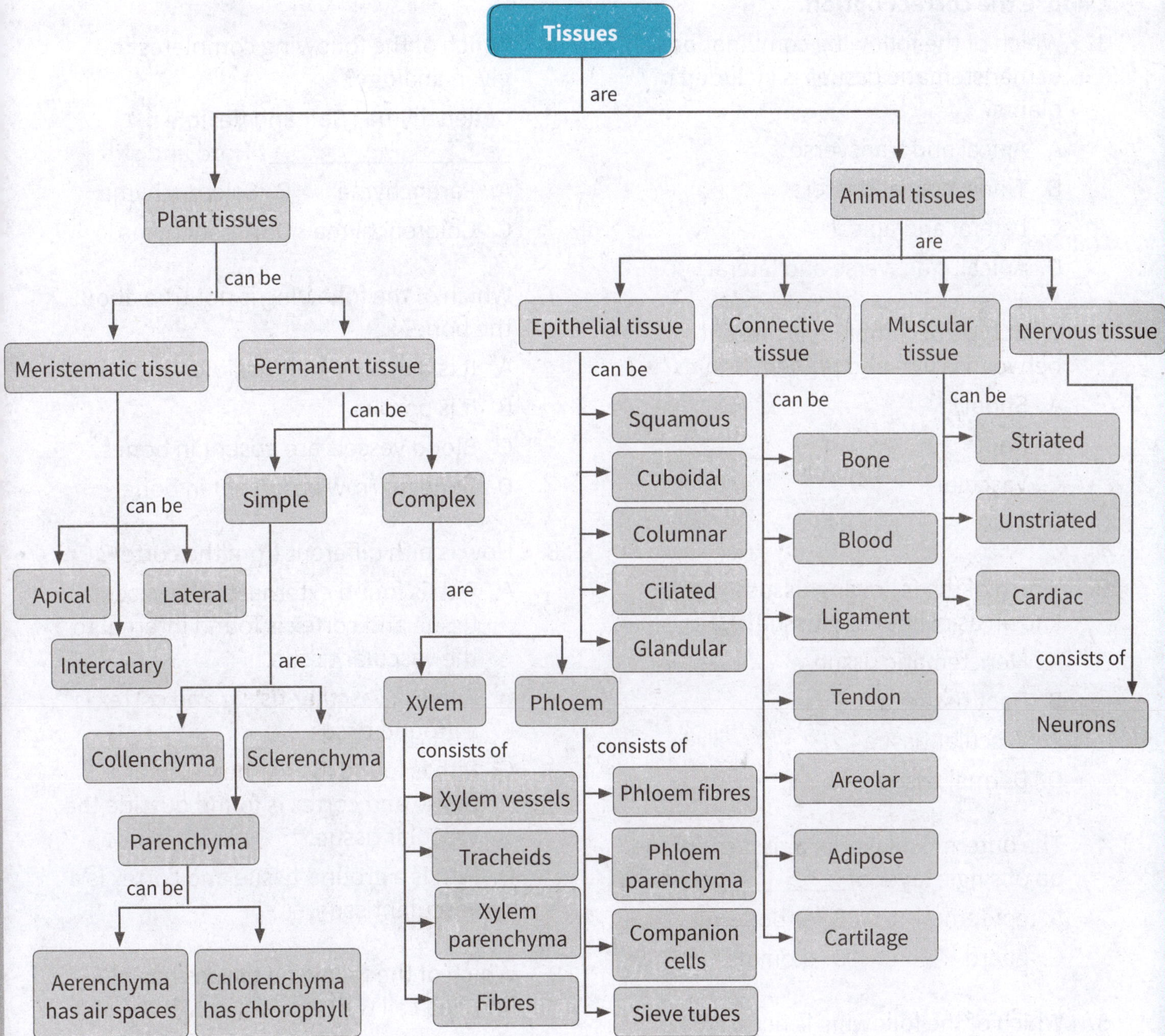
Tissues
are
Plant tissues
can be
Meristematic tissue
can be
Apical
Lateral
Intercalary
Permanent tissue
can be
Simple
are
Collenchyma
Sclerenchyma
Parenchyma
can be
Aerenchyma has air spaces
Chlorenchyma has chlorophyll
Complex
are
Xylem
consists of
Xylem vessels
Tracheids
Xylem parenchyma
Fibres
Phloem
consists of
Phloem fibres
Phloem parenchyma
Companion cells
Sieve tubes
Animal tissues
are
Epithelial tissue
can be
Squamous
Cuboidal
Columnar
Ciliated
Glandular
Connective tissue
can be
Bone
Blood
Ligament
Tendon
Areolar
Adipose
Cartilage
Muscular tissue
can be
Striated
Unstriated
Cardiac
Nervous tissue
consists of
Neurons

# SELF-ASSESSMENT 1

**Choose the correct option.**

1. Which of the following combinations of meristematic tissues is included in plants?
   A. Apical and transverse
   B. Transverse and lateral
   C. Lateral and apical
   D. Apical, transverse and lateral

2. What type of cambium is present between xylem and phloem tissues?
   A. Shoot
   B. Root
   C. Vascular
   D. Cork

3. Which of the following tissues is also known as conducting tissue?
   A. Meristematic tissue
   B. Root tissue
   C. Vascular tissue
   D. Dermal tissue

4. The outermost layer of a tissue is made up of single layer of __________cells.
   A. epidermal B. endodermal
   C. guard D. stomata

5. Which of the following is not a type of connective tissue?
   A. Blood B. Neuron
   C. Bone D. Cartilage

6. Which of the following completes the given analogy?
   Collenchyma : Soft and flexible ::
   ___________________ : Hard and stiff
   A. Parenchyma B. Sclerenchyma
   C. Chlorenchyma D. Aerenchyma

7. Which of the following is not true about the bone?
   A. It is hard and non-flexible.
   B. It is porous.
   C. Blood vessels are absent in bones.
   D. Bone marrow is present in bone.

8. How is pith different from the cortex?
   A. Pith is found external to the vascular tissue and cortex is found internal to the vascular tissue.
   B. Pith is a vascular tissue and cortex is a ground tissue.
   C. Pith is found inside the vascular tissue and cortex is found outside the vascular tissue.
   D. Pith is a ground tissue and cortex is a vascular tissue.

9. Which of the following tissues has lignified cell wall?
   A. Parenchyma B. Collenchyma
   C. Sclerenchyma D. Cambium

10. Which of the following completes the given analogy?
Blood : Connective tissue :: Ligaments : ______________
   A. Muscular tissue
   B. Fibrous connective tissue
   C. Skeletal tissue
   D. Nerve tissue

11. Which of the following is the key difference between meristematic and permanent tissues?
   A. Photosynthetic ability
   B. Ability to divide
   C. Ability to move
   D. Complexity to perform a certain function

12. Which of the following muscle tissues function throughout their life continuously, without fatigue?
   A. Skeletal muscles
   B. Cardiac muscles
   C. Smooth muscles
   D. Voluntary muscles

13. Which of the following statements is not true with respect to permanent tissues?
   A. Cells are small in size.
   B. Cells lack the power of cell division.
   C. Cytoplasm is present as a layer along the cell wall.
   D. Cells may either be living or dead.

14. Which of the following is not a function of parenchyma cells?
   A. Storage of food and minerals
   B. Wound healing and repair
   C. Regeneration and grafting
   D. Mechanical strength and elasticity

15. Identify the incorrect pair.
   A. Tracheids—Non-living cells
   B. Vessels—Living cells
   C. Companion cells—Living cells
   D. Xylem fibres—Non-living cells

16. Identify the correct type of tissues found in bones and bark of trees, respectively.
   A. Connective tissue and sclerenchyma tissue
   B. Cuboidal epithelial tissue and parenchyma tissue
   C. Complex permanent tissue and epithelial tissue
   D. Columnar epithelial tissue and collenchyma tissue

17. Which of the following actions is the result of the functioning of smooth muscles?
   A. The movement of the passage of food in the intestine.
   B. The movement of hands and legs.
   C. The rhythmic contraction and relaxation of the heart.
   D. The transmission of signals from one part of the body to another.

18. Which of the following completes the given analogy?
Plant cell wall : ______________ :: Horns of animals : Keratin
   A. Cellulose  B. Amino acid
   C. Lipid  D. Protein

19. Which of the following types of cells forms a gland in animals?
   A. Connective  B. Epithelial
   C. Nervous  D. Muscle

20. Which of the following indicates the features of striated muscles?
   A. Cylindrical, multinucleate and unbranched
   B. Spindle, unbranched and unnucleated
   C. Cylindrical, striped and nucleated
   D. Cylindrical, striped and branched

21. **Statement I:** Cardiac muscles are composed of branched network of fibres.

   **Statement II:** Intercalated discs are present at intervals in the cardiac muscle fibres.
   A. Statement I is correct and statement II is incorrect.
   B. Statement II is correct and statement I is incorrect.
   C. Both statements are correct.
   D. Both statements are incorrect.

22. Match the following.

| | Column I | | Column II |
|---|---|---|---|
| a. | Sieve tube | i. | Conduction of food through sieve tube |
| b. | Companion cells | ii. | Conduction of food |
| c. | Phloem parenchyma | iii. | Mechanical support |
| d. | Phloem fibres | iv. | Storage |

   A. a→i; b→ii; c→iii; d→iv
   B. a→ii; b→i; c→iv; d→iii
   C. a→iv; b→iii; c→i; d→ii
   D. a→iii; b→iv; c→ii; d→i

23. Which of the following tissues would be damaged if two long bones are dislocated in an individual?
   A. Tendon break
   B. Skeletal muscle break
   C. Ligament break
   D. Areolar tissue break

24. **Assertion (A):** The girth of the plant increases with the growth and development of the plant.

   **Reason (R):** Lateral meristem occurs almost parallel to the long axis of the root, stem and branches.
   A. Both A and R are true and R is the correct explanation of A.
   B. Both A and R are true but R is not the correct explanation of A.
   C. A is true but R is false.
   D. A is false but R is true.

25. Microscopic observation of the epithelial tissue shows that the thin and flat cells that are arranged edge-to-edge appear like closely packed tiles. These cells could be found in the ________________.
   A. inner lining of the stomach
   B. inner lining of the mouth
   C. outer surface of the ovary
   D. inner lining of the fallopian tube

# SELF-ASSESSMENT 2

**Choose the correct option.**

26. Which of the following is the basis for the classification of tissues into meristematic and permanent?
    A. The dividing capacity of the tissues
    B. The water-absorption capacity of the tissues
    C. The position of the tissues
    D. The size of the tissues

27. Which of the following plant tissues is found at the plant tips and helps in increasing the length of the plant?
    A. Lateral meristem
    B. Apical meristem
    C. Vascular bundle
    D. Cambium

28. Which of the following tissues gives flexibility to plants?
    A. Parenchyma
    B. Chlorenchyma
    C. Collenchyma
    D. Aerenchyma

29. In which of the following organs is the cartilage not present?
    A. Nose
    B. Ears
    C. Kidney
    D. Larynx

30. Which of the following tissues is made of dead cells?
    A. Parenchyma
    B. Sclerenchyma
    C. Chlorenchyma
    D. Aerenchyma

31. Which of the following is not a part of the phloem?
    A. Sieve tube
    B. Companion cells
    C. Vessels
    D. Fibres

32. Which of the following muscles is responsible for the movement of food in the alimentary canal?
    A. Stratified
    B. Striated
    C. Unstriated
    D. Cardiac

33. Which of the following completes the given analogy?
    Ligaments : Bone to bone :: Tendon : ________________
    A. Bone to muscle
    B. Muscle to vessels
    C. Muscle to muscle
    D. Vessels to bone

34. Which of the following is a characteristic feature of collenchyma?
   A. Elongated cells with the deposition of cellulose and pectin all over the cell wall
   B. Isodiametric cells with the deposition of cellulose and pectin at the corners
   C. Elongated cells with irregular thickening at the corner
   D. Isodiametric cells with thickening all over the cell wall

35. Which of the following completes the given analogy?
   Study of plants : Botany :: Study of tissues : ____________
   A. Cytology B. Embryology
   C. Histology D. Pathology

36. Which of the following tissues in a human body acts as an insulator?
   A. Lipoproteins B. Adipose tissue
   C. Mucous layer D. Lymphoid tissue

37. Which of the following completes the given analogy?
   Neutrophil : Polynucleus ::
   ____________ : Single large nucleus
   A. Eosinophil B. Basophil
   C. Erythrocytes D. Lymphocytes

38. Which of the following statements is incorrect?
   A. Smooth muscles are also found in the iris of the eye.
   B. Nervous tissue is made of neurons that receive and conduct impulses.
   C. Muscles of the heart are called voluntary muscles.
   D. Muscles contain special proteins called contractile proteins.

39. Which of the following epithelial cells helps in the absorption of digested food in the intestine?
   A. Striated squamous epithelium
   B. Columnar epithelium
   C. Pseudo-stratified epithelium
   D. Cuboidal epithelium

40. Identify the incorrect pair.
   A. Adipose tissue—Fat storage
   B. Nervous tissue—Purification of blood
   C. Blood—Connective tissue
   D. Tendons—Connect bone to muscles

41. Which of the following is a voluntary action?
   A. Pumping of heart
   B. Movement of food in the stomach
   C. Moving your legs
   D. Movement of the diaphragm

42. Which of the following features is ensured by the presence of tissues in a multicellular organism?
   A. Faster development
   B. Division of labour
   C. Higher productive potential
   D. Body strength

43. Identify the odd one out.
   A. Ligament B. Epithelium
   C. Tendon D. Blood

44. Which is the most abundant animal tissue in an organism?
   A. Epithelium
   B. Muscular
   C. Connective
   D. Nerve

45. Which of the following tissues is responsible for receiving, interpreting, and producing a response to stimuli?

A. Muscular tissue B. Nervous tissue

C. Epithelial tissue D. Connective tissue

46. **Statement I:** Voluntary muscles show light and dark bands.

**Statement II:** Involuntary muscles do not show light or dark bands.

A. Statement I is correct and statement II is incorrect.

B. Statement II is correct and statement I is incorrect.

C. Both statements I and II are correct.

D. Both statements I and II are incorrect.

47. Match the following.

| Column I | | Column II |
|---|---|---|
| a. Meristematic tissue | i. | Differentiated cells without the ability to divide |
| b. Permanent tissue | ii. | Conducts food from leaves to all parts of the plant |
| c. Xylem | iii. | Undifferentiated actively dividing cells |
| d. Phloem | iv. | Conducts water from roots to all parts of a plant |

A. a→i; b→ii; c→iii; d→iv

B. a→iii; b→i; c→iv; d→ii

C. a→iii; b→iv; c→ii; d→i

D. a→iv; b→iii; c→i; d→ii

48. On observing a plant cell under a microscope, cells with thick wall, elongated in shape and possessing thickened cellulose and pectin were found. What could be the type of the cell?

A. Parenchyma

B. Collenchyma

C. Sclerenchyma

D. Vascular tissue

49. **Assertion (A):** A nail hammered to a plant at a height of 3 feet will not show any change in its height even after years.

**Reason (R):** Apical meristem is present at the tip of the shoot and the root.

A. Both A and R are true and R is the correct explanation of A.

B. Both A and R are true but R is not the correct explanation of A.

C. A is true but R is false.

D. A is false but R is true.

50. Which of the following tissues can be found in the hump of a camel and the blubbers in a whale?

A. Areolar tissue

B. Muscular tissue

C. Tendons

D. Adipose tissue

Chapter 7

# Diversity in Living Organisms

## PRE-TEST

**Choose the correct option.**

1. Identify the odd one out based on the growing height of a human.
   A. 10-year-old
   B. 11-year-old
   C. 14-year-old
   D. 60-year-old

2. Which of the following can be grouped with human beings in animal classification?
   A. Apes
   B. Dogs
   C. Tigers
   D. Starfish

3. Identify the odd one among the following.
   A. Bacteria  B. Moss
   C. Ferns  D. Algae

4. Which of the following would belong to the family of 'cats'?
   A. Bear  B. Tiger
   C. Antelope  D. Dog

5. The other name of a seed leaf is ___________.
   A. cotyledon  B. embryo
   C. spore  D. thallus

## KEYWORDS

**Angiosperms:** Plants with seeds inside the fruit and that bear flowers

**Bilateral symmetry:** Divisibility of an organism into identical right and left halves, creating mirror images through a single vertical plane

**Biodiversity:** The diverse variety of living organisms present in a particular region

**Class:** Taxonomy rank that comes below 'Phylum or Division' and above 'Order'

**Diploblastic:** Organisms derived from two embryonic germ layers

**Division:** Taxonomy rank that comes below 'Kingdom' and above 'Class' with reference to plants

**Ectoderm:** The outermost germ layer of an animal embryo that forms nail, hair, epidermis, etc.

**Endoderm:** The innermost germ layer of an animal embryo that forms the stomach, colon, urinary bladder, etc.

**Family:** Taxonomy rank that comes below 'Order' and above 'Genus'

**Genus:** Taxonomy rank that comes below 'Family' and above 'Species'

**Groups:** A group of organisms within a species that differ in simple ways from its parent group

**Gymnosperms:** Plants with naked seeds and that do not bear flowers

**Kingdom Animalia:** Kingdom comprising of all the existing or extinct animals

**Kingdom Fungi:** Kingdom of multicellular organisms with a eukaryotic cell organization

**Kingdom Monera:** Kingdom of unicellular organisms with a prokaryotic cell organization

**Kingdom Plantae:** Kingdom comprising of all the existing or extinct plants

**Kingdom Protista:** Kingdom of unicellular organisms with a eukaryotic cell organization

**Kingdom:** Highest category in taxonomic classification

**Mesoderm:** The middle germ layer between ectoderm and endoderm of an animal embryo, which forms bones, cartilage, etc.

**Nomenclature:** A way of identifying the various life forms which include a generic and a specific name

**Order:** Taxonomy rank that comes below 'Class' and above 'Family'

**Phylum:** Taxonomy rank that comes below 'Kingdom' and above 'Class' with reference to animals

**Radial symmetry:** Divisibility of an organism into equally-spaced portions around a central point

**Species:** Organisms belonging to the same genus which can interbreed

**Symbiotic relation:** The relation between two organisms that live together for the benefit of one or both

**Taxonomy:** A branch of biology which deals with the identification, nomenclature and classification of organisms

**Triploblastic:** Organisms (mainly animals) derived from all the three embryonic germ layers

# Concept Map

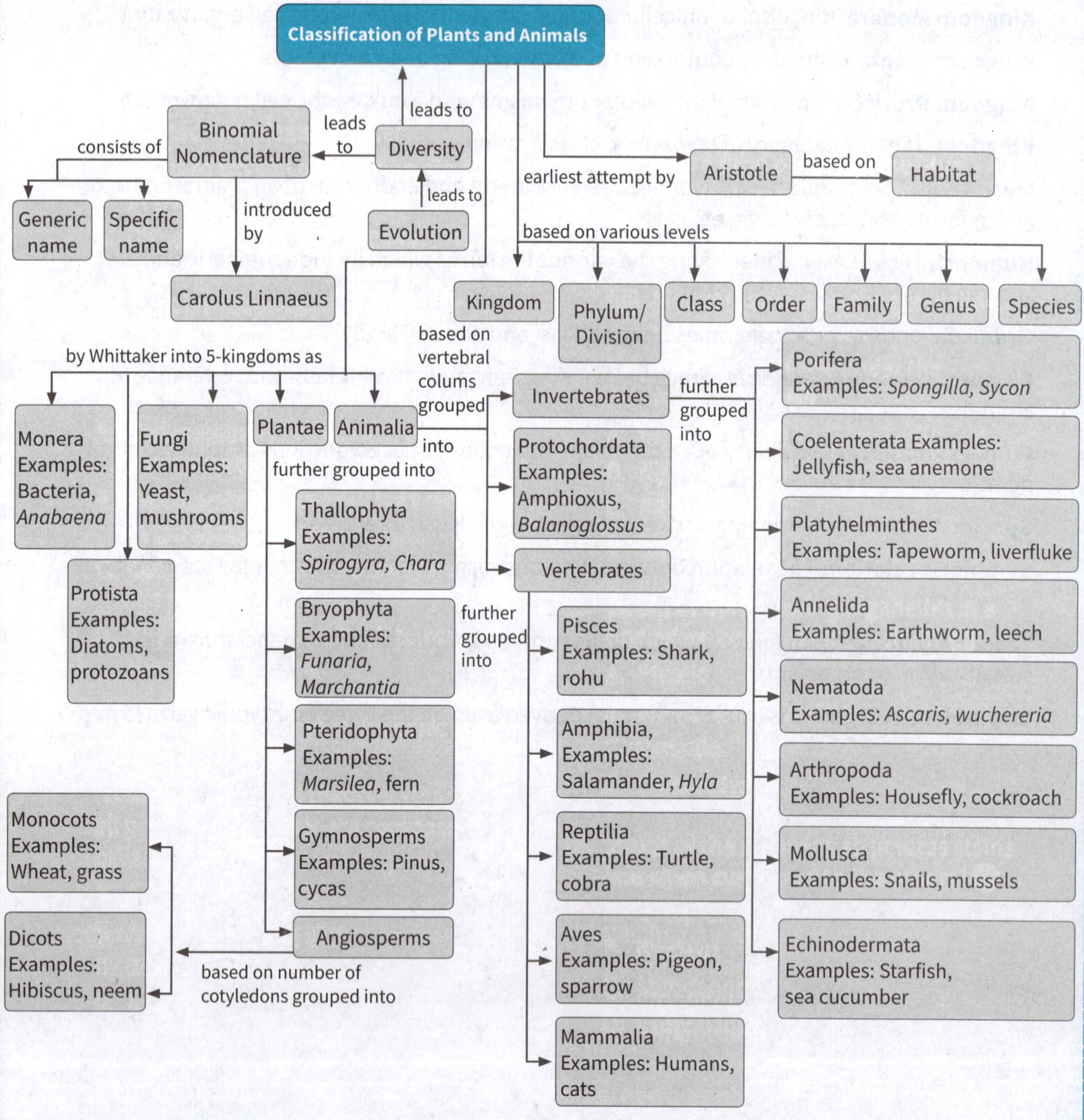
Classification of Plants and Animals
leads to
Diversity
leads to
Evolution
leads to
Binomial Nomenclature
consists of
Generic name
Specific name
introduced by
Carolus Linnaeus
earliest attempt by
Aristotle
based on
Habitat
based on various levels
Kingdom
Phylum/ Division
Class
Order
Family
Genus
Species
by Whittaker into 5-kingdoms as
Monera Examples: Bacteria, *Anabaena*
Fungi Examples: Yeast, mushrooms
Protista Examples: Diatoms, protozoans
Plantae
Animalia
further grouped into
Thallophyta Examples: *Spirogyra, Chara*
Bryophyta Examples: *Funaria, Marchantia*
Pteridophyta Examples: *Marsilea*, fern
Gymnosperms Examples: Pinus, cycas
Angiosperms
based on number of cotyledons grouped into
Monocots Examples: Wheat, grass
Dicots Examples: Hibiscus, neem
based on vertebral colums grouped into
Invertebrates
further grouped into
Porifera Examples: *Spongilla, Sycon*
Coelenterata Examples: Jellyfish, sea anemone
Platyhelminthes Examples: Tapeworm, liverfluke
Annelida Examples: Earthworm, leech
Nematoda Examples: *Ascaris, wuchereria*
Arthropoda Examples: Housefly, cockroach
Mollusca Examples: Snails, mussels
Echinodermata Examples: Starfish, sea cucumber
Protochordata Examples: Amphioxus, *Balanoglossus*
Vertebrates
further grouped into
Pisces Examples: Shark, rohu
Amphibia, Examples: Salamander, *Hyla*
Reptilia Examples: Turtle, cobra
Aves Examples: Pigeon, sparrow
Mammalia Examples: Humans, cats

# SELF-ASSESSMENT 1

**Choose the correct option.**

1. Which of the following characteristics was used by Aristotle to classify living organisms?
   A. Habitat
   B. Eating habits
   C. Type of movement
   D. Modes of reproduction

2. Who among the following classified the kingdom Monera into Archaebacteria and Eubacteria?
   A. Carl Woese
   B. Ernst Haeckel
   C. Robert Whittaker
   D. Aristotle

3. Which of the following kingdoms consists of autotrophs?
   A. *Animalia* B. *Protista*
   C. *Plantae* D. *Monera*

4. Which of the following is known as 'seed-bearing plants'?
   A. *Pteridophytes* B. *Bryophytes*
   C. *Thallophytes* D. Phanerogams

5. Which of the following refers to 'flatworms'?
   A. Coelenterata
   B. Porifera
   C. Platyhelminthes
   D. Annelida

6. Identify the odd one out from the following.
   A. *Paramoecium* B. *Amoeba*
   C. *Euglena* D. *Penicillium*

7. Identify the symbiotic relationship shown in the picture.

   A. Lichen
   B. *Lactobacillus*
   C. Algae
   D. African Oxpecker

8. Which of the following organisms used cilia for locomotion?
   A. *Euglena*
   B. *Paramoecium*
   C. *Amoeba*
   D. *Aspergillus*

9. Which of the following has stem and leaf-like structures but do not conduct water and food from one part to another?
   A. *Cladophora*
   B. *Funaria*
   C. *Ulothrix*
   D. *Ulva*

10. Which of the following is cryptogamae?
   A. *Paphiopedilum*
   B. *Ipomoea*
   C. *Marsilea*
   D. Grass

11. Which of the following completes the given analogy?
   Animals : Phylum :: Plants: ________.
   A. Genus B. Division
   C. Species D. Family

12. Which of the following does not have a specialized conductive tissue?
   A. *Marsilea* B. *Riccia*
   C. *Horsetail* D. Ferns

13. Which of the following does not possess a naked embryo?
   A. *Ulva* B. *Ulothrix*
   C. *Cladophora* D. *Paphiopedilum*

14. Which of the following is referred to as a non-motile animal?
   A. *Sycon*
   B. Sea anemone
   C. Liver flukes
   D. *Planaria*

15. **Assertion (A):** *Hydra* and sea anemone are classified under phylum Coelenterata.
   **Reason (R):** They have two-layered body with tentacles around their mouth.
   A. A is true R is false.
   B. A is false R is true.
   C. Both A and R are true.
   D. Both A and R are false.

16. Which of the following organisms' body is bilaterally symmetrical?
   A. *Planaria*
   B. *Hydra*
   C. *Spongilla*
   D. Sea anemone

17. Which of the following has 'pseudocoelom'?
   A. *Wuchereria* B. *Nereis*
   C. Earthworm D. Leech

18. Which of the following contains the skeleton made up of calcium carbonate?
   A. Prawn B. Earthworm
   C. Sea urchin D. Housefly

19. Which of the following is separated by a notochord?
   A. Nervous system and gut
   B. Coelomic cavity and muscle tissue
   C. Spiny skin and coelomic cavity
   D. Open circulatory system and kidney-like organ

20. Which of the following organisms has a two-chambered heart?
   A. Anglerfish
   B. *Balanoglossus*
   C. Turtle
   D. King Cobra

21. Identify the correct pair among the following.
   A. Prawn—Jointed legs
   B. *Ascaris*—Open circulatory system
   C. *Wuchereria*—Blood filled cavity
   D. Spider—Water driven tube system

22. Identify the characteristics of leeches.
    (i) Their body is bilaterally symmetrical.
    (ii) They possess pseudocoelom.
    (iii) They are triploblastic.
    (iv) They have a segmented body.
    A. (i), (ii) and (iii) B. (ii), (iii) and (iv)
    C. (i), (iii) and (iv) D. (i), (ii) and (iv)

23. **Assertion (A):** Bryophytes are known as the amphibians of the plant kingdom.
    **Reason (R):** The body of bryophytes consists of stem and leaf-like structures.
    A. A is true R is false.
    B. A is false R is true.
    C. A is true but R is the incorrect explanation of A.
    D. A is true and R is the correct explanation of A.

24. Which of the following is true about the body cavity of *Annelida*?
    A. The body cavity is absent.
    B. Organs are packed in the body structure.
    C. Tentacles play the role of body cavity.
    D. The body cavity is replaced by pores throughout.

25. Which of the following is the criteria used to divide angiosperms into two groups?
    A. Number of cotyledons
    B. Number of spores
    C. Presence of differentiated plant body
    D. Presence of vascular tissue

# SELF-ASSESSMENT 2

**Choose the correct option.**

26. Which of the following describes biodiversity?
    A. Variety of life in a particular area
    B. Movement of life in different areas
    C. Adaptations of some organisms
    D. Habitat of some organisms

27. Which of the following has a cell wall and is a saprophyte?
    A. *Aspergillus*
    B. *Ulothrix*
    C. *Funaria*
    D. *Marchantia*

28. Which of the following grows from a seed?
    A. Fruit
    B. Spores
    C. Thallus
    D. Cones

29. Which of the following belongs to the phylum Porifera?
    A. *Euplectella*
    B. Sea anemone
    C. *Hydra*
    D. *Planaria*

30. Identify the largest group of Kingdom Animalia.
    A. Nematoda B. Annelida
    C. Arthropoda D. Coelenterata

31. Which of the following is true about Lichens?
    A. They are a combination of fungi and protozoa.
    B. They are a combination of algae and protozoa.
    C. They are a combination of algae and fungus.
    D. They are a combination of algae, fungi and protozoa.

32. If a plant does not have a well-defined body, it is classified as ___________.
    A. pteridophytes
    B. thallophytes
    C. bryophytes
    D. gymnosperms

33. Which of the following are the characteristics of thallophyta?
    (i) They have a well-differentiated body design.
    (ii) They live in aquatic habitat.
    (iii) Plants in this group are called algae.
    (iv) They photosynthesize.
    A. (i), (ii) and (iii)
    B. (ii), (iii) and (iv)
    C. (i), (iii) and (iv)
    D. (i), (ii) and (iv)

34. Which of the following has sporocarp?
    A. *Chara* B. *Ulva*
    C. *Marsilea* D. *Spirogyra*

35. Which of the following is not similar to algae in its structure and function?
A. *Spirogyra*
B. *Funaria*
C. *Cladophora*
D. *Ulva*

36. Which among the following has two seed leaves?
A. *Paphiopedilum*
B. *Pinus*
C. *Cycas*
D. *Ipomoea*

37. Which of the following is perennial, evergreen and woody?
A. *Fern*
B. *Pinus*
C. *Paphiopedilum*
D. *Ipomoea*

38. Which of the following is a parasitic Platyhelminthes?
A. Planaria
B. Tapeworm
C. Liver fluke
D. Both B and C

39. Which of the following can be found in our intestines?
A. Roundworm B. Earthworm
C. Leech D. *Nereis*

40. Which of the following has blood-filled coelomic cavity with jointed legs?
A. Crabs
B. Antedon
C. Sea cucumber
D. Starfish

41. Which of the following completes the given analogy?
Mollusca : __________ ::
Echinodermata : Starfish
A. Octopus
B. Housefly
C. Sea urchin
D. Sea cucumber

42. Match the following.

| Column A | Column B |
|---|---|
| a. Mollusca | i. *Balanoglossus* |
| b. Protochordata | ii. Scorpion |
| c. Arthropoda | iii. *Pila* |

A. a→i; b→ii; c→iii
B. a→iii; b→ii; c→i
C. a→ii; b→iii; c→i
D. a→iii; b→i; c→ii

43. Which of the following has a skeleton entirely made up of cartilage?
A. Octopus B. Chiton
C. *Pila* D. Shark

44. Which class does a common house lizard belong to?
A. Amphibia B. Pisces
C. Aves D. Reptilia

45. Though platypus and echidna are mammals, they are similar to crocodiles in __________.
A. laying eggs
B. having a four-chambered heart
C. exoskeleton of scales
D. having four-chambered heart and laying eggs

46. Which kingdom of animals matches with the characteristics listed below?

(i) They are eukaryotes.

(ii) They are multicellular.

(iii) They do not have a cell wall.

A. Animalia B. Plantae

C. Protista D. Monera

47. Which of the following completes the given analogy?

Pisces : Gills :: Porifera : __________.

A. Tube system

B. Pores

C. Open circulatory system

D. Coelomic cavity

48. Why is phylum Platyhelminthes called flatworms?

A. They have a flat coelom.

B. They have a flat head.

C. Their body is triploblastic.

D. Their body is flattened dorsiventrally.

49. Identify the classes of the kingdom Animalia described below.

(i) They have bilaterally symmetrical body.

(ii) They have pseudocoelom.

(iii) They have triploblastic and cylindrical body.

A. (i), (ii) and (iii)—Nematoda

B. (i)—Platyhelminthes; (ii)—Annelida; (iii)—Nematoda

C. (i), (ii) and (iii)—Annelida

D. (i) and (ii)—Mollusca; (iii)—Nematoda

50. Identify the classes of vertebrates described below.

(i) They have mucus gland in their skin.

(ii) They have three-chambered heart.

(iii) They live both on land and in water.

A. (i), (ii) and (iii)—Amphibia

B. (i) and (ii)—Aves; (iii)—Amphibia

C. (i), (ii) and (iii)—Reptilia

D. I and III—Amphibia; II—Pisces

Chapter 8

# Motion

## PRE-TEST

**Choose the correct option.**

1. The distance covered by an object in a given unit of time is called __________.
   A. speed  B. displacement
   C. acceleration  D. momentum

2. Identify the correct statement.
   A. A distance–time graph can be a curve.
   B. A distance–time graph is always a straight line.
   C. A distance–time graph is always a curve.
   D. A distance–time graph can never be a curve.

3. A distance–time graph is a ______.
   A. bar graph  B. pie chart
   C. Venn diagram  D. line graph

4. Which of the following statements is correct if the distance-time graph is a straight line at an angle (less than 90° with x-axis.
   (i) The speed of the object is changing with time.
   (ii) The object is moving with a constant speed.
   A. Only (i) is correct.
   B. Only (ii) is correct.
   C. Both (i) and (ii) are correct.
   D. Both (i) and (ii) are incorrect.

5. The standard unit of distance is _______.
   A. metre  B. second
   C. metre per second  D. newton

## KEYWORDS

**Acceleration:** The rate of change in velocity

**Displacement:** The shortest distance between the final position and the initial position of the motion of the object

**Distance-time graph:** The graph of distance against time which shows how the position of an object changes with respect to time

**Equations of motion:** The relations among velocity, distance, time and acceleration

**Non-uniform motion:** The motion in which an object covers unequal distances in equal intervals of time or equal distances in unequal intervals of time

**Uniform motion:** The motion in which an object covers equal distances in equal intervals of time

**Velocity-time graph:** The graph of velocity against time which shows how the velocity changes with respect to time

**Velocity:** The rate of change in displacement

# Concept Map

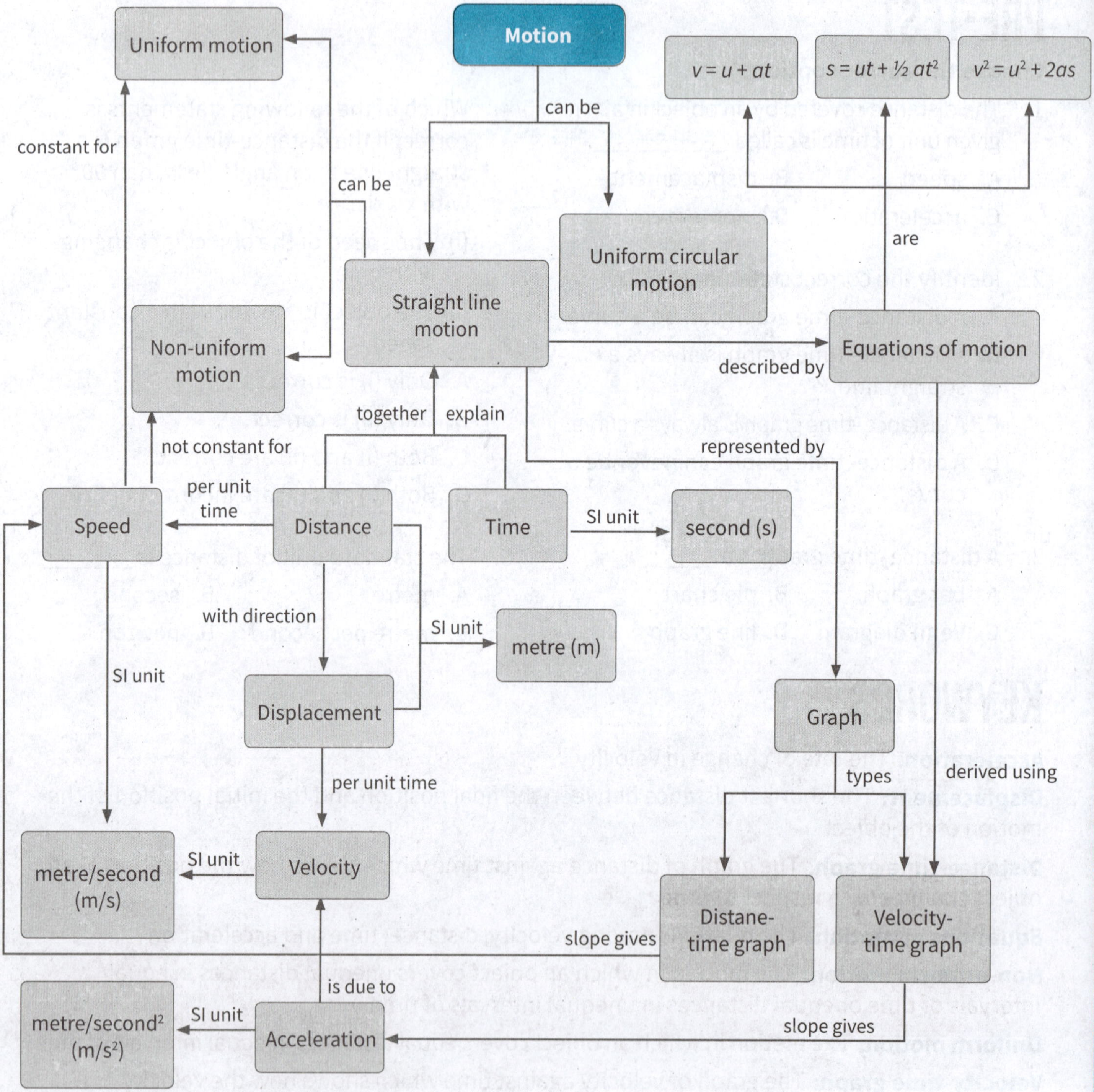

Motion
can be
Uniform motion
constant for
can be
Straight line motion
Uniform circular motion
Non-uniform motion
not constant for
together explain
described by
Equations of motion
are
$v = u + at$
$s = ut + \frac{1}{2}at^2$
$v^2 = u^2 + 2as$
represented by
Speed
per unit time
Distance
Time
SI unit
second (s)
with direction
SI unit
metre (m)
SI unit
Displacement
Graph
types
derived using
per unit time
metre/second (m/s)
SI unit
Velocity
slope gives
Distane-time graph
Velocity-time graph
is due to
metre/second² (m/s²)
SI unit
Acceleration
slope gives

Chapter 8 Motion

# SELF-ASSESSMENT 1

**Choose the correct option.**

1. If a bus moving on a straight road increases its speed uniformly from rest to 20 m/s over a time interval of 1 min, then the distance travelled during this time interval is __________.
   A. 150 m
   B. 300 m
   C. 600 m
   D. 900 m

2. Which of the following statements is true?
   A. The distance covered by an object is always less than its displacement.
   B. The distance covered by an object is always greater than its displacement.
   C. The distance covered by an object can be more than or equal to the displacement.
   D. The distance covered by an object can be less than or equal to its displacement.

3. A person throws a ball upwards with a certain velocity. If it attains a height of 5 m and comes back, then ________.
   A. the total distance covered by the ball is 5 m
   B. the total distance travelled by the ball is zero
   C. the total displacement is 10 m
   D. the total displacement is zero

4. An object travels 4 km from P to Q towards North and then 3 km from Q to R towards West. What is its displacement?
   A. 25 km  B. 7 km
   C. 1 km  D. 5 km

5. A car is driven from New Delhi to Haryana. The initial reading and the final reading of the odometer are 13100 km and 14500 km, respectively. What is the distance travelled by the car?
   A. 14500 km
   B. 13100 km
   C. 1400 km
   D. 27600 km

6. If two bodies of different masses X and Y are dropped from different heights $H_1$ and $H_2$, then the ratio of the time taken by the two bodies to drop through these distances is _______.
   A. $H_1/H_2$  B. $H_2/H_1$
   C. $(H_1/H_2)^{1/2}$  D. $H_1^2/H_2^2$

7. When a body covers a certain distance in direct proportion to the square of the time elapsed, then the acceleration is said to be _________.
   A. increasing
   B. decreasing
   C. constant
   D. zero

8. Observe the data regarding the motion of two different objects X and Y given in the table and identify the correct answer.

| Time (am) | Distance travelled by X (km) | Distance travelled by Y (km) |
|---|---|---|
| 8:00 | 0 | 0 |
| 8:30 | 5 | 5 |
| 9:00 | 10 | 15 |
| 9:30 | 15 | 30 |

A. Both X and Y are in uniform motion.
B. Both X and Y are in non-uniform motion.
C. Only X is in non-uniform motion.
D. Only Y is in non-uniform motion.

9. Pick the odd one out.
A. km
B. m
C. kg
D. cm

10. A car travels 40 km in 1 hour and then travels 50 km in next 2 hours. What is the average speed of the object?
A. 30 km/h
B. 40 km/h
C. 50 km/h
D. 60 km/h

11. The magnitude of average velocity of an object is equal to its average speed when ___________.
A. the object moves in a circular path
B. the object moves in a straight line
C. the object moves in a rectangular path
D. the object moves in a curved path

12. The distance between two points P and Q is 120 m. An object goes from point P to Q and then returns to point P in 1 minute 40 seconds. What is its average velocity?
A. 2.4 m/s B. 0
C. 1.2 m/s D. 3.6 m/s

13. A signal from a point X in the space reached a point Y on the Earth in 2 seconds. What is the distance between X and Y? (The signal travels at a speed of light, i.e. $3 \times 10^8$ m/s).
A. $6 \times 10^8$ m B. $1.5 \times 10^8$ m
C. 900 m D. $5.4 \times 10^{10}$ m

14. The driver of a car increases its speed from 30 km/h to 70 km/h at a uniform rate. What is the average velocity of the car?
A. 100 km/h B. 40 km/h
C. 50 km/h D. 45 km/h

15. Observe the given graph and identify the correct statement.

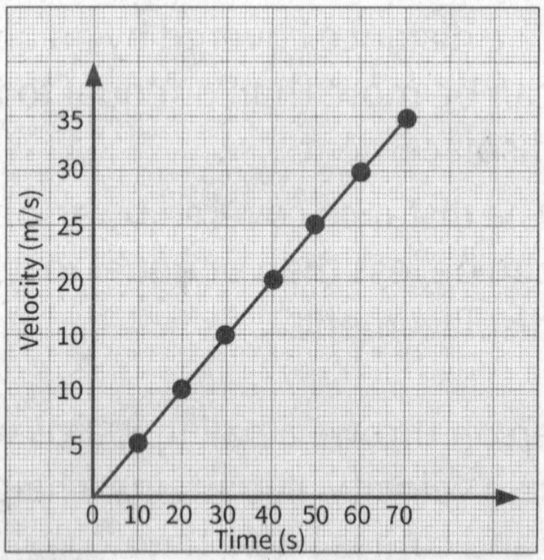


A. Velocity increases equally in equal intervals of time.
B. Acceleration of the object increases with time.
C. Velocity decreases equally in equal intervals of time.
D. Velocity of the object is uniform.

16. Starting from rest, an object attains a velocity of 8 m/s in 25 s. Then, the velocity of the object comes down to 4 m/s in the next 5 s. Which of the following is true when the whole motion of the object is considered?

A. Uniformly accelerated motion

B. Non-uniformly accelerated motion

C. Uniform motion

D. Average velocity is zero

17. Which of the following quantities is measured by the area under the velocity-time graph?

A. Magnitude of velocity

B. Magnitude of displacement

C. Magnitude of acceleration

D. Average speed

18. A person is travelling on a bike at a speed of 36 km/h. He applied brakes and the acceleration produced is $-0.2\ m/s^2$. Find how far the bike will go before it comes to rest.

A. 324 m     B. 250 m

C. 0     D. 100 m

19. An object is said to have uniform acceleration when __________.

A. its velocity changes uniformly with time

B. it is in uniform motion

C. its velocity remains same

D. its magnitude of speed and velocity are same

20. The rate of change of displacement is __________.

A. velocity     B. distance

C. speed     D. acceleration

21. When an object moves in a circular path at a uniform speed, it is said to be in __________.

A. curvilinear motion

B. rectilinear motion

C. uniform circular motion

D. uniformly accelerated motion

22. Which of the following equations of motion is correct?

A. $v = u + (1/2)at$

B. $s = ut + at^2$

C. $as = v^2 - u^2$

D. $v = u + at$

23. The unit of acceleration is __________.

A. m/s     B. $m/s^{-2}$

C. $ms^{-2}$     D. $m/s^{-1}$

24. An object travels 20 m in 10 s. What is the speed of the object?

A. 200 m/s

B. 30 m/s

C. 10 m/s

D. 2 m/s

25. Which of the following statements are true?

(i) The distance travelled by an object is always equal to its magnitude of displacement.

(ii) The slope of the distance-time graph represents the speed of the particle.

(iii) The rate of change of displacement of a particle is its velocity.

A. Only (i) and (ii) are true.

B. Only (ii) and (iii) are true.

C. Only (i) and (iii) are true.

D. All (i), (ii) and (iii) are true.

# SELF-ASSESSMENT 2

**Choose the correct option.**

26. The odometer of a car reads 22000 km at the start of a trip and 23800 km at the end of the trip. If the trip took 30 h, what is the average speed of the car?
    A. 30 km/h
    B. 40 km/h
    C. 50 km/h
    D. 60 km/h

27. An object travels from a point X to another point Y in 10 seconds. The distance between X and Y is 30 m. It travels again from Y to another point Z and covers 40 m. The average speed of the object during the whole journey is 2 m/s. How long the object takes to travel from Y to Z?
    A. 70 s B. 25 s
    C. 10 s D. 7 s

28. In the given velocity-time graph, the distance travelled by the object between 5 s and 7 s is ______.

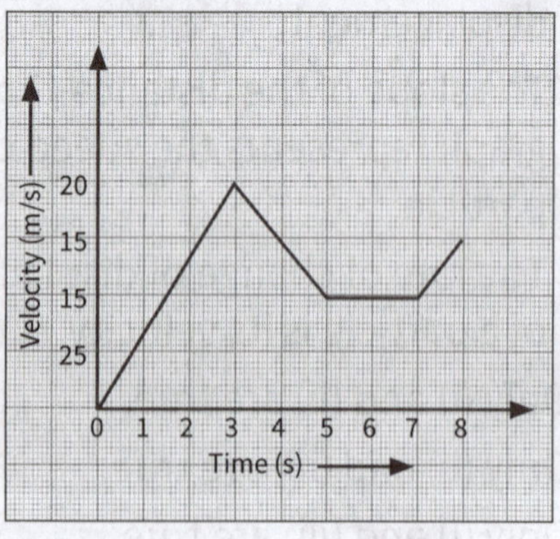


    A. 30 m B. 15 m
    C. 2 m D. 17 m

29. A particle is travelling at a constant speed. What can we understand from this statement?
    A. The position of the particle remains constant as time passes.
    B. The acceleration of the particle is uniform.
    C. The particle covers equal distances in equal intervals of time.
    D. The particle does not change its direction of motion.

30. The velocity of a body is given by the equation, $v = 6 - 0.02t$, where $t$ is the time taken. Which of the following types of motion is exhibited by the body?
    A. Uniform motion
    B. Negative acceleration
    C. Uniform velocity
    D. Uniform acceleration

31. An object is moving along a circular path of radius 1 cm with uniform speed. What is the ratio of the distance covered and the displacement in half revolution?
    A. $1 : \pi$ B. $\pi : 2$
    C. $2 : \pi$ D. $\pi : 1$

32. How do the directions of velocity and acceleration act when brakes are applied to a moving vehicle?
    A. In the same direction
    B. Perpendicular to each other
    C. Opposite to each other
    D. None of these

33. A car covers equal displacements in equal intervals of time. Which of the following is exhibited by the car?
   A. Uniform velocity
   B. Non-uniform velocity
   C. Positive acceleration
   D. Negative acceleration

34. Which among the following is correctly matched?
   A. Speed—cm
   B. Displacement—s
   C. Time—km/h
   D. Acceleration—$km/h^2$

35. From the given graph, which object is moving with the slowest speed?

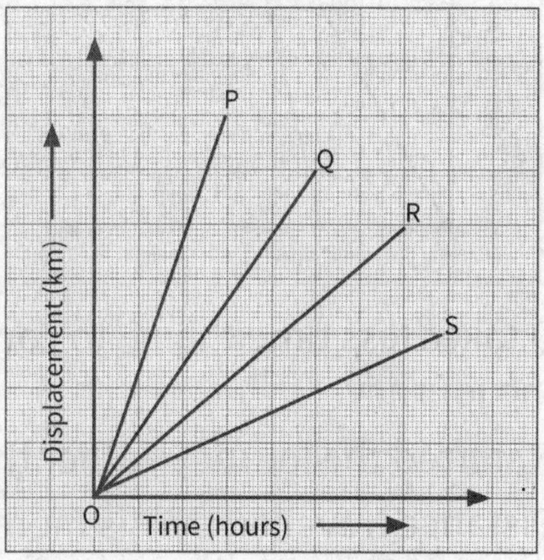


   A. P
   B. Q
   C. R
   D. S

36. An object moving with an initial velocity of 10 m/s is subjected to a uniform acceleration of – 8 $m/s^2$. Find the displacement in the next 2 seconds.
   A. 0
   B. 36 s
   C. 4 s
   D. 16 s

37. Which of the following distance–time graphs describes the possible motion of the object ?

A. 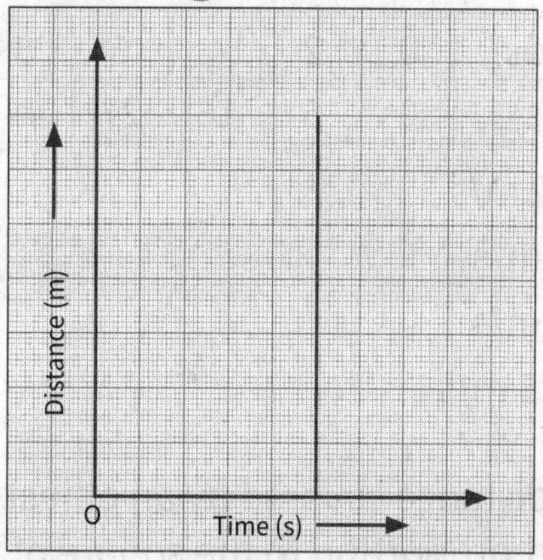


B. 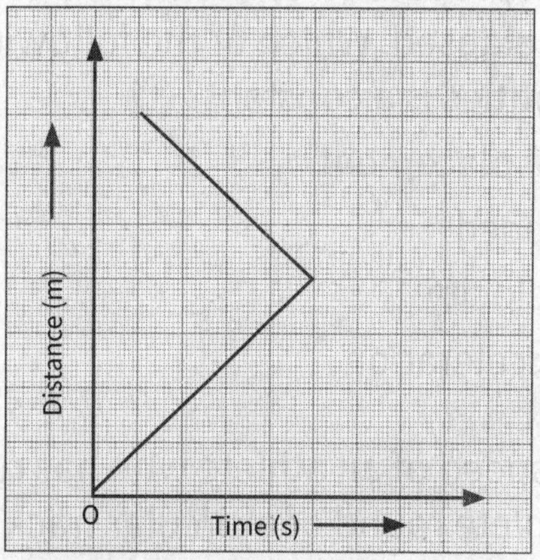


C. 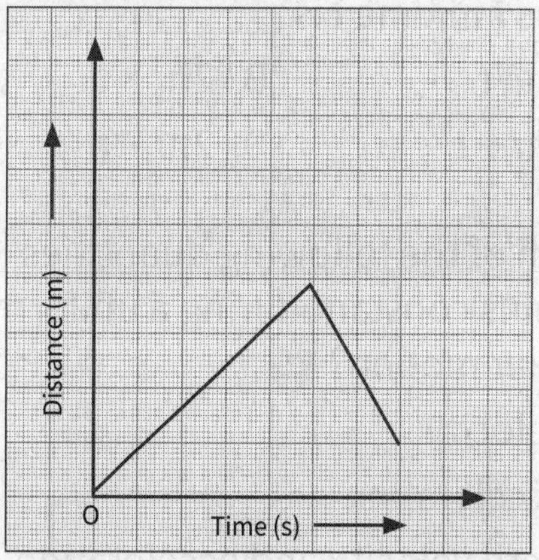


D. 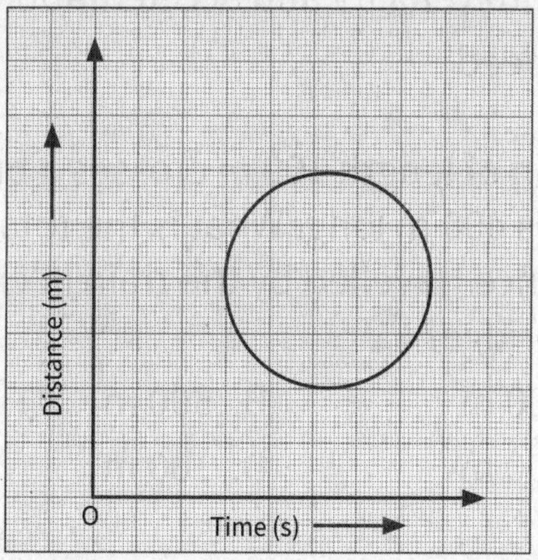

38. Read the given data and identify the average velocity between $t = 4$ s and $t = 8$ s.

| $t$ (seconds) | 0 | 2 | 4 | 6 | 8 | 10 |
|---|---|---|---|---|---|---|
| $s$ (metres) | 0 | 5 | 16 | 27 | 44 | 64 |

A. 22 m/s
B. 7 m/s
C. 8 m/s
D. 5.5 m/s

39. The distance covered by an object is in direct proportion to the square of the time elapsed. Which of the following quantities is a constant?

A. Displacement
B. Speed
C. Velocity
D. Acceleration

40. The speed of an athlete who has run a complete round of a circular track of radius $r$ in time $t$ is ________________.

A. $2\pi r/t$ B. $2\pi r \times t$
C. $2\pi r + t$ D. $2\pi r - t$

41. Which of the following quantities remains constant during a uniform circular motion?

A. Velocity
B. Acceleration
C. Both velocity and acceleration
D. Speed

42. A train of length 100 m crosses a bridge that is 400 m long. What is the total distance travelled by the train in crossing the bridge?

A. 600 m B. 500 m
C. 400 m D. 100 m

43. A 150 m long train crosses a bridge that is 450 m long in 50 seconds with a constant velocity. What is the velocity of the train?

A. 6 m/s
B. 78 m/s
C. 12 m/s
D. 14 m/s

44. The distance-time graphs of two objects P and Q are shown below. Which of the following statements is not correct based on the given graph?

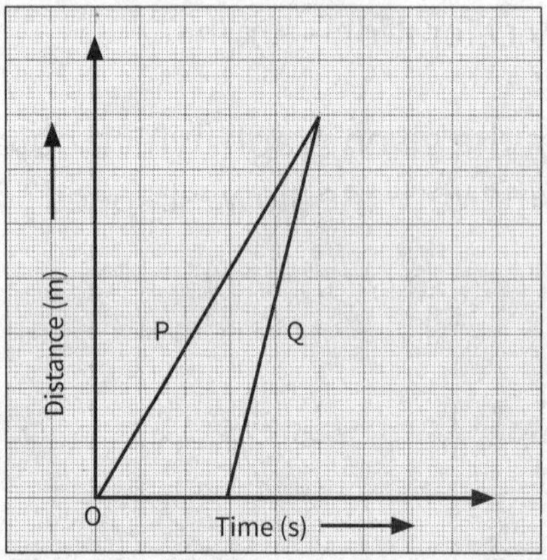


A. Q takes less time than P to complete the journey.
B. P started the journey earlier than Q.
C. Distance travelled by P is more than that of Q.
D. Distance travelled by both P and Q is same.

45. An object is moving along a circular path at a constant speed. The direction of acceleration is __________.

A. in the direction of velocity
B. opposite to the direction of velocity
C. towards the centre of the circular path
D. away from the centre of the circular path

46. A ball dropped from a certain height falls down with a constant acceleration of 9.8 $m/s^2$. It means that ____________.

A. the ball moves 9.8 m/s

B. the velocity of the ball as it reaches the ground is 9.8 m/s

C. the ball falls 9.8 m during the first second of its fall

D. the velocity of the ball increases by 9.8 m/s each second

47. Which of the following statements are true?

(i) It is possible for a body to have its velocity and acceleration perpendicular to each other.

(ii) It is possible for a body to have its velocity and acceleration opposite to each other.

(iii) It is possible for a body to be in circular motion with a constant velocity.

A. Only (i) and (ii) are true.

B. Only (ii) and (iii) are true.

C. Only (i) and (iii) are true.

D. All (i), (ii) and (iii) are true.

48. A man is riding his bike at a constant speed of 8 m/s on a straight road. He increases the speed of the bike to 18 m/s in 5 seconds. Calculate the acceleration.

A. 2 $m/s^2$

B. 6 $m/s^2$

C. 9.5 $m/s^2$

D. 13 $m/s^2$

49. The slope of a velocity-time graph gives ____________.

A. velocity

B. displacement

C. acceleration

D. time

50. The device which measures distance travelled by a vehicle is known as____________.

A. speedometer

B. tachometer

C. odometer

D. optical pyrometer

Chapter 9

# Force and Laws of Motion

## PRE-TEST

**Choose the correct option.**

1. Which of the following is not an effect of force?
   A. A force can decrease the temperature of a body.
   B. A force can increase the speed of a moving body.
   C. A force can make a moving body stop.
   D. A force can change the direction of a moving body.

2. Which among the following is an example of contact force?
   A. Electrostatic force
   B. Gravitational force
   C. Frictional force
   D. Magnetic force

3. __________ force only causes attraction.
   A. Electrostatic   B. Gravitational
   C. Frictional   D. Magnetic

4. A scooter travels at a uniform speed of 30 km/h. What would be the time taken by the scooter to travel a distance of 150 km?
   A. 4500 h   B. 0.2 h
   C. 5 h   D. 120 h

5. _______ force is always a resistive force?
   A. Gravitational
   B. Frictional
   C. Magnetic
   D. Electrostatic

## KEYWORDS

**Balanced forces:** Two or more forces acting on a body whose resultant is zero

**Conservation of momentum:** In an isolated system, the total momentum remains constant

**First law of motion:** An object continues to be in a state of rest or of uniform motion in a straight line unless acted upon by an unbalanced force

**Inertia:** The natural tendency of objects to resist a change in their state of rest or of uniform motion

**Momentum:** The product of the mass and velocity of an object

**Second law of motion:** The rate of change in the momentum of an object is proportional to the applied unbalanced force in the direction of the force

**Third law of motion:** To every action, there is an equal and opposite reaction

**Unbalanced forces:** Two or more forces acting on a body, whose resultant is not zero

# Concept Map

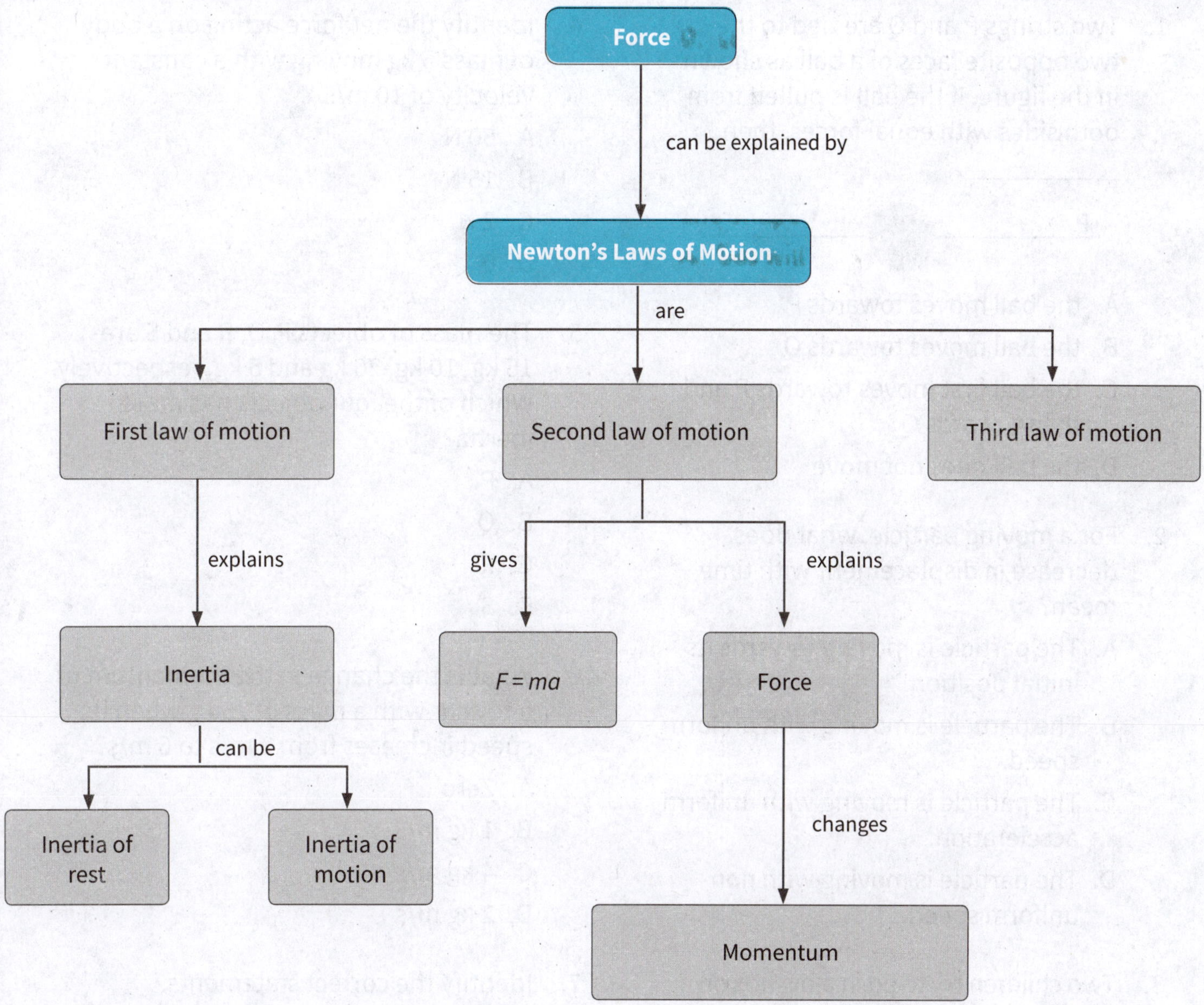
Force
can be explained by
Newton's Laws of Motion
are
First law of motion
Second law of motion
Third law of motion
explains
gives
explains
Inertia
F = ma
Force
can be
changes
Inertia of rest
Inertia of motion
Momentum

Chapter 9 Force and Laws of Motion

# SELF-ASSESSMENT 1

**Choose the correct option.**

1. Two strings P and Q are tied to the two opposite faces of a ball as shown in the figure. If the ball is pulled from both sides with equal forces, then ____________.

   A. the ball moves towards P
   B. the ball moves towards Q
   C. the ball first moves towards P and then towards Q
   D. the ball does not move

2. For a moving particle, what does decrease in displacement with time mean?
   A. The particle is moving towards its initial position.
   B. The particle is moving with uniform speed.
   C. The particle is moving with uniform acceleration.
   D. The particle is moving with non-uniform speed.

3. Two children try to push a big box on a rough floor but It does not move. Why?
   A. The friction balances the pushing force.
   B. The friction and the pushing force act in the same direction.
   C. The friction is less than the pushing force.
   D. There is no friction acting between the box and the floor.

4. Identify the net force acting on a body of mass 5 kg moving with a constant velocity of 10 m/s.
   A. 50 N
   B. 15 N
   C. 2 N
   D. 0

5. The mass of objects P, Q, R and S are 15 kg, 10 kg, 20 kg and 5 kg, respectively. Which of the four objects has more inertia?
   A. P
   B. Q
   C. R
   D. S

6. What is the change in the momentum of a toy car with a mass of 250 g when its speed increases from 2 m/s to 6 m/s?
   A. Zero
   B. 1 kg m/s
   C. 4 kg m/s
   D. 2 kg m/s

7. Identify the correct statements.
   (i) A ball at rest on a plane ground continues to be in the state of rest.
   (ii) A ball rolling on a plane ground has the tendency to come to rest.
   A. Only (i) is correct.
   B. Only (ii) is correct.
   C. Both (i) and (ii) are correct.
   D. Both (i) and (ii) are incorrect.

8. The tendency of an object to continue its state of rest is ____________.
   A. inertia of motion
   B. inertia of rest
   C. inertia of direction
   D. acceleration

9. Which among the following statements is not true?
   A. The inertia of an object is measured by its mass.
   B. Heavier objects offer larger inertia.
   C. All bodies have the same inertia.
   D. A train has more inertia than a cart.

10. When we shake the branches of a tree, some of the leaves may get detached from it because of the ____________.
    A. inertia of rest
    B. inertia of motion
    C. momentum of the leaves
    D. balanced forces acting on the leaves

11. If a person throws a ball weighing 250 g vertically upwards at a speed of 4 m/s, then the momentum of the ball at the highest point of its flight will be ____________.
    A. 1 kg m/s  B. 1000 kg m/s
    C. 4 kg m/s  D. Zero

12. The impact produced by moving objects when stopped suddenly depends on their ____________.
    A. mass only
    B. velocity only
    C. mass and velocity
    D. inertia

13. If the mass of a body and the force acting on it are doubled then its acceleration ____________.
    A. also doubles
    B. reduces to half
    C. remains the same
    D. becomes zero

14. A force acts on a box of mass 15 kg for a duration of 3 s. It increases the object's velocity from 5 m/s to 9 m/s. What is the magnitude of the applied force?
    A. 10 N  B. 15 N
    C. 20 N  D. 25 N

15. Neena wants to accelerate an object of mass 5 kg at 2 $m/s^2$. Anita wants to accelerate an object of mass 3 kg at 5 $m/s^2$. Raj wants to accelerate an object of 2 kg mass at 4 $m/s^2$. Who has to apply the greater force?
    A. Neena
    B. Anita
    C. Both Neena and Anita
    D. Raj

16. John is standing carrying a box on his head. The box is exerting a force of 50 N on John's head. If this force is taken to be the action, identify the reaction force.
    A. The force applied by the Earth on the box
    B. The force applied by John's head on the box
    C. The force applied by the Earth on John's head
    D. The force applied by the box on the Earth

17. A force acting on an object of mass 100 g accelerates it and displaces it through 500 cm in 1 s. If the initial velocity of the object is zero, what is the magnitude of the force applied?
   A. 0.05 N
   B. 0.5 N
   C. 0.1 N
   D. 1 N

18. An object having mass 3 kg at rest moves under the action of a force for 4 s with an acceleration of 2.5 m $s^{-2}$. What is the gain in the momentum of the object?
   A. 0
   B. 7.5 kg m/s
   C. 15 kg m/s
   D. 30 kg m/s

19. A man is able to pull a vegetable cart because of the ________.
   A. force exerted by the cart on the man
   B. force exerted by the ground on the cart
   C. force exerted by the ground on the man
   D. force exerted by man on the cart

20. In a shooting competition, contestants have the options to use rifles of different weights but the bullets used are of a fixed weight. What would they prefer and why?
   A. Light rifles, as they can be carried easily
   B. Heavy rifles, as they can be held firmly
   C. Light rifles, as handling them is easy
   D. Heavy rifles, as they have less recoil

21. Ram is standing on a boat in still water near the shore. If he jumps towards the shore, the boat will __________.
   A. move towards the shore
   B. move away from the shore
   C. remain stationary
   D. sink down

22. Which of the following is the unit of momentum?
   A. m $s^{-1}$ B. kg m/$s^{-1}$
   C. kg m $s^{-2}$ D. kg m/s

23. According to Newton's third law, the action and reaction always act on __________.
   A. a single object
   B. two different objects
   C. two sides of a same object
   D. Both B and C

24. Which of the following statements are correct?
   (i) Dust particles fall when a mat is beaten with a stick—Inertia
   (ii) Flight of a rocket—Newton's first law of motion
   A. Only (i) is correct.
   B. Only (ii) is correct.
   C. Both (i) and (ii) are correct.
   D. Both (i) and (ii) are incorrect.

25. The tendency of an object to continue its state of motion is __________.
   A. inertia of motion
   B. inertia of rest
   C. momentum
   D. acceleration

## Chapter 9 Force and Laws of Motion

# SELF-ASSESSMENT 2

**Choose the correct option.**

26. Two strings P and Q are tied to two opposite faces of a wooden block as shown in the figure. If the block is pulled from both sides with a force of 10 N from point P and that of 15 N from point Q then ________________.

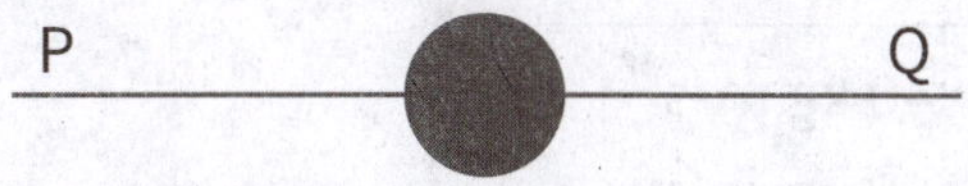


   A. the block moves towards P
   B. the block moves towards Q
   C. the block first moves towards P and then towards Q
   D. the block will not move

27. **Assertion (A):** If an object is pulled from both sides with equal forces, the object will not move.
   **Reason (R):** Balanced force acting on an object cannot bring it to motion.
   A. A and R are true but R is not the correct explanation of A.
   B. A and R are true and R is the correct explanation of A.
   C. A is true but R is false.
   D. A is false but R is true.

28. Which of the following reasons makes it difficult to achieve a zero unbalanced force on moving objects in practical situations?
   A. Presence of balanced force
   B. Presence of frictional force
   C. Presence of gravitational force
   D. Presence of muscular force

29. Which among the following statements is true?
   A. A plastic ball has more inertia than a metal ball of the same size.
   B. A car has more inertia than a bus.
   C. A five-rupee coin has less inertia than a one-rupee coin.
   D. An elephant has more inertia than a rabbit.

30. We tend to fall in the forward direction when a moving car applies brakes suddenly because of ____________.
   A. inertia of rest B. inertia of motion
   C. momentum D. unbalanced force

31. Raj is swirling a stone attached to a thread. After a few seconds, he lets go of the thread. The stone moves away from the circular path. Identify the types of inertia involved in this situation.
   A. Inertia of rest and inertia of motion
   B. Inertia of rest and inertia of direction
   C. Inertia of motion and inertia of direction
   D. Inertia of rest, Inertia of motion, and inertia of direction

32. Recoil of a gun and rocket propulsion are the illustrations of the ______________.
   A. first law of motion
   B. second law of motion
   C. third law of motion
   D. balanced forces on the gun

33. A ball of mass 1 kg is sliding with a constant velocity of 5 m/s on a frictionless horizontal plane. The force required to keep the object moving with the same velocity is ____________.

A. 0

B. 5 N

C. 0.2 N

D. 6 N

34. Identify the correct statements.

(i) The SI unit of weight is newton.

(ii) If we apply a constant force on a body, the body moves with a constant acceleration.

A. Only (i) is correct.

B. Only (ii) is correct.

C. Both (i) and (ii) are correct.

D. Both (i) and (ii) are incorrect.

35. X weighing 40 kg is walking with a uniform velocity of 2 m/s. What is the momentum of X?

A. 80 kg m/s B. 42 kg m/s

C. 20 kg m/s D. 38 kg m/s

36. Identify the property which allows an object to continue in its state of rest in the absence of a force.

A. Acceleration B. Momentum

C. Inertia D. Weight

37. If a wooden ball is moving with a uniform acceleration, then which of the following statements is true?

A. Balanced forces are acting on it.

B. The velocity of the body always increases.

C. The velocity of the body always decreases.

D. A constant force is acting on it.

38. A force of 20 N acts on an object for a time of 3 s. The velocity of the body increases from 5 m/s to 11 m/s. What is the mass of the body?

A. 20 kg

B. 10 kg

C. 4 kg

D. 1 kg

39. A 20-kg object is kept in a moving trolley of mass 30 kg. If the system is moving with a velocity of 2 m/s, then the momentum of the object-trolley system is ______________.

A. 40 kg m/s

B. 60 kg m/s

C. 100 kg m/s

D. 25 kg m/s

40. A constant force of 50 N acts on an object of mass 20 kg which is initially at rest. The velocity acquired by the body at the end of tenth second is ____________.

A. 25 m/s B. 50 m/s

C. 100 m/s D. 250 m/s

41. While catching a ball, a cricket player moves his hand a little backwards to __________.

A. reduce the velocity of the ball

B. reduce the force exerted on the hands

C. reduce the mass of the ball

D. reduce the time of impact of the ball and the hand

42. According to the third law of motion, to every action, there is an equal and opposite reaction. What would be the angle between action and reaction?

A. 0° B. 90°

C. 180° D. 360°

43. A ball of mass 300 g is thrown horizontally at a speed of 90 km/h. The momentum of the ball is ______.

A. 27000 kg m/s

B. 7.5 kg m/s

C. 27 kg m/s

D. 0

44. When the coin at the bottom of a pile of carom coins is hit horizontally with a striker, only the coin being hit moves because of ______________.

A. inertia of motion of the coin which is hit

B. inertia of motion of the coins on the top

C. inertia of rest of the coin which is hit

D. inertia of rest of the coins on the top

45. A bus with passengers is moving at a speed of 54 km/h. Brakes are applied at a constant force of 6000 N, and it stops after 5 s. The mass of the bus including its passengers is ___________.

A. 2000 kg

B. 1000 kg

C. 32400 kg

D. 1200 kg

46. 1 N is equal to _____________.

A. 1 kg $m/s^{-2}$

B. 1 kg $m/s^2$

C. 1 g cm/s

D. 1 g $cm/s^2$

47. Identify the correct statement based on the given table.

| Time (s) | 0 | 2 | 4 | 6 | 8 | 10 |
|---|---|---|---|---|---|---|
| Distance (m) | 0 | 6 | 12 | 18 | 24 | 30 |

A. A constant force is acting on the object in the opposite direction of motion.

B. An unbalanced force is acting on the object.

C. A non-uniform force is acting on the object in the direction of motion.

D. No forces are acting on the object.

48. The product of mass and velocity gives ___________.

A. force B. momentum

C. density D. acceleration

49. Newton's first law of motion is also called _______________.

A. law of inertia

B. law of momentum

C. law of acceleration

D. law of velocity

50. Which of the following statements are correct?

(i) Action and reaction forces always act on different objects.

(ii) Action and reaction forces are always equal in magnitude.

A. Only (i) is correct.

B. Only (ii) is correct.

C. Both (i) and (ii) are correct.

D. Both (i) and (ii) are incorrect.

Chapter 10

# Gravitation

## PRE-TEST

**Choose the correct option.**

1. __________ force is not a contact force.
   A. Muscular  B. Frictional
   C. Spring  D. Gravitational

2. Identify the correct statements.
   (i) Gravitational force is an attractive force.
   (ii) Gravitational force can either be a force of attraction or a force of repulsion between the two charged particles.
   A. Only (i) is correct.
   B. Only (ii) is correct.
   C. Both (i) and (ii) are correct.
   D. Both (i) and (ii) are incorrect.

3. Identify the physical quantity required to change the speed or the direction of motion of an object.
   A. Mass  B. Force
   C. Density  D. Volume

4. Which of the following statements is correct?
   A. Earth is the largest planet in the solar system.
   B. All planets are equidistant from the sun.
   C. The moon revolves around the Earth.
   D. The sun's gravitational force pushes the planets away from it.

5. X is a fundamental property of all objects and is a measurement of the amount of matter in an object. X is the quantitative measurement of inertia. What is X?
   A. Force
   B. Energy
   C. Mass
   D. Acceleration

## KEYWORDS

**Archimedes' Principle:** When a body is partially or completely immersed in a fluid, it experiences an apparent loss of weight which is equal to the weight of the fluid displaced by the immersed part of the body

**Buoyancy:** The force exerted on an object that is fully or partly immersed in a fluid

**Density:** The mass of the substance per unit volume

**Gravitation:** The force of attraction between all the masses in the universe

**Relative density:** The ratio of density of a substance to the density of water

**Universal law of gravitation:** The force of attraction between any two objects is proportional to the product of their masses and inversely proportional to the square of the distance between them

**Weight:** The force with which a body is attracted to the Earth

# Concept Map

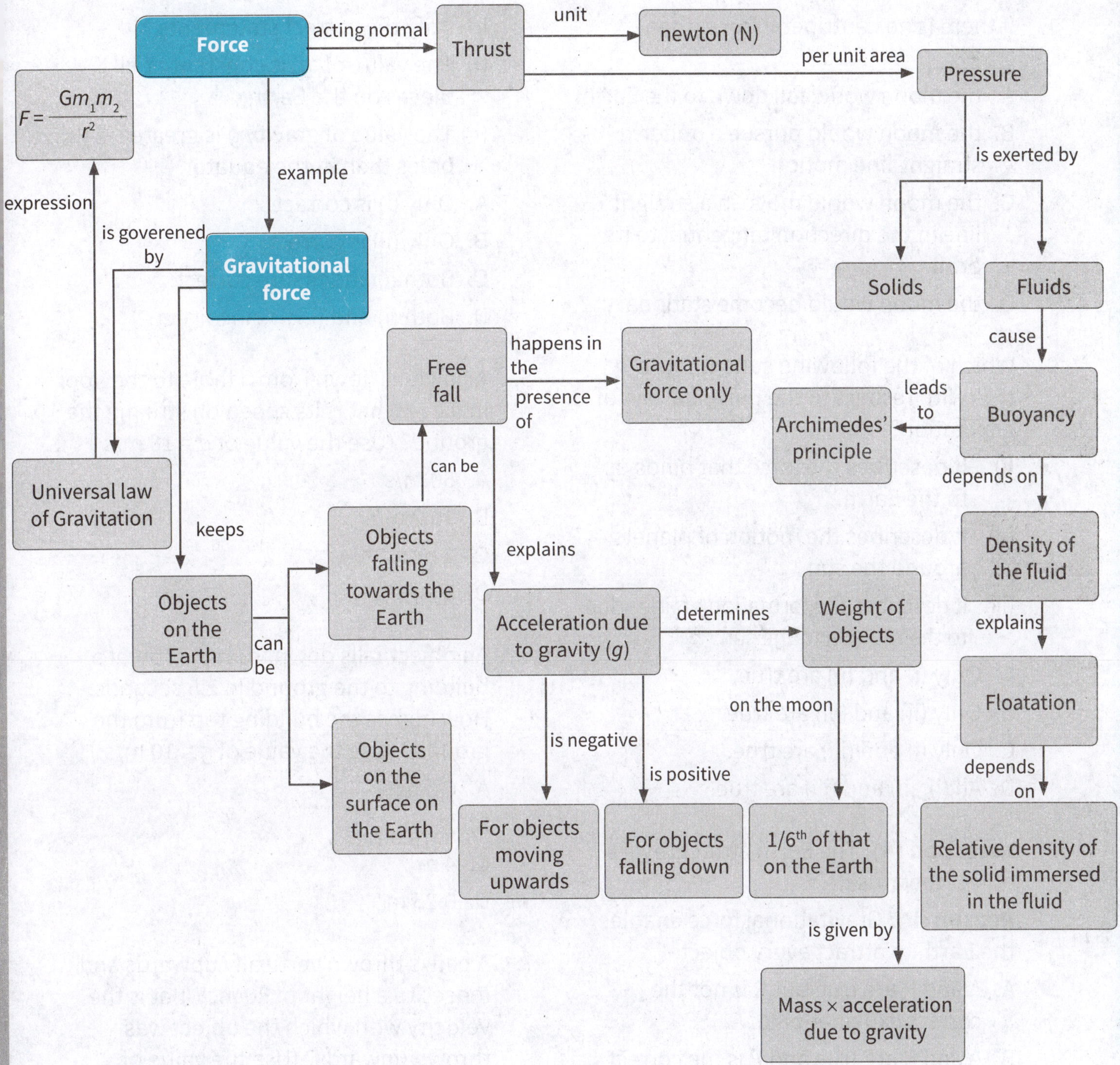
Force
acting normal
Thrust
unit
newton (N)
per unit area
Pressure
$F = \frac{Gm_1m_2}{r^2}$
expression
example
is goverened by
Gravitational force
is exerted by
Solids
Fluids
cause
Free fall
happens in the presence of
Gravitational force only
leads to
Archimedes' principle
Buoyancy
can be
depends on
Universal law of Gravitation
keeps
Objects falling towards the Earth
explains
Density of the fluid
Objects on the Earth
can be
Acceleration due to gravity ($g$)
determines
Weight of objects
explains
on the moon
Floatation
Objects on the surface on the Earth
is negative
is positive
depends on
For objects moving upwards
For objects falling down
1/6th of that on the Earth
Relative density of the solid immersed in the fluid
is given by
Mass × acceleration due to gravity

# SELF-ASSESSMENT 1

**Choose the correct option.**

1. If there is no centripetal force, then ___________.
   A. the moon would fall down to the Earth
   B. the moon would pursue a uniform straight-line motion
   C. the moon would move in a straight line in the direction tangential to its orbit
   D. the moon would become stationary

2. Which of the following statements are true with respect to the universal law of gravitation?
   (i) It describes the force that binds us to the Earth.
   (ii) It describes the motion of planets around the sun.
   (iii) It describes the formation of tides due to the moon and the sun.
   A. Only (i) and (ii) are true.
   B. Only (ii) and (iii) are true.
   C. Only (i) and (iii) are true.
   D. All (i), (ii) and (iii) are true.

3. **Assertion (A):** The Earth attracts every object towards it.
   **Reason (R):** Gravitational force enables the Earth to attract every object.
   A. A and R are true but R is not the correct explanation of A.
   B. A and R are true and R is the correct explanation of A.
   C. A is true but R is false.
   D. A is false but R is true.

4. Identify the correct statements.
   (i) The value of '$g$' is constant at all places on the Earth.
   (ii) The value of gravity $g$ is greater at the poles than at the equator.
   A. Only (i) is correct.
   B. Only (ii) is correct.
   C. Both (i) and (ii) are correct.
   D. Both (i) and (ii) are incorrect.

5. A ball falls down from a table to the floor in 0.2 s. What is its speed on striking the ground? (Use the value of $g = 10$ m/s$^2$)
   A. 50 m/s
   B. 10.2 m/s
   C. 2 m/s
   D. 9.8 m/s

6. An object falls down from the top of a building to the ground in 2.5 seconds. How high is the building top from the ground? (Use the value of $g = 10$ m/s$^2$)
   A. 62. 5 m
   B. 25 m
   C. 4 m
   D. 6.25 m

7. A ball is thrown vertically upwards and it rises to a height of 20 m. What is the velocity with which the object was thrown upwards? (Use the value of $g = 10$ m/s$^2$)
   A. 12 m/s
   B. 400 m/s
   C. 200 m/s
   D. 20 m/s

8. Which of the following statements are correct?
   (i) The SI unit of mass and weight is same.
   (ii) The SI unit of weight is newton (N).
   A. Only (i) is correct.
   B. Only (ii) is correct.
   C. Both (i) and (ii) are correct.
   D. Both (i) and (ii) are correct.

9. Which among the following statements is not true?
   A. The value of gravity *g* is constant at a given place.
   B. The mass of an object remains the same everywhere.
   C. The weight of an object on the moon is 1/6 times greater than its weight on the Earth.
   D. The weight of an object depends on its location.

10. What is the weight of an object on the Earth if its mass is 20 kg?
   A. 20 N
   B. 98 N
   C. 196 N
   D. 0 N

11. The weight of an object on the moon is $(1/6)^{th}$ of its weight on the Earth because ________________.
   A. the mass and radius of the Earth are equal to that of the moon.
   B. the mass and radius of the Earth are more than that of the moon.
   C. the mass and radius of the Earth are less than that of the moon.
   D. there is no gravitational force between the Earth and the moon.

12. Sandeep took an empty plastic bottle closed with an airtight stopper through its mouth. He pushed it into a bucket containing water. When he released the bottle, it bounced back to the surface. What could be the reason?
   A. Upward force by the water = Weight of the bottle
   B. Upward force by the water $<$ Weight of the bottle
   C. Buoyant force = 0
   D. Upward force by the water $>$ Weight of the bottle

13. If we place a cork and a nail on the surface of water, the cork floats while the nail sinks. Which of the following statements will be the correct reasons for this statement?
   (i) The density of the cork is less than the density of water.
   (ii) The upthrust of water on the cork is greater than the weight of the cork.
   (iii) The weight of the nail is greater than the upthrust of water.
   A. Only (i) and (ii) are correct.
   B. Only (ii) and (iii) are correct.
   C. Only (i) and (iii) are correct.
   D. All (i), (ii) and (iii) are correct.

14. Which of the following statements is not true?
   A. A solid exerts pressure on the surface due to its weight.
   B. The pressure exerted on a given surface is inversely proportional to the thrust acting on the surface.
   C. At a given place, the weight of an object is directly proportional to its mass.
   D. Gravitation is a weak force unless large masses are involved.

15. It is difficult to hold a school bag having a strap made of a thin and strong string because ________________.
    A. pressure is inversely proportional to the applied force
    B. pressure is directly proportional to the surface area
    C. pressure is independent of the surface area
    D. pressure is inversely proportional to the surface area

16. A ball is thrown upwards at a speed $u$ from the top of a building. The ball reaches the ground with a velocity $5u$. What is the height of the building?
    A. $3u^2/g$
    B. $4u^2/g$
    C. $6u^2/g$
    D. $12u^2/g$

17. A rectangular tank of dimension 5 m × 5 m × 8 m is filled with water. What is the thrust acting on the bottom of the tank? (Use the value of $g = 10\ m/s^2$ and density of water $= 10^3\ kg/m^3$)
    A. 2000 N
    B. $200 \times 10^5$ N
    C. $20 \times 10^5$ N
    D. $2000 \times 10^5$ N

18. Ajay immersed an object in water. Its loss in weight is equal to ________.
    A. the weight of the water
    B. the weight of the object
    C. the difference in the weights of the object in air and in water
    D. the upthrust of water on the object

19. A rectangular wooden block is placed on a platform in different ways such that different faces of it touch the platform. In all these cases, the block exerts ____________.
    A. the same thrust and pressures
    B. the same thrust but different pressures
    C. different thrusts but same pressures
    D. different thrusts and pressures

20. If we compare the pressure exerted by a sharp needle and a blunt needle on the same surface, then we can say that ____________.
    A. the pressure exerted by the sharp needle is more
    B. the pressure exerted by a blunt needle is more
    C. the pressure exerted by both the needles is equal
    D. the pressure exerted by the needles does not depend on the sharpness

21. The force of gravitation between two objects does not depend upon __________.
    A. the product of their masses
    B. the sum of their masses
    C. the separation between them
    D. the gravitational constant

22. What would happen if the gravitational force of the Earth disappeared?
    A. Mass of a body on the surface of the Earth becomes zero.
    B. Weight of a body on the surface of the Earth becomes zero.
    C. Both the mass and weight become zero.
    D. Neither the weight nor the mass becomes zero.

23. When an object is thrown upwards the direction of gravitational force ________.

A. acts in the direction of the motion

B. becomes zero as the body moves up

C. increases as the body moves up

D. acts in the opposite direction of the motion

24. 1 kg of weight is equal to __________.

A. 1 N B. 9.8 N

C. 98 N D. 980 N

25. The SI unit of universal gravitational constant G is ______________.

A. $Nm^2\ kg^{-2}$ B. $N^2m^2\ kg^{-2}$

C. $Nm^2\ kg^2$ D. $Nm^{-2}\ kg^2$

# SELF-ASSESSMENT 2

**Choose the correct option.**

26. Identify the correct statements.
    (i) The mass of an object is the force of gravity exerted by the Earth on it.
    (ii) The force of attraction of the Earth on an object is the weight of the object.
    A. Only (i) is correct.
    B. Only (ii) is correct.
    C. Both (i) and (ii) are correct.
    D. Both (i) and (ii) are incorrect.

27. An object falls down from a table to the floor in 0.2 s. What is its average speed during its journey? (Given $g = 10\ m/s^2$)
    A. 4 m/s    B. 1 m/s
    C. 2 m/s    D. 9.8 m/s

28. Which of the following is the source of the centripetal force that a planet requires to revolve around the sun?
    A. Electrostatic force
    B. Gravitational force
    C. Electromagnetic force
    D. Frictional force

29. A ball is thrown vertically upwards and it rises to a height of 20 m. What is the time taken by the object to reach the highest point? (Use value of $g = 10\ m/s^2$)
    A. 30 s    B. 10 s
    C. 1 s    D. 2 s

30. What is the mass of a body when its weight on the Earth is 98 N?
    A. 98 kg    B. 1 kg
    C. 10 kg    D. 9.8 kg

31. What would be the weight of an object on the Earth if it weighs 20 N on the surface of the moon?
    A. 6.66 N
    B. 26 N
    C. 14 N
    D. 120 N

32. Which of the following statements are correct?
    (i) The net force exerted by a body in a particular direction is thrust.
    (ii) The force per unit area is pressure.
    A. Only (i) is correct.
    B. Only (ii) is correct.
    C. Both (i) and (ii) are correct.
    D. Both (i) and (ii) are not correct.

33. Two objects X and Y of different masses are at a distance *d* from each other. If they are now kept at a distance 4*d*, then the gravitational force becomes __________.
    A. 1/16 times smaller
    B. 1/16 times bigger
    C. 1/4 times smaller
    D. 1/4 times bigger

34. Nails have pointed tip, knives have sharp edges and buildings have wide foundations because ______________.

A. force acting on a smaller area exerts a larger pressure

B. force acting on a larger area exerts a larger pressure

C. force acting on a smaller area exerts a lesser pressure

D. force and pressure are independent of each other

35. Which of the following statements are correct?

(i) The objects of density less than that of a liquid sink in the liquid.

(ii) The objects of density greater than that of a liquid float on the liquid.

A. Only (i) is correct.

B. Only (ii) is correct.

C. Both (i) and (ii) are correct.

D. Both (i) and (ii) are not correct.

36. If the volume of a 200-g sealed container is 100 $cm^3$, then the density of the container is ______________.

A. 2 $kg/m^3$ B. ½ $g/cm^3$

C. 2 $kg/cm^3$ D. 2 $g/cm^3$

37. Imagine there is no gravitational force of attraction between the Earth and a satellite revolving around it. What will happen?

A. The satellite continues to move in its orbit with the same velocity.

B. The satellite becomes stationary in its orbit.

C. The satellite moves away from its orbit tangentially.

D. The satellite falls towards the Earth.

38. Four metal balls P, Q, R and S have equal masses. The size of R and S are twice as that of P and Q. P and Q are kept at a distance of *d* from each other while objects R and S are kept at a distance of 2*d* from each other. Which of the following is correct?

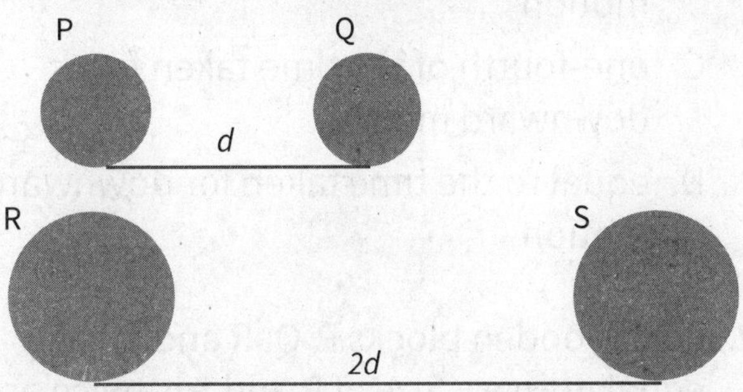


A. Force between P and Q is equal to the between R and S.

B. Force between P and Q is four times the force between R and S.

C. Force between P and Q is half the force between R and S.

D. Force between P and Q is one-fourth the force between R and S.

39. If a body is projected vertically upwards with an initial velocity of *u* and it goes to a maximum height *h* before coming to the ground, then the value of *h* is given by ______________.

A. $(v^2 - u^2)/2g$ B. $(u^2 - v^2)/2g$

C. $(v^2 + u^2)/2g$ D. $(u^2 + v^2)/2g$

40. An object X of mass 1 kg and another object Y of mass 2 kg are dropped from the same height. What is the acceleration due to gravity on X and Y?

A. $g$ on X is 9.8 $m/s^2$ and $g$ on Y is 19.6 $m/s^2$

B. $g$ on X is 9.8 $m/s^2$ and $g$ on Y is 9.8 $m/s^2$

C. $g$ on X is 19.6 $m/s^2$ and $g$ on Y is 9.8 $m/s^2$

D. $g$ on X is 19.6 $m/s^2$ and $g$ on Y is 19.6 $m/s^2$

41. A stone thrown vertically upwards reaches its maximum height and then falls down to the Earth. The time taken for upward motion is ______________.
   A. twice the time taken for downward motion
   B. half of the time taken for downward motion
   C. one-fourth of the time taken for downward motion
   D. equal to the time taken for downward motion

42. Four wooden blocks P, Q, R and S have equal masses. Size of R and S is twice as that of P and Q. Given that the distance between P and Q = distance between R and S = *d*. So, the force between P and Q is ________________.
   A. equal to the force between R and S
   B. twice the force between R and S
   C. half the force between R and S
   D. one-fourth the force between R and S

43. Two objects, P and Q, are dropped from a certain height in vacuum. The mass of P is twice as that of Q. Based on the given statement, choose the correct possibility.
   A. Both P and Q reach the ground at the same time.
   B. Object P reaches first.
   C. Object Q reaches first.
   D. Time of fall depends on the size of the objects.

44. Two objects, X and Y, of equal masses are kept at a distance of 2 m from each other attract with a force of $F$. If their masses are doubled, the force between them is equal to ______________.
   A. $F$ B. $2F$
   C. $4F$ D. $8F$

45. Which of the following statements are correct?
   (i) Gravitational force between two objects is directly proportional to the product of their masses.
   (ii) Gravitational force between two objects is inversely proportional to the square of the distance between them.
   (iii) Gravitational force between two objects is inversely proportional to the product of their masses.
   A. Only (i) and (ii) are correct.
   B. Only (ii) and (iii) are correct.
   C. Only (i) and (iii) are correct.
   D. All (i), (ii) and (ii) are correct.

46. Identify the correct statements.
   (i) Acceleration due to gravity is the same for all objects falling towards the Earth.
   (ii) Acceleration due to gravity on the surface of a planet depends on the mass of the planet.
   A. Only (i) is correct.
   B. Only (ii) is correct.
   C. Both (i) and (ii) are correct.
   D. Both (i) and (ii) are incorrect.

47. P and Q are objects that are placed in a liquid. P sinks and Q floats. Identify the most appropriate conclusion for the situation.

A. P is denser than the liquid and Q is less dense than the liquid.

B. Q is denser than the liquid and P is less dense than the liquid.

C. Both P and Q are less dense than the liquid.

D. Q is denser than P.

48. What would be the effect on the gravitational force between two objects if the distance between them is reduced to half?

A. It increases by 2 times.

B. It decreases by 2 times.

C. It increases by 4 times.

D. It decreases by 4 times.

49. The gravitational pull exerted by the Earth on a body is called its _______.

A. weight

B. mass

C. density

D. inertia

50. The value of universal gravitational constant was determined by __________.

A. Galileo Galilei

B. Isaac Newton

C. Johannes Kepler

D. Henry Cavendish

Chapter 11

# Work and Energy

## PRE-TEST

**Choose the correct option.**

1. Which of the following equations of motion is not correct?
   A. $v = u + at$  B. $s = ut + \frac{1}{2} at^2$
   C. $2as = v^2 + u^2$  D. $s = (v^2 - u^2)/2a$

2. The rate of change of displacement is __________.
   A. momentum
   B. velocity
   C. magnitude of displacement
   D. acceleration

3. The SI unit of universal gravitational constant G is ______________.
   A. $N^2 m\ kg^{-2}$  B. $N\ m^2 kg^{-2}$
   C. $N\ m^2 kg^2$  D. $N\ m^{-2} kg^2$

4. If an object is thrown upwards, then ______________.
   A. the force of gravity acts in the direction of motion
   B. the force of gravity acts in the opposite direction of motion
   C. the force of gravity is zero as the body moves up
   D. the force of gravity increases as the body moves up

5. Which of the following formulae represents the weight of an object $W$?
   A. $W = ma$
   B. $W = mgh$
   C. $W = mg$
   D. $W = m$

## KEYWORDS

**Energy:** The capability of an object or a system to do work

**Kinetic energy:** Energy possessed by an object by the virtue of its motion

**Law of conservation of energy:** Energy can neither be created nor be destroyed; it can only be transformed from one form to another

**Potential energy:** The energy possessed by a body due to its change in position or configuration

**Power:** The rate of doing work or work done in unit time

**Work done:** The magnitude of the force multiplied by the distance moved by the object in the direction of the applied force

# Concept Map

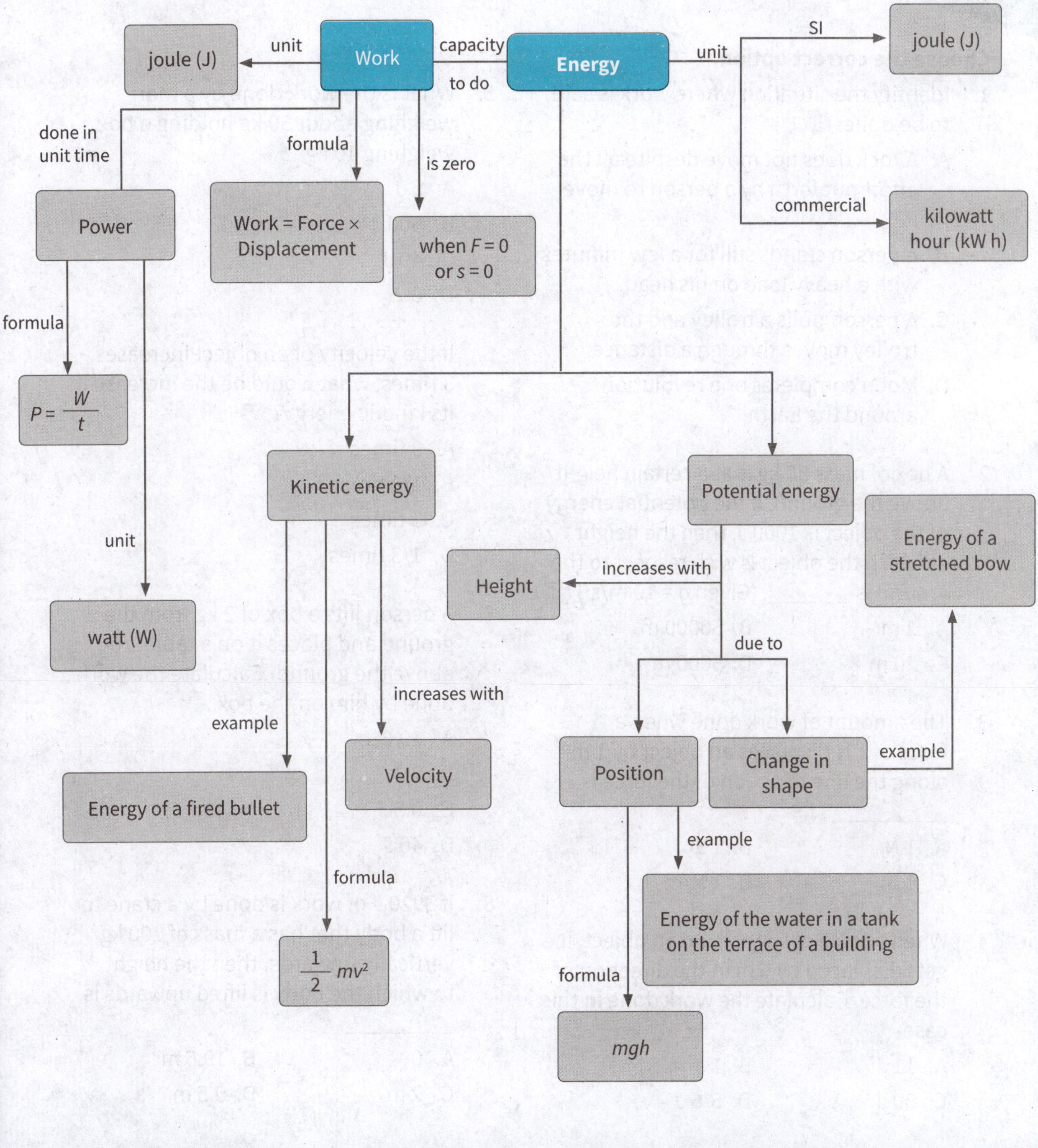
Work
Energy
capacity
to do
unit
joule (J)
SI
joule (J)
commercial
kilowatt hour (kW h)
done in unit time
formula
is zero
Power
Work = Force × Displacement
when $F = 0$ or $s = 0$
formula
$P = \frac{W}{t}$
unit
watt (W)
Kinetic energy
Potential energy
Energy of a stretched bow
increases with
Height
due to
example
Energy of a fired bullet
increases with
Velocity
Position
Change in shape
example
example
formula
Energy of the water in a tank on the terrace of a building
formula
$\frac{1}{2}mv^2$
$mgh$

# SELF-ASSESSMENT 1

**Choose the correct option.**

1. Identify the situation where work is said to be done.
   A. A rock does not move despite all the effort put forth by a person to move it.
   B. A person stands still for a few minutes with a heavy load on his head.
   C. A person pulls a trolley and the trolley moves through a distance.
   D. Moon completes one revolution around the Earth.

2. A box of mass 50 kg is at a certain height above the ground. If the potential energy of the object is 1000 J, then the height at which the object is with respect to the ground is _______. (Given $g = 10\ m/s^2$)
   A. 2 m B. 50000 m
   C. 20 m D. 5000 m

3. The amount of work done when a force of 1 N displaces an object by 1 m along the line of action of the force is __________.
   A. 1 N B. 1 J
   C. 1 m D. 1 N/m

4. When a force of 5 N acts on an object, it gets displaced by 6 m in the direction of the force. Calculate the work done in this case.
   A. 11 J B. 1 J
   C. 30 J D. 5/6 J

5. What is the work done by a man weighing about 50 kg holding a box weighing 10 kg?
   A. 5 J
   B. 500 J
   C. 40 J
   D. 0

6. If the velocity of an object increases 3 times, what would be the increase in its kinetic energy?
   A. 9 times
   B. 1/9 times
   C. 3 times
   D. 1/3 times

7. A person lifts a box of 2 kg from the ground and places it on a table 1 m above the ground. Calculate the work done by him on the box.
   A. 19.6 J
   B. 2 J
   C. 0.5 J
   D. 40 J

8. If 3920 J of work is done by a crane to lift a body that has a mass of 200 kg vertically upwards, then the height to which the body is lifted upwards is __________.
   A. 0 B. 19.6 m
   C. 2 m D. 0.5 m

9. Two people together exert a force of 150 N to drag a metal box through 4 m. How much work is done in dragging the box?

A. 300 J  B. 1200 J
C. 600 J  D. 2400 J

10. Which of the following statements are correct?

(i) An object having a capability to do work is said to possess energy.
(ii) The object which does the work loses energy.
(iii) The object on which the work is done gains energy.

A. Only (i) and (ii) are correct.
B. Only (ii) and (iii) are correct.
C. Only (i) and (iii) are correct.
D. (i), (ii) and (iii) are correct.

11. **Assertion (A):** The unit of energy is the same as that of work, that is, joule (J).
**Reason (R):** The energy possessed by a body is measured in terms of its capacity of doing work.

A. Both A and R are true and R is the correct explanation of A.
B. Both A and R are true, but R is not the correct explanation of A.
C. Only A is true.
D. Only B is true.

12. Two identical objects, X and Y, are moving along a floor and X is moving relatively slower than Y. Which of the following statements is true with respect to the given situation?

A. X can do more work than Y.
B. Y can do more work than X.
C. Both X and Y can do the same amount of work.
D. X and Y cannot do any work.

13. The kinetic energy of a body moving with a certain velocity is ________.

A. greater than the work done on it to make it acquire that velocity
B. less than the work done on it to make it acquire that velocity
C. equal to the work done on it to make it acquire that velocity
D. independent of the work done

14. If a metal ball of mass 6 kg is moving with a uniform velocity of 3 m/s, then its kinetic energy is ________.

A. 9 J  B. 18 J
C. 27 J  D. 54 J

15. If a body moving with a uniform velocity of 36 km/h possesses energy of 250 J, then its mass Is ________.

A. 0.38 kg  B. 5 kg
C. 6.9 kg  D. 10 kg

16. The kinetic energy of a body of mass *m* moving with a velocity of 10 m/s is 50 J. Calculate the kinetic energy of the body when its velocity is doubled.

A. 200 J  B. 100 J
C. 50 J  D. 0

17. **Assertion (A):** The potential energy of an object increases with an increase in its height from the ground.
**Reason (R):**Work is done on the object against gravity while it is being raised.

A. Both A and R are true but R is not the correct explanation of A.
B. Both A and R are true and R is the correct explanation of A.
C. Only A is true.
D. Only B is true.

18. What would be the work done $W$ on the object against gravity when an object of mass $m$ is being raised through a height $h$ from the ground?

A. $W = 0$ B. $W = mg$

C. $W = (1/2) mv^2$ D. $W = mgh$

19. What is the energy possessed by an object of mass 10 kg when it is at a height of 10 m above the ground? (Given $g = 10$ m/ s²)

A. 0 J B. 100 J

C. 1000 J D. 10000 J

20. Which of the following pairs is correctly matched?

(i) Rubbing both hands together for warmth—$E_k$ to Thermal Energy

(ii) A falling object speeding up—Gravitational, $E_p$ to $E_k$

(iii) Electric lamp—Light energy to Electric Energy

A. Only (i) is correct.

B. Only (i) and (ii) are correct.

C. Only (i) and (iii) are correct.

D. (i), (ii) and (iii) are correct.

21. An object that has the mass of 2 kg is dropped from a height of 15 m. What is its potential energy after falling till 5 m? (Given $g$ =10 m/s²)

A. 100 J B. 200 J

C. 300 J D. 0

22. Identify the quantity that measures the rate of work done, that is, how fast or slow the work is done.

A. Law of conservation of momentum

B. Kinetic energy

C. Potential energy

D. Power

23. Electrical energy used in a month is usually expressed in terms of units. Identify the relation between 1 unit and kilowatt hour.

A. 1 unit = 100 kW h

B. 1 unit = 1000 kW h

C. 1 unit= 1 kW h

D. 1 unit= 10000 kW h

24. The power rating of an iron box is 1000 W. How much energy does it use in 5 hours?

A. 5 units

B. 250 units

C. 5000 units

D. $5 \times 10^{-3}$ units

25. We can say that power of a system is 1 W when the rate of consumption of energy is ____________.

a. 1 J/s$^{-1}$

b. 1 J

c. 1 J s

D. 1 J/s

Chapter 12

# Sound

## PRE-TEST

**Choose the correct option.**

1. A ball oscillates 20 times in 4 seconds. What is its frequency?

   A. 20 Hz  B. 10 Hz
   C. 5 Hz  D. 0.2 Hz

2. There is a difference in the voices of men, women and children due to ________.

   A. difference in food pipe
   B. difference in lungs
   C. difference in vocal cords
   D. difference in wind pipe

3. The unit of frequency is ____________.

   A. metre  B. hertz
   C. metre/second  D. second

4. If a wave completes 100 vibrations in 25 s, then its frequency is ____________.

   A. 2500 Hz  B. 4 Hz
   C. 0.25 s  D. 1

5. Female voice is shrill compared to the male voice because ______________.

   A. frequency of female voice is more than that of male voice
   B. frequency of male voice is more than that of female voice
   C. amplitude of female voice is more than that of male voice
   D. amplitude of male voice is more than that of female voice

## KEYWORDS

**Frequency:** The number of oscillations completed per unit time

**Infrasonic sound:** Sound waves with frequencies below the audible range (< 20 Hz)

**Intensity of sound:** The amount of sound energy passing each second through a given unit area

**Law of reflection of sound:** The directions in which the incident sound and the reflected sound make equal angles with the normal to the reflecting surface and the three lie in the same plane

**Loudness:** A physiological response of the ear to the intensity of sound

**Pitch:** The shrillness of sound experienced by the listener

**Time period:** Time taken by the wave to travel a distance that is equal to its wavelength

**Ultrasonic sound:** Sound waves with frequencies above the audible range (> 20 kHz)

**Wavelength:** The distance between two consecutive compressions or two consecutive rarefactions

# Concept Map

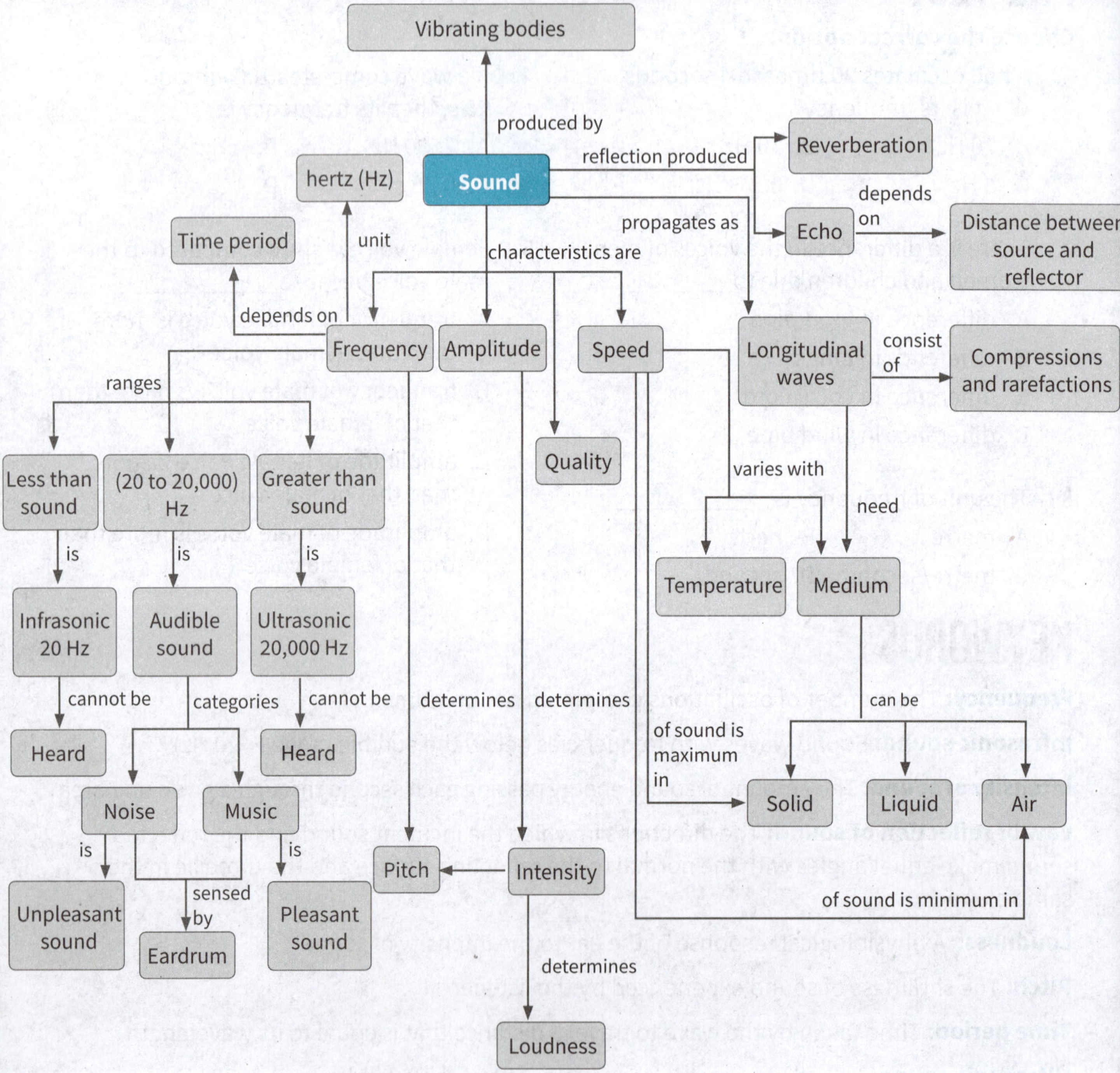
Vibrating bodies
produced by
Sound
reflection produced
Reverberation
hertz (Hz)
unit
Time period
depends on
propagates as
Echo
depends on
Distance between source and reflector
characteristics are
Frequency
Amplitude
Speed
Longitudinal waves
consist of
Compressions and rarefactions
ranges
Less than sound
(20 to 20,000) Hz
Greater than sound
Quality
varies with
need
Temperature
Medium
is
Infrasonic 20 Hz
Audible sound
Ultrasonic 20,000 Hz
cannot be
categories
cannot be
determines
determines
can be
Heard
Heard
of sound is maximum in
Noise
Music
Solid
Liquid
Air
is
is
Pitch
Intensity
sensed by
of sound is minimum in
Unpleasant sound
Eardrum
Pleasant sound
determines
Loudness

Chapter 12 Sound

# SELF-ASSESSMENT 1

**Choose the correct option.**

1. Identify X and Y from the given figure.

   A. X and Y—Rarefaction
   B. X and Y—Compression
   C. X—Compression; Y—Rarefaction
   D. X—Rarefaction; Y—Compression

2. If the time period of a sound wave increases, then its frequency will ____________.
   A. remain the same
   B. increase
   C. decrease
   D. first increase then decrease

3. Two persons on the moon cannot hear each other as ____________.
   A. the moon's atmosphere does not allow sound waves to pass
   B. the moon's atmosphere absorbs the sound produced
   C. sound waves can only travel in vacuum
   D. the moon has no atmosphere around it

4. Which of the following completes the given analogy? __________: Longitudinal wave :: Light : Transverse wave
   A. Ripples on the surface of water
   B. Sound wave
   C. Vibrations in a guitar string
   D. A Mexican wave in a sports stadium

5. Compressions are regions where ___.
   A. density is high, pressure is low
   B. density is low, pressure is high
   C. density as well as pressure is low
   D. density as well as pressure is high

6. The wavelength of a sound wave in air is ____________.
   A. the distance between two consecutive compressions
   B. the distance between a compression and a rarefaction
   C. the distance between two consecutive crests
   D. the distance between a crest and trough

7. Identify the correct statements.
   (i) The faster the vibration of the source, the higher is the frequency of a sound.
   (ii) The faster the vibration of the source, the higher is the pitch of a sound.
   A. Only (i) is correct.
   B. Only (ii) is correct.
   C. Both (i) and (ii) are correct.
   D. Both (i) and (ii) are incorrect.

8. Observe the given figures and identify the wave shape for a high-pitched sound.

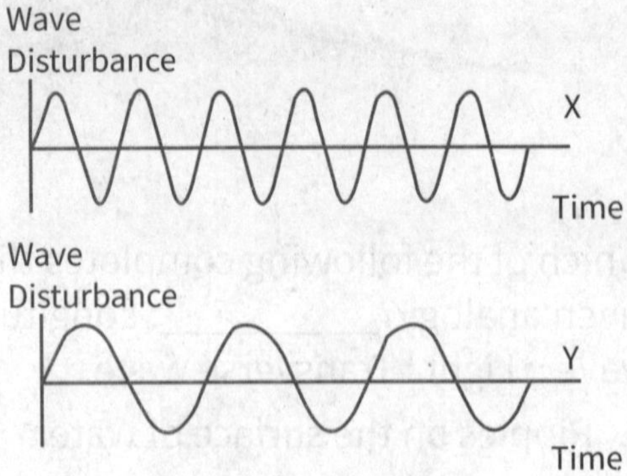


A. X is high-pitched sound.
B. Y is high-pitched sound.
C. Both X and Y represent high-pitched sound.
D. Both X and Y represent low-pitched sound.

9. Which among the following statements are true?
   (i) A sound of single frequency is a tone.
   (ii) The sound which is produced due to a mixture of frequencies is the pitch.
   (iii) Noise is unpleasant to the ear.

A. Only (i) and (ii) are true.
B. Only (i) and (iii) are true.
C. Only (ii) and (iii) are true.
D. (i), (ii) and (iii) are true.

10. Which of the following completes the given analogy?
    ____________: Pitch :: Amplitude: Loudness

A. Amplitude
B. Time period
C. Oscillation
D. Frequency

11. What is the wavelength of a sound wave whose frequency is 100 Hz and speed is 400 m/s in a given medium?

A. $\frac{1}{4}$ m
B. 40000 m
C. 4 m
D. $\frac{1}{4} \times 10^{-4}$ m

12. A sound wave has a frequency of 800 Hz and wave length 50 cm. Identify the time taken by the wave to travel 2 km.

A. 5 s
B. 1 s
C. 40 s
D. 4 s

13. Amay is listening to a tone of 200 Hz standing at a distance of 150 m from the musical instrument. Identify the time period.

A. 30,000 s
B. $\frac{4}{3}$ s
C. 5 s
D. 0.005 s

14. Arrange the media iron, air and water in accordance with the speed of sound through them in an ascending order.

A. Iron < Water < Air
B. Water < Air < Iron
C. Iron < Air < Water
D. Air < Water < Iron

15. The sound of a thunder is heard a little later than the flash of light is seen. Identify the correct reason for the given statement.

A. Speed of sound > Speed of light
B. Speed of sound = Speed of light
C. Speed of sound < Speed of light
D. Speed of sound in air = Zero

16. Identify the correct statements.
    (i) The speed of sound decreases when we go from solid to gaseous state.
    (ii) In any medium, the speed of sound increases with the increase in temperature.
    A. Only (i) is correct.
    B. Only (ii) is correct.
    C. Both (i) and (ii) are correct.
    D. Both (i) and (ii) are incorrect.

17. Reena made a sound near a steep rock face and heard the echo after 1 s. Identify the distance of the rock face from Reena. (The speed of the sound is 342 m/s.)
    A. 342 m    B. 171 m
    C. 644 m    D. 1 m

18. Ceilings of music concert halls are curved to ____________.
    A. increase the speed of sound
    B. distribute sound in all directions
    C. decrease the speed of sound
    D. increase the intensity and loudness of the sound

19. Which of the following completes the given analogy?
    Rhinoceroses: Infrasound:
    ____________: Ultrasound
    A. Elephants    B. Giraffes
    C. Dolphins    D. Whales

20. A watercraft sends an ultrasound to the ocean floor. It returns and is detected after 4 s. Identify the distance of the ocean floor from the ship. (Given the speed of ultrasound is 1500 m/s.)
    A. 6000 m    B. 1200 m
    C. 3000 m    D. 1500 m

21. When a mechanical wave travels in a medium, identify the quantity that is transferred from one place to another with the wave.
    A. Velocity
    B. Mass
    C. Energy
    D. Density

22. Which of the following waves can be produced in a slinky?
    A. Transverse wave only
    B. Longitudinal wave only
    C. Both longitudinal and transverse waves
    D. No waves can be produced in slinky

23. The time taken for one complete oscillation by the particle of the medium is called ____________.
    A. frequency of the sound wave
    B. time period of the sound wave
    C. intensity of the sound wave
    D. wavelength of the sound wave

24. How does the brain interpret the frequency of an emitted sound?
    A. With the intensity of the sound wave
    B. With the loudness of the sound wave
    C. With the pitch of the sound wave
    D. With the wavelength of the sound wave

25. The audible range of sound for human beings extends from about ________.
    A. 20 Hz to 20,000 kHz
    B. 20 kHz to 20,000 kHz
    C. 20 Hz to 20,000 Hz
    D. 2 Hz to 20,000 Hz

Chapter 12 Sound

# SELF-ASSESSMENT 2

**Choose the correct option.**

26. Rarefactions are the regions where __________.
    A. density is high and the pressure is low
    B. density is low and the pressure is high
    C. density as well as the pressure is low
    D. density as well as the pressure is high

27. Identify the correct statements.
    (i) The frequency of the wave determines its loudness.
    (ii) The pitch is determined by the amplitude of a wave.
    A. Only (i) is correct.
    B. Only (ii) is correct.
    C. Both (i) and (ii) are correct.
    D. Both (i) and (ii) are not correct.

28. Through which of the following media sound travels the slowest?
    A. Iron
    B. Water
    C. Oil
    D. Air

29. Harminder heard the echo of his own sound in 5 s. What is the distance between the reflecting surface and the source of sound? (Given the speed of sound is 342 m/s)
    A. 342 m
    B. 171 m
    C. 1710 m
    D. 855 m

30. A ship sends out an ultrasound that returns from an object near to the sea bed in 2.5 seconds. Identify the distance between the ship and the reflected surface. (Given the speed of sound is 1500 m/s)
    A. 3750 m B. 1500 m
    C. 1875 m D. 1775 m

31. If a wave source produces 40 crests and 40 troughs in 0.5 s, then the frequency of the wave is __________.
    A. 80 Hz B. 160 Hz
    C. 8 Hz D. 20 Hz

32. Which of the following represents the distance between a crest and trough?
    A. λ B. 2λ
    C. λ/2 D. λ/4

33. A longitudinal wave travels from North to South in air. Identify the direction in which the particles of air move.
    A. East—West B. North—East
    C. North—South D. South—West

34. What is the frequency of the sound represented by the given graph?

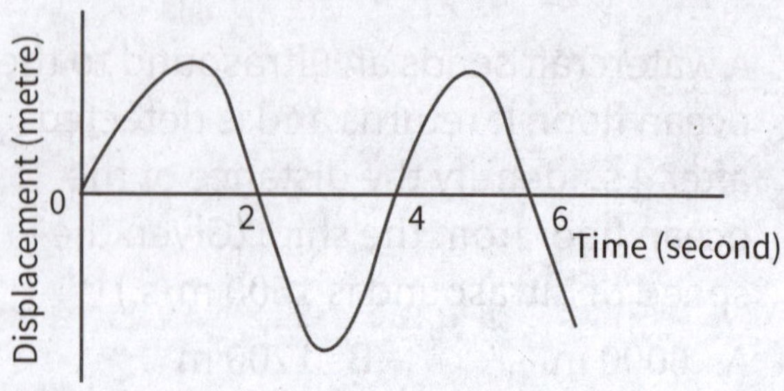


    A. 4 Hz B. 2 Hz
    C. 0.5 Hz D. 0.25 Hz

35. A region in a medium can be called high pressure or low pressure from the ________.

A. total number of particles in that region
B. number of particles per unit volume in that region
C. size of the medium
D. length of the medium

36. Which of the following represents the amplitude of the wave in the given diagrams?

A.
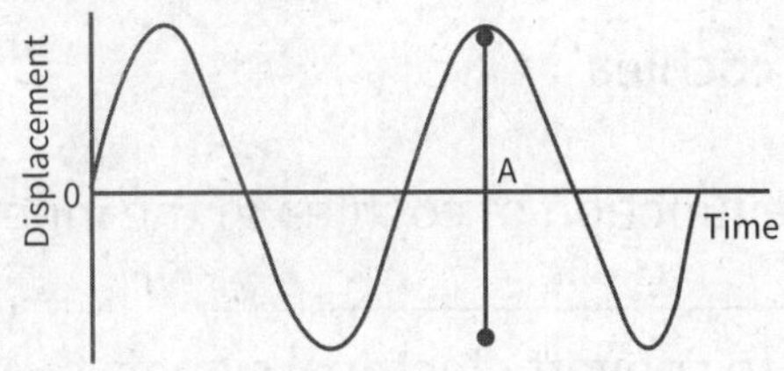


B.
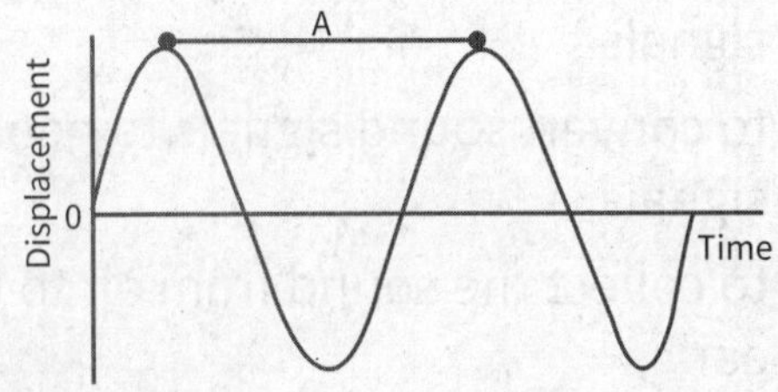


C.
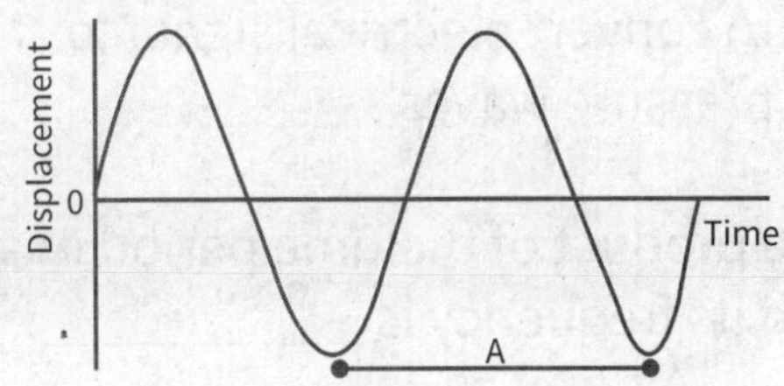


D.
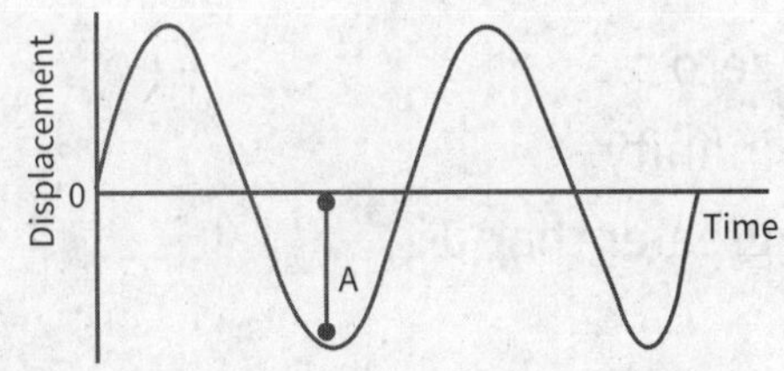


37. The number of compressions and rarefactions passing through a region in a medium in one second is called ________.

A. frequency
B. wavelength
C. time period
D. amplitude

38. If a longitudinal wave has a frequency of 200 Hz and a wavelength of 50 cm then, what is the time taken by the wave to travel 1 km?

A. 10,000 s
B. 10 s
C. 1000 s
D. 100 s

39. The sound waves produced from the tightened strings of a guitar ________.

A. have a high pitch
B. have a low pitch
C. fluctuates from low pitch to high pitch
D. have low frequency

40. Jairam stood facing a huge wall at a distance of 170 m from it and shouted. What is the time interval when he hears an echo? (Speed of sound = 340 m/s)

A. 0.5 s
B. 1 s
C. 2 s
D. 4 s

41. Identify the quantity that does not alter when a sound wave travels from one medium to another.

A. Intensity
B. Loudness
C. Velocity
D. Frequency

42. Identify the properties that change during the reflection of a sound wave.

A. Frequency, wavelength and speed
B. Frequency and wavelength
C. Wavelength and speed
D. Frequency and speed

43. Which of the following statements is true?
   A. Compressions are always seen in transverse waves.
   B. Compressions and rarefactions do not co-exist in a wave
   C. Speed of sound is medium dependent.
   D. Light and sound travel with the same speed.

44. A tuning fork of frequency 300 Hz completes 60 vibrations. Find the distance travelled by sound in air. (Given the speed of sound = 340 m/s)
   A. 5 m B. 68 m
   C. 60 m D. 1620 m

45. A sound produced due to mixture of frequencies which is pleasant to hear is called ______________.
   A. note B. tone
   C. pitch D. loudness

46. Identify the property that enables the sound of a patient's heartbeat to reach the doctor's ears through stethoscope.
   A. Multiple reflection
   B. Single reflection
   C. Absorption
   D. Direct transmission

47. SONAR stands for ______________.
   A. sound navigation and reflection
   B. sound navigation and ranging
   C. sound output navigation and ranging
   D. ultrasound navigation and ranging

48. The part of the ear which collects sound from the surroundings is called ______________.
   A. middle ear
   B. inner ear
   C. pinna
   D. cochlea

49. The function of cochlea in the inner ear is ______________.
   A. to convert electrical signals to sound signals
   B. to convert sound signals to neural signals
   C. to collect the sound from air to the ear
   D. to convert electrical signal to pressure waves

50. The product of the time period of a wave and its frequency is ______________.
   A. 1
   B. zero
   C. infinity
   D. greater than 1

Chapter 13

# Why Do We Fall Ill?

## PRE-TEST

**Choose the correct option.**

1. Which of the following diseases can spread in a park?
   A. Common cold B. Cholera
   C. Typhoid D. Diarrhoea

2. Identify the odd one among the following.
   A. Cholera B. Pneumonia
   C. Diarrhoea D. Amoebiasis

3. Which of the following spreads disease?
   A. Cockroach B. Honeybee
   C. Grasshopper D. Butterfly

4. Which of the following prevents waterborne diseases?
   A. Repairing leaking taps immediately
   B. Consuming boiled and filtered water
   C. Drinking recycled water directly
   D. Consuming filtered rainwater

5. Identify the odd one out.
   A. Human beings
   B. Mosquitoes
   C. Dogs
   D. Frogs

## KEYWORDS

**Acute diseases:** Diseases that comes on rapidly and last for a short duration of time

**Chronic diseases:** Long-term diseases that last a lifetime

**Communicable diseases:** A disease, caused by infectious pathogens, that spreads from one person to another through air, water, sexual contact, physical contact, blood-to-blood contact or from an infected mother to her baby

**Food Chain:** Series of organisms connected with one another based on their food habit (It always begins with a producer or an autotroph)

**Health:** Physical, mental and social well-being of a person

**Hygiene:** Practices and conditions that help to maintain health and prevent spread of diseases

**Immunization:** The process by which a person is made immune or resistant to an infectious disease, typically by the administration of a vaccine

**Infectious agents:** Abiotic and biotic factors that cause illness

**Vaccine:** A substance containing a harmless form of the germs that cause a particular disease; injected to people or taken orally to prevent from getting a disease

# Concept Map

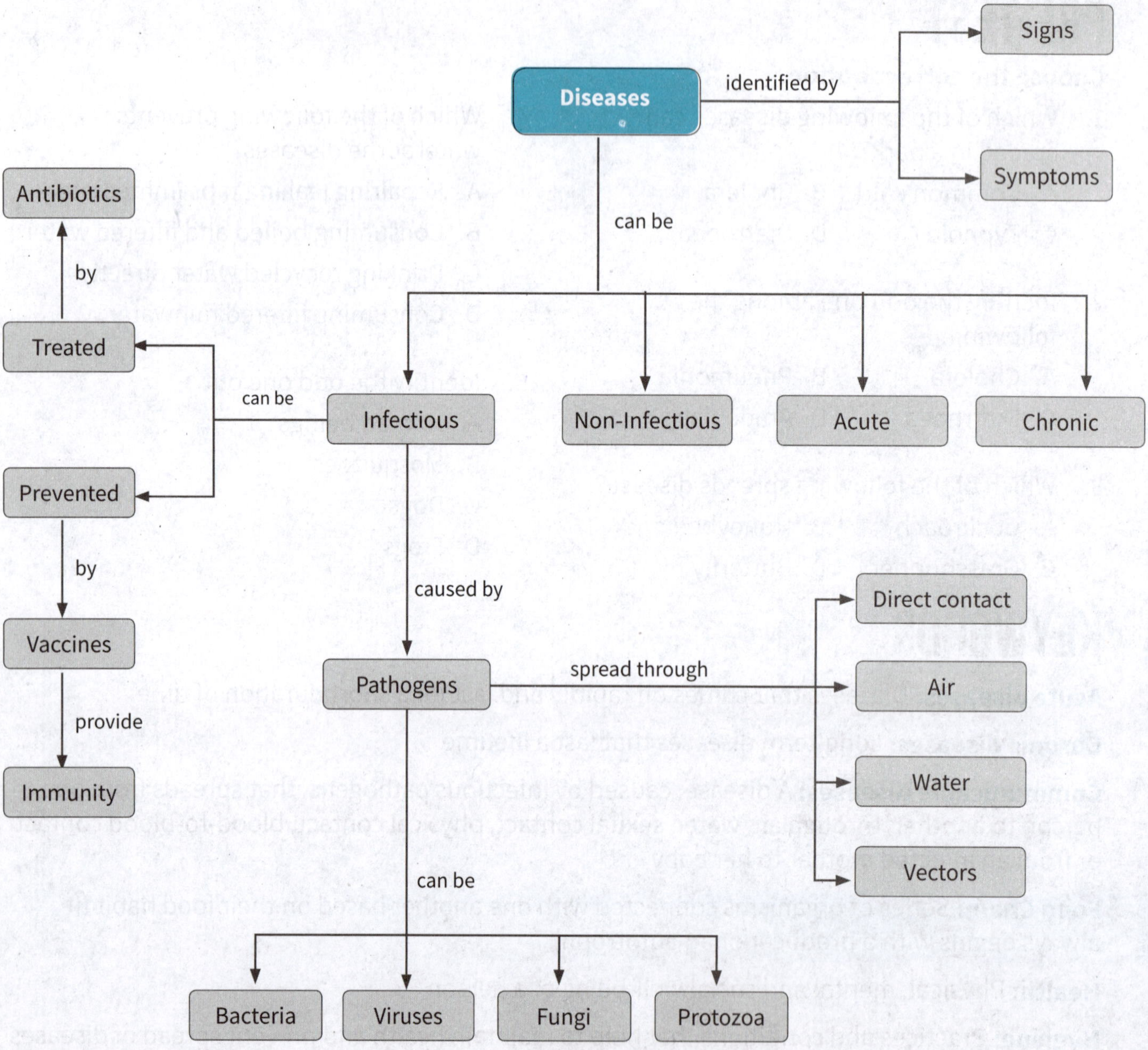

Diseases
identified by
Signs
Symptoms
can be
Infectious
Non-Infectious
Acute
Chronic
can be
Treated
by
Antibiotics
Prevented
by
Vaccines
provide
Immunity
caused by
Pathogens
spread through
Direct contact
Air
Water
Vectors
can be
Bacteria
Viruses
Fungi
Protozoa

Chapter 13 Why Do We Fall Ill?

# SELF-ASSESSMENT 1

**Choose the correct option.**

1. Which of the following describes a disease?
   A. Disturbed ease
   B. Disrupted health
   C. Disturbance in health
   D. Modes of reproduction

2. Which of the following does not cause ill health?
   A. Impure drinking water
   B. Closed drainage
   C. Collection of solid waste
   D. Stagnant water

3. Which of the following is the main symptom of lung diseases?
   A. Fits B. Breathlessness
   C. Vomiting D. Headache

4. Which of the following can spread the common cold?
   A. Sneezing by an infected person without covering his mouth
   B. Sneezing by a normal person by covering his mouth
   C. Sneezing by a normal person without covering his mouth
   D. Sitting next to a normal person

5. Which of the following is the best medicine for peptic ulcer?
   A. Antacids B. Citric-rich food
   C. Antibiotics D. Protein-rich food

6. Which of the following is considered to be a chronic disease?
   A. Dry cough
   B. Asthma
   C. Common cold
   D. Stomach pain

7. Which among the following is an effective method to purify unclean water at home?
   A. Chlorination
   B. Boiling for 20 minutes
   C. Decantation
   D. Filtration

8. Which of the following is a bacterial infection?
   A. Common cold
   B. Typhoid
   C. Corona
   D. Malaria

9. Which of the following completes the given analogy?
   Fungi : Skin infection :: Protozoa : ____________.
   A. Cholera
   B. Tuberculosis
   C. Malaria
   D. Anthrax

10. Which of the following is not an intestinal worm?
    A. Human pinworm
    B. Giant roundworm
    C. Tapeworm
    D. Leech

11. Which of the following is a vector for the disease chikungunya?
    A. Grasshopper
    B. Mosquito
    C. Honeybee
    D. Red worm

12. Which of the following diseases is highly infectious?
    A. Foodborne diseases
    B. Waterborne diseases
    C. Airborne diseases
    D. Animal-borne diseases

13. Identify the disease that is not caused by sexual contact.
    A. AIDS
    B. Syphilis
    C. Gonorrhoea
    D. Cholera

14. Match the following.

| | Column I | | Column II |
|---|---|---|---|
| a. | HIV | i. | Jaundice |
| b. | Liver | ii. | Headache |
| c. | Brain fever | iii. | Sexual contact |

A. a→i; b→ii; c→iii
B. a→ii; b→i; c→iii
C. a→ii; b→iii; c→i
D. a→iii; b→i; c→ii

15. Which of the following is the full form of AIDS?
    A. Active immune disease syndrome
    B. Assumed immune deficiency syndrome
    C. Acquired immune disease symptom
    D. Acquired immune deficiency syndrome

16. Identify the non-viral infection.
    A. Smallpox
    B. Ebola
    C. H1N1
    D. Anthrax

17. Identify the incorrect pair from the following.
    A. Immune system—Number of microbes
    B. Rabies Vector—Dog
    C. Bacterial nuclei—Crowded area
    D. Leech—Gangrene

18. Which of the following pollutes air, soil and water?
    A. Untreated open sewage
    B. Cow dung cakes
    C. Vermicompost pits
    D. Paper waste and leaf litter

19. Which of the following is not a tissue-specific disease?
    A. Sickle cell anaemia
    B. HIV
    C. Goitre
    D. Jaundice

20. Identify the odd one from the following.
   A. Bone fracture  B. Skin burn
   C. Flu  D. Alzheimer's

21. Which of the following statements are true about chronic disease?
   (i) This form of disease is severe.
   (ii) It has a long-term effect on the health.
   (iii) The onset of such a disease is rapid.
   (iv) No symptoms are observed.
   A. (i) and (ii) only
   B. (ii) (iii) and (iv) only
   C. (ii) only
   D. (i) and (iii) only

22. Which of the following fits into the intersection part of the given Venn diagram?

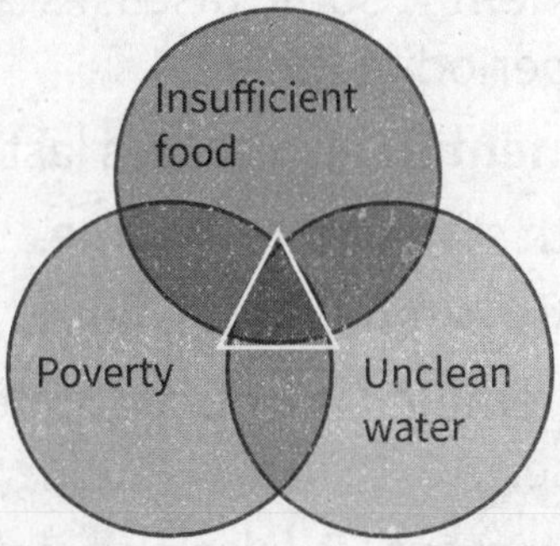


   A. Loose motion caused by viral infection
   B. Headache caused by drinking unclean water
   C. Blindness due to malnourishment
   D. Diseases due to poverty

23. Which of the following blocks the biochemical pathway of bacteria?
   (i) Antibiotics
   (ii) Vaccines
   (iii) Antifungal creams
   (iv) Antiviral injections
   A. (i), (ii) and (iii) only
   B. (i) and (iv) only
   C. (i), (ii), (iii) and (iv)
   D. (i) only

24. **Statement I:** Cancer is caused by genetic abnormalities.
   **Statement II:** Cancer does not spread from person to person.
   **Statement III:** Cancer is spread by viral infection.
   A. Statement I, statement II and statement III—True
   B. Statement I and statement II—True; Statement III—False
   C. Statement I, statement II and Statement III—False
   D. Statement I and statement III—False; Statement II—True

25. Which of the following is caused by non-infectious agents?
   A. Cholera
   B. High fever
   C. Skin allergy
   D. High blood pressure

**Chapter 13 Why Do We Fall Ill?**

# SELF-ASSESSMENT 2

**Choose the correct option.**

26. Which of the following does not affect the severity of a disease?
    A. Target tissue
    B. Acute or chronic disease
    C. Immunity of the person
    D. The number of pathogens in the body

27. Which of the following completes the given analogy?
    Elephantiasis : Filarial worm :: Rabies : ______________
    A. *E. coli* bacteria
    B. Rabies virus
    C. *Salmonella typhi*
    D. Ebola virus

28. Which of the following does not have a vaccine?
    A. HIV    B. Typhoid
    C. Tetanus    D. Dengue

29. Edward Jenner developed the vaccine against ____________.
    A. polio
    B. asthma
    C. lactose intolerance
    D. small pox

30. Which of the following multiplies slower than the others?
    A. Bacterium    B. Virus
    C. Fungus    D. Worm

31. Which of the following actions will help a physician to diagnose a disease?
    (i) Observing the symptoms and signs
    (ii) Lab test reports
    (iii) Body temperature
    (iv) Colour of the skin
    A. (i) and (ii) only
    B. (ii) and (iv) only
    C. (i), (ii) and (iii) only
    D. (iii) and (iv) only

32. **Statement I:** Some diseases last for a short period of time.
    **Statement II:** All diseases last longer.
    A. Both statements are true.
    B. Both statements are false.
    C. Statement I is true but statement II is false.
    D. Statement I is false and statement II is true.

33. **Assertion (A):** Excessive weight and blood pressure affects the health of a person.
    **Reason (R):** High blood pressure is caused by obesity.
    A. Both A and R are true and R is the correct explanation of A.
    B. Both A and R are true, but R is not the correct explanation of A.
    C. A is true but R is false.
    D. R is true but A is false.

34. Which of the following statements is true about peptic ulcer disease?
   A. It is caused by *Helicobacter pylori*.
   B. It is caused by untimely food habits.
   C. It is caused by lack of exercise.
   D. It is caused by wearing tight stomach belts.

35. Which of the following is the correct match?
   A. Bacteria—Chikungunya
   B. Protozoa—Dengue fever
   C. Fungi—Skin diseases
   D. Protozoa—Thyroid disorders

36. Which of the following affects the immune system?
   A. Influenza virus
   B. HIV
   C. Smallpox virus
   D. Ebola virus

37. Which of the following is an acute disease?
   A. Cancer of liver
   B. Type 1 diabetes
   C. Swine flu
   D. Ebola

38. Read the following statements and identify the correct options.
   i. The sign of active immune system is the production of the fluid (a)________.
   ii. After an injury, the (b)________is commonly observed.
   A. (a)—sweat, (b)—fracture
   B. (a)—urine, (b)—haemorrhage
   C. (a)—pus, (b)—inflammation
   D. (a)—saliva, (b)—shrinking of cells

39. The different measures that are needed to be taken for the prevention of corona virus are:
   (i) Wearing masks in public places
   (ii) Washing hands frequently
   (iii) Taking vaccine for flu
   (iv) Drinking plenty of water
   (v) Avoiding crowded places
   Which of the following represents the correct steps?
   A. (i), (ii), (iv) and (v) only
   B. (i) and (iii) only
   C. (i), (ii) and (iii) only
   D. (iii), (iv) and (v) only

40. Which of the following is a disease of the muscular system?
   A. Polio
   B. Colour blindness
   C. Night blindness
   D. Rickets

41. Identify the way by which HIV cannot be spread.
   A. Sexual contact
   B. Physical contact
   C. Blood transfusion
   D. Animal vector

42. **Assertion (A):** Oral polio vaccine (OPV) is voluntarily given to children.
   **Reason (R):** OPV prevents polio attack.
   A. Both A and R are true and R is the correct explanation of A.
   B. Both A and R are true but R is not the correct explanation of A.
   C. A is true but R is false.
   D. R is true but A is false.

43. **Statement I:** Contagious diseases are vector borne.

**Statement II:** Contagious diseases spread by air only.

**Statement III:** Contagious diseases are always chronic.

A. Statement I, statement II and statement III—True

B. Statement I—True; Statement II and statement III—False

C. Statement I, statement II and statement III—False

D. Statement I, statement II—True; Statement III—False

44. Which of the following reduces peptic ulcer infections?

A. Antibiotics

B. Vaccine

C. Hormonal injections

D. Blood transfusion

45. Which of the following statements is incorrect?

A. Sewage water can be reused for irrigation after removing the impurities.

B. Stagnant sewage water does not cause illness in the neighbourhood.

C. Sewage water is treated before being drained into the seas and oceans.

D. Sewage water can be reused with treatment for any domestic purpose.

46. Which of the following completes the given analogy?

Diabetes : ___________ :: Bone fracture : Immobilization

A. Unable to process iodized salt

B. Unable to process blood glucose

C. Unable to process omega-3 fatty acids

D. Unable to process iron-rich food

47. While going abroad, we are requested to get vaccinated against certain diseases. Why?

A. To avoid being carrier of infection

B. To get immunity to a new disease

C. Both A and B

D. None of these

48. Which of the following does not alter our metabolism?

A. Saline  B. Diet

C. Exercise  D. Hormones

49. Which of the following could reduce the inflammation in the knee due to injury?

A. Applying weight

B. Applying pressure

C. Immobilization and relaxation

D. Leaving as it is

50. Which of the following diseases is caused by a protozoan which is oval-shaped with a long whip-like structure?

A. Kala-azar  B. SAARS

C. AIDS  D. Pneumonia

Chapter 14

# Natural Resources

## PRE-TEST

**Choose the correct option.**

1. What percentage of the Earth is covered with water?
   A. 50% B. 71%
   C. 90% D. 95%

2. What is smog composed of?
   A. Fog and smoke
   B. Snow and smoke
   C. Dust and water vapour
   D. Fog and water vapour

3. Which of the following contaminates water?
   A. Rain B. Sewage
   C. Aquatic animals D. Tube wells

4. What is the role of the ozone layer in the atmosphere?
   A. It causes rainfall.
   B. It helps in the movement of clouds.
   C. It protects from ultraviolet radiations.
   D. It helps in the navigation of aeroplanes.

5. Identify the correct reason for water pollution.
   A. Melting of glaciers
   B. Increase of forests
   C. Presence of aquatic animals
   D. Fertilizer dissolved in water

## KEYWORDS

**Acid rain:** Oxides of sulphur and nitrogen present in the atmosphere mixes with water vapour and precipitate as rain

**Air pollution:** Contamination of the air with substances harmful for both living organisms and non-living things

**Carbon cycle:** The circulation of carbon between the atmosphere and environment

**Greenhouse effect:** An effect related to the increase of the average temperature all over the world caused by greenhouse gases

**Nitrogen cycle:** The circulation of elementary nitrogen in the atmosphere to land and soil and back to the atmosphere

**Oxygen cycle:** The cyclic movement of oxygen within and between its three main reservoirs, namely atmosphere, biosphere and lithosphere

**Water cycle:** The circulation of water from the land to sea in a cyclic manner

**Water pollution:** Addition of certain substances in the water that reduces its quality and changes its colour and smell

**Wind:** The circulation of air in the atmosphere

# Concept Map

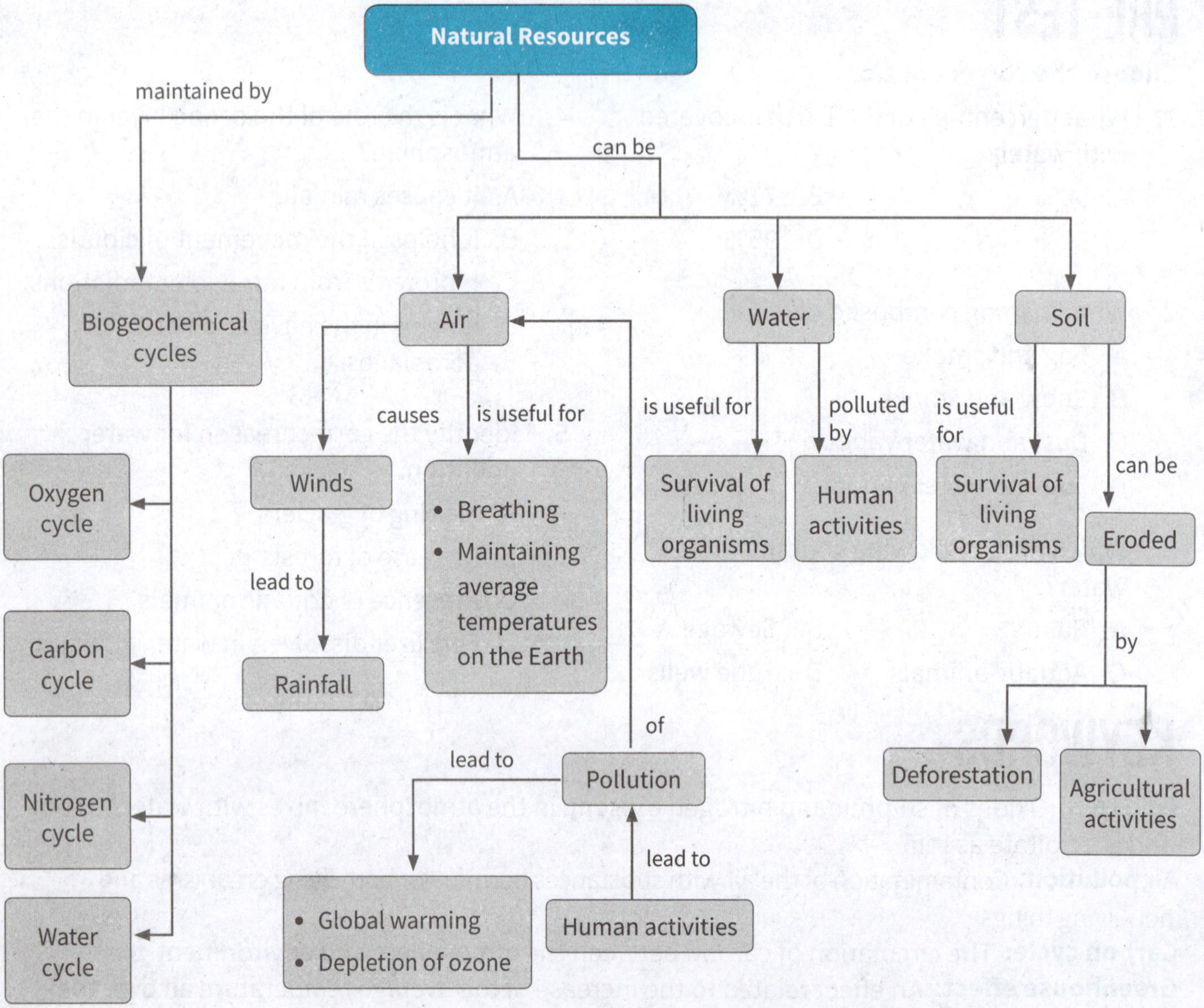
Natural Resources
maintained by
can be
Biogeochemical cycles
Oxygen cycle
Carbon cycle
Nitrogen cycle
Water cycle
Air
causes
is useful for
Winds
lead to
Rainfall
• Breathing
• Maintaining average temperatures on the Earth
of
Pollution
lead to
• Global warming
• Depletion of ozone
lead to
Human activities
Water
is useful for
Survival of living organisms
polluted by
Human activities
Soil
is useful for
Survival of living organisms
can be
Eroded
by
Deforestation
Agricultural activities

PART 1

Chapter 14 Natural Resources

# SELF-ASSESSMENT 1

**Choose the correct option.**

1. What is the major component found in the atmosphere of Venus and Mars?
   A. Nitrogen
   B. Carbon dioxide
   C. Oxygen
   D. Hydrogen

2. Identify the layer of soil that contains humus.
   A. Bottom soil
   B. Topsoil
   C. Middle soil
   D. Soil between rocks

3. Where can the nitrogen-fixing bacteria be found in plants?
   A. In the roots
   B. In the leaves
   C. In the stem
   D. In the fruits

4. Identify the elemental form of carbon found on the Earth.
   A. Graphite
   B. Water
   C. Common salt
   D. Nitrogen oxide

5. What percentage of oxygen in elemental form is found on the Earth?
   A. 78% B. 50%
   C. 37% D. 21%

6. Identify the factor that decides the quality of soil.
   A. Amount of air
   B. Amount of water
   C. Amount of humus
   D. Amount of pollutants

7. Which among the following is the effect of deforestation?
   (i) Rainfall
   (ii) Soil erosion
   (iii) Loss of biodiversity
   (iv) Increase in wind
   A. (ii) and (iii) only
   B. (i) and (iv) only
   C. (i), (iii) and (iv) only
   D. (i), (ii) and (iv) only

8. What is the correct description of the greenhouse effect?
   A. Absorption of carbon dioxide by the plants in the atmosphere
   B. Release of carbon dioxide by the animals to the atmosphere
   C. Trapping of radiations by the Earth's atmosphere
   D. Circulation of air in the form of wind

9. Which of the following is correct about soil erosion?
   A. It is reversible.
   B. It is difficult to reverse.
   C. It improves the quality of soil.
   D. It increases the biodiversity in an area.

10. What do plants generally do with nitrates?
   A. They convert it into nitrogen.
   B. They convert it into food.
   C. They convert it into amino acids.
   D. They convert it into oxygen.

11. Identify the process through which carbon is incorporated into life forms.
   A. Respiration
   B. Photosynthesis
   C. Evaporation
   D. Combustion

12. Identify the processes that release carbon dioxide into the atmosphere.
   (i) Cooking
   (ii) Heating
   (iii) Transportation
   (iv) Photosynthesis
   A. (i) and (iii)
   B. Only (iv)
   C. (ii) and (iv)
   D. (i), (ii) and (iii)

13. Which of the following is the result of an increase in the carbon dioxide content in the atmosphere?
   A. Global warming
   B. Rainfall
   C. Clouds
   D. Decrease in greenhouse gases

14. How is oxygen found in its combined form on the Earth's crust and air?
   A. Ozone
   B. Hydroxide
   C. Carbon dioxide
   D. Water vapour

15. Identify the major process by which oxygen is returned to the atmosphere.
   A. Photosynthesis
   B. Respiration
   C. Combustion
   D. Transportation

16. Which among the following processes use oxygen in the atmosphere?
   (i) Combustion
   (ii) Photosynthesis
   (iii) Global warming
   (iv) Respiration
   A. (i) and (ii) only
   B. (i) and (iv) only
   C. (iii) and (iv) only
   D. (i), (ii) and (iii) only

17. Identify the abiotic components of biosphere.
   (i) Air
   (ii) Water
   (iii) Living organisms
   (iv) Soil
   A. (i) and (ii)
   B. Only (iii)
   C. (i), (ii) and (iii)
   D. (i), (ii) and (iv)

18. Which of the following decides the rainfall pattern of a region?
   A. Clouds B. Water vapour
   C. Sunlight D. Wind pattern

19. Identify the particles that get suspended in air due to increased burning of fossil fuels.
   A. Dust B. Smoke
   C. Hydrocarbons D. Nitrogen

20. Where could we find freshwater in frozen form on the Earth's surface?
   (i) At North Pole
   (ii) In sea
   (iii) On snowy mountains
   (iv) At South Pole
   A. (i), (ii) and (iv) only
   B. (i), (ii) and (iii) only
   C. (i), (iii) and (iv) only
   D. (iii) and (iv) only

21. **Assertion (A):** All organisms require water for their survival.
   **Reason(R):** Cellular processes take place in aqueous medium.
   A. A is correct. R is incorrect
   B. A is incorrect R is correct.
   C. A and R are correct and R is the correct explanation for A.
   D. A and R are correct but R is not the correct explanation of A.

22. Which among the following is the result of the presence of suspended particles in air during cold weather?
   A. Poor vision
   B. Rainfall
   C. Increase in wind speed
   D. Increase in temperature

23. Identify the cause for the doubling of carbon dioxide concentration in the atmosphere.
   A. Cooking at hotels
   B. Burning of fossil fuels
   C. Respiration by animals
   D. Forest fires

24. Which among the following plays a role in the nitrogen cycle?
   (i) Lightning
   (ii) Rain
   (iii) Nitrogen-fixing bacteria
   (iv) Roots of plants
   A. (i) and (ii) only
   B. (ii) and (iv) only
   C. (i), (iii) and (iv) only
   D. (i), (ii), (iii) and (iv)

25. In which direction does the air flow in coastal regions during night-time?
   A. Towards sea
   B. Towards land
   C. There will be no movement
   D. Towards sky

# SELF-ASSESSMENT 2

**Choose the correct option.**

26. What is the range of temperature on the surface of moon?
    A. 0 °C to 50 °C
    B. –190 °C to 110 °C
    C. –90 °C to 130 °C
    D. 50 °C to 100 °C

27. Identify the factors that influence wind in an area.
    (i) Rotation of the Earth
    (ii) Water vapour
    (iii) Mountain ranges
    (iv) Moon
    A. (i) and (iii)
    B. (ii) and (iv)
    C. Only (iii)
    D. Only (iv)

28. Which of the following causes low visibility during cold weather?
    A. Sunlight
    B. Water vapour
    C. Smog
    D. Wind

29. Which of the following contains decayed living organisms?
    A. Moss
    B. Algae
    C. Humus
    D. Lichen

30. Which of the following is a major factor that determines the biodiversity in an area?
    A. Wind
    B. Quality of topsoil
    C. Water cycle
    D. Ground water

31. Does nitrogen fixation happen in the presence of oxygen? Why or why not?
    A. Yes, oxygen protects the nitrogen-fixing bacteria.
    B. No, oxygen destroys the root.
    C. Yes, oxygen reacts with other gases.
    D. No, oxygen inhibits the production of enzyme by the nitrogen-fixing bacteria.

32. Identify the situation that leads to global warming.
    A. Increase in the amount of carbon dioxide
    B. Decrease in the amount of carbon dioxide
    C. Increase in the amount of rainfall
    D. Decrease in the wind speed

33. Which among the following contains carbon in a combined state?
    (i) Proteins
    (ii) Carbohydrates
    (iii) Fats
    (iv) Vitamins
    A. (ii) only
    B. (i), (iii) and (iv) only
    C. (i), (ii), (iii) and (iv)
    D. (ii), (iii) and (iv) only

34. Which of the following statements is correct about combustion?
   A. Carbon dioxide is released into the atmosphere.
   B. Oxygen goes back to the atmosphere.
   C. Both carbon dioxide and oxygen go back to the atmosphere.
   D. Carbon dioxide in the atmosphere is used.

35. How does some portion of groundwater come to the surface of the Earth?
   A. Rain
   B. Flood
   C. Canals
   D. Springs

36. Identify the processes involved in the water cycle.
   (i) Combustion
   (ii) Evaporation
   (iii) Condensation
   (iv) Respiration
   A. (i) only
   B. (ii) and (iii) only
   C. (i) and (iv) only
   D. (i), (ii), (iii) and (iv)

37. From where do marine animals get nutrients?
   A. Water
   B. Air
   C. Land
   D. Plants

38. Which physical process is involved in converting nitrogen into nitrates?
   A. Evaporation B. Condensation
   C. Transpiration D. Lightning

39. How does nitrogen in the atmosphere reach land?
   A. Through wind B. Through sunlight
   C. Through rain D. Through rainbow

40. Which of the following is responsible for converting nitrates or nitrites into elemental nitrogen?
   A. Bacteria B. Wind
   C. Oxygen D. Carbon dioxide

41. Which form of nitrogen can be used by life forms on the Earth?
   A. Dinitrogen
   B. Nitrates
   C. Elemental form
   D. Nitric acid

42. What phenomenon keeps tropical plants warm during cold climate?
   A. Global warming
   B. Watering
   C. Exposing to sunlight
   D. Greenhouse effect

43. Identify the constituent of the atmosphere that contains three atoms of oxygen.
   A. Oxide
   B. Ozone
   C. Nitrogen dioxide
   D. Carbon monoxide

44. What is the function of ozone in the atmosphere?
   A. Absorbing harmful radiations
   B. Cooling the atmosphere
   C. Helping in the navigation of aeroplanes
   D. Providing nutrients to aquatic animals

45. Identify the man-made compound that causes depletion of the ozone layer.

A. Carbon dioxide
B. Nitrogen oxides
C. Chlorofluorocarbons
D. Carbon monoxide

46. Identify the characteristics of chlorofluorocarbons.

(i) Unstable
(ii) Biodegradable
(iii) Very stable
(iv) Not biodegradable

A. Only (i)
B. Only (iii)
C. (i) and (ii)
D. (iii) and (iv)

47. Identify the forms in which oxygen is found on the Earth's crust.

(i) Oxides of metals
(ii) Carbonates
(iii) Nitrates
(iv) Minerals

A. (i), (ii), (iii) and (iv)
B. (i) only
C. (i), (ii) and (iii) only
D. (i) and (iv) only

48. Find the odd one out.

A. Respiration
B. Combustion
C. Photosynthesis
D. Formation of oxides of nitrogen

49. Identify the forms in which carbon is found in different minerals.

(i) Carbonate
(ii) Hydroxide
(iii) Hydrogen carbonate salts
(iv) Nitrites

A. (i) and (ii) only
B. (i) and (iii) only
C. (ii) and (iv) only
D. (ii), (iii) and (iv) only

50. **Assertion (A):** All the rainwater that falls to the ground does not reach the sea.

**Reason (R):** Sea lies far away from the land.

A. A and R are correct and R is the correct explanation for A.
B. A and R are correct but R is not the correct explanation for A.
C. A is correct but R is incorrect.
D. A is incorrect R is correct.

Chapter 15

# Improvement in Food Resources

## PRE-TEST

**Choose the correct option.**

1. Which among the following contributed towards the increase in food production?
   A. Industrial revolution
   B. Green revolution
   C. Glorious revolution
   D. Global revolution

2. Which among the following is related to the white revolution?
   A. Milk
   B. Egg
   C. Salt
   D. Sugar

3. Identify the cereal from the following.
   A. Soya bean B. Pea
   C. Maize D. Green gram

4. The majority of people in India are dependent on ___________ for their livelihood.
   A. cattle rearing B. fishing
   C. bee-keeping D. agriculture

5. Which among the following does not belong to the category of livestock?
   A. Sheep B. Cattle
   C. Zebra D. Goat

## KEYWORDS

**Animal husbandry:** Scientific management of feeding, breeding and disease control of animal livestock

**Cattle farming:** Raising milch animals such as cow, buffalo and goat for milk and agricultural practices such as ploughing, irrigation and transportation

**Fertilizers:** Commercially-produced plant nutrients

**Inland fisheries:** Fishing from freshwater resources

**Inter-cropping:** Growing two or more crops in the same field in a definite pattern

**Manure:** Decomposed animal excreta and plant wastes

**Marine fisheries:** Fishing from seawater

**Mixed cropping:** Growing two or more crops at the same time in the same piece of land

**Organic farming:** Farming system with minimal or no use of chemical fertilizer or pesticides

**Poultry farming:** Raising poultry animals such as hen, turkey and ducks for egg and meat

# Concept Map

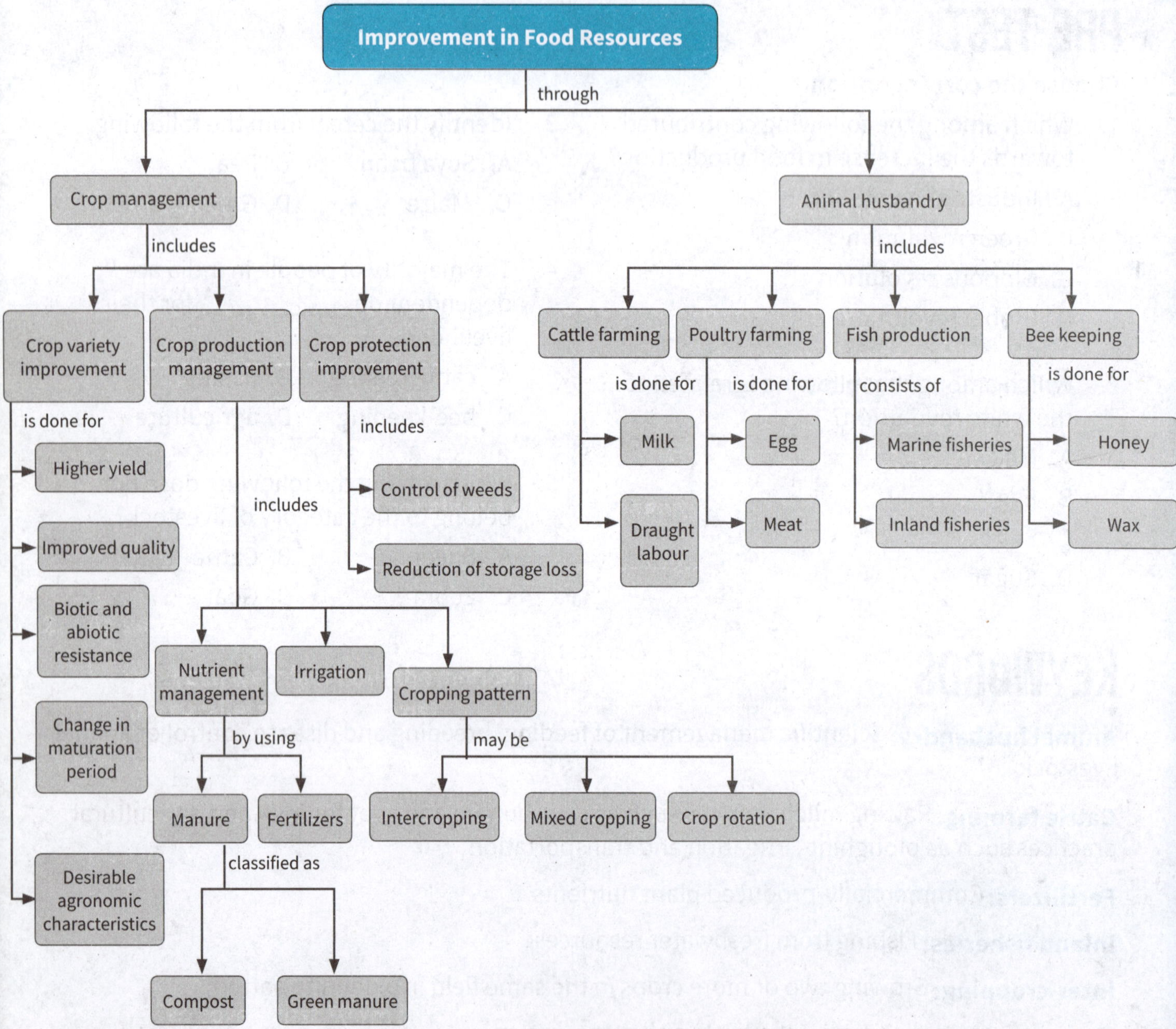

Improvement in Food Resources
through
Crop management
includes
Crop variety improvement
is done for
Higher yield
Improved quality
Biotic and abiotic resistance
Change in maturation period
Desirable agronomic characteristics
Crop production management
includes
Nutrient management
by using
Manure
classified as
Compost
Green manure
Fertilizers
Irrigation
Cropping pattern
may be
Intercropping
Mixed cropping
Crop rotation
Crop protection improvement
includes
Control of weeds
Reduction of storage loss
Animal husbandry
includes
Cattle farming
is done for
Milk
Draught labour
Poultry farming
is done for
Egg
Meat
Fish production
consists of
Marine fisheries
Inland fisheries
Bee keeping
is done for
Honey
Wax

# SELF-ASSESSMENT 1

**Choose the correct option.**

1. Cereals are rich in ______________.
   A. vitamins B. carbohydrates
   C. proteins D. lipids

2. Which of the following provides us with protein?
   A. Green gram B. Rice
   C. Wheat D. Sunflower

3. Identify the correct description of a photoperiod.
   A. Duration of wind
   B. Duration of rain
   C. Duration of heat
   D. Duration of sunlight

4. Identify the duration of the kharif season.
   A. January to June
   B. June to October
   C. October to March
   D. November to April

5. Which of the following crops are grown during rabi season?
   (i) Wheat (ii) Paddy
   (iii) Mustard (iv) Cotton
   A. (i) and (iii) are grown.
   B. (ii) and (iv) are grown.
   C. (i) and (ii) are grown.
   D. (ii) and (iii) are grown.

6. Which of the following is decomposed to prepare manure?
   (i) Plastic waste
   (ii) Plant waste
   (iii) Animal excreta
   (iv) Unused utensils
   A. (i), (ii) and (iv) only
   B. (i) and (iv) only
   C. (ii) and (iii) only
   D. (i), (ii), (iii) and (iv)

7. Which of the following are commercially and chemically produced plant nutrients?
   A. Organic pesticides
   B. Organic weedicides
   C. Vermicompost
   D. NPK fertilizers

8. Which of the following is the result of an excess use of fertilizers?
   A. Water pollution
   B. Air pollution
   C. Dehydration
   D. Flood

9. Identify the farming system with minimal or no use of chemical fertilizers.
   A. Subsistence farming
   B. Organic farming
   C. Commercial farming
   D. Mixed farming

10. Identify the cause behind crop failure in most of the areas.
    A. Chemical fertilizers
    B. Manure
    C. Poor monsoon
    D. Moisture in the soil

11. Identify the elaborately and extensively used irrigation system.
    A. Tanks
    B. Canals
    C. River lift system
    D. Wells

12. Growing of two or more crops simultaneously in the same piece of land in a specific pattern is called ________.
    A. intercropping B. mixed farming
    C. crop rotation D. crop protection

13. In which of the following ways do insects generally attack plants?
    (i) Shed the fruits
    (ii) Cut the root
    (iii) Suck the cell sap
    (iv) Bore the stem
    A. (ii) only
    B. (iii) and (iv) only
    C. (i) and (ii) only
    D. (ii), (iii) and (iv) only

14. Which of the following methods are included in the common use of pesticides?
    (i) Vaccicide (ii) Herbicide
    (iii) Insecticide (iv) Fungicide
    A. (i) and (ii) only
    B. (ii), (iii) and (iv) only
    C. (iii) and (iv) only
    D. (i), (ii) and (iii) only

15. Identify the process followed to destroy weeds and pests in the field.
    A. Ploughing
    B. Harvesting
    C. Incineration
    D. Irrigation

16. What is the scientific management of animal livestock called?
    A. Animal assisted-interventions
    B. Animal welfare
    C. Animal research
    D. Animal husbandry

17. Identify the main purposes of cattle husbandry.
    (i) Milk production
    (ii) Harvesting
    (iii) Ploughing
    (iv) Irrigation
    A. (i) and (ii) only
    B. (i) and (iii) only
    C. (ii) only
    D. (iii) and (iv) only

18. Identify the non-Indian breed of cow.
    A. Sahiwal B. Gir
    C. Red Sindhi D. Jersey

19. Identify the meaning of milch animals.
    A. Draught animals
    B. Meat producers
    C. Dairy animals
    D. Egg producers

20. Identify the disease of cattle caused by an external parasite.
    A. Lung disease B. Eye disease
    C. Liver disease D. Skin disease

21. Identify the period of milk production in dairy animals.

A. Breeding period

B. Lactation period

C. Incubation period

D. Grazing period

22. Identify the food requirement of dairy animals.

(i) Hay and grass

(ii) Wheat bran and neem cake

(iii) Fresh fruits and vegetables

(iv) Broken rice and soya pulp

A. (i) and (ii) only

B. (ii) and (iii) only

C. (i), (ii), and (iv) only

D. (iii) only

23. Which of the following helps to reduce the size of egg-laying bird in poultry farming?

A. Cross-breeding

B. Supplying less food

C. Rearing in cages

D. Exposing to high temperature

24. Which of the following prevents the reduction and loss of poultry due to infectious diseases?

A. Providing adequate water

B. Vaccination

C. Rearing in separate cages

D. Providing proper feed

25. The quality of honey depends on the _______.

A. bee species

B. fruits of the plants

C. nectar of flowers

D. size of beehive

# SELF-ASSESSMENT 2

**Choose the correct option.**

26. Which of the following provides us with necessary fat when consumed?
    A. Wheat B. Sunflower
    C. Black gram D. Pea

27. Which of the following are required by crops for their growth and to complete their life cycle?
    (i) Climatic conditions
    (ii) Temperature
    (iii) Photoperiods
    (iv) Hydrogen
    A. (i), (ii) and (iii) only
    B. (ii), (iii) and (iv) only
    C. (iii) and (iv) only
    D. (i) and (iv) only

28. Identify the duration of the rabi season.
    A. January to June
    B. June to October
    C. November to April
    D. October to March

29. Identify the crops grown during the kharif season.
    (i) Pea (ii) Cotton
    (iii) Paddy (iv) Mustard
    A. (i) and (iv) only
    B. (ii) and (iii) only
    C. (ii) and (iv) only
    D. (i) and (iii) only

30. Identify the desired characteristics for crop variety improvement.
    (i) Disease resistance
    (ii) High yield
    (iii) Product quality
    (iv) Response to fertilizers
    A. (i) and (ii) only
    B. (iii) and (iv) only
    C. (i), (ii), (iii) and (iv)
    D. (iv) only

31. Identify the different ways in which cross breeding can be done between genetically dissimilar plants.
    (i) Self-pollination
    (ii) Inter-varietal
    (iii) Inter-specific
    (iv) Cross pollination
    A. (i) and (iv) only
    B. (ii) and (iii) only
    C. (i), (ii) and (iv) only
    D. (i), (ii), (iii) and (iv)

32. Identify the factor that allows farmers to take up different farming practices and technology.
    A. Access to technology
    B. Land
    C. Awareness
    D. Money

33. How does manure affect sandy soil?
 A. Absorbs water in the soil
 B. Increases the nitrogen content in the soil
 C. Increases the water-holding capacity of the soil
 D. Decreases nutrients in the soil

34. Which of the following is supplied by fertilizers to ensure good vegetative growth?
 (i) Oxygen
 (ii) Nitrogen
 (iii) Potassium
 (iv) Phosphorus
 A. (i) and (ii) only
 B. (ii) and (iv) only
 C. (i), (ii), (iii) and (iv)
 D. (ii), (iii) and (iv) only

35. Which of the following is used as a biofertilizer for grain storage in organic farming?
 A. Neem leaves
 B. Pesticides
 C. Livestock excreta
 D. Insects

36. Identify the fresh initiatives taken to increase the availability of water for agricultural purposes.
 (i) River lift systems
 (ii) Rainwater harvesting
 (iii) Building of canals
 (iv) Watershed management
 A. (i), (ii) and (iv) only
 B. (ii) and (iv) only
 C. (i) and (iii) only
 D. (i), (ii), (iii) and (iv)

37. Why are crops grown in rows in the intercropping method?
 A. Due to the difference in water requirement
 B. Due to the difference in nutrient requirement
 C. In order to share land for cultivation
 D. For ease in harvesting

38. How do weeds decrease the yield of plants or crops?
 A. Weeds absorb all of the nutrients from plants.
 B. Weeds provide more nutrients.
 C. Weeds facilitate bacteria that hinders the growth of plants.
 D. Weeds prevent pests.

39. What are the unwanted plants in the cultivated field called?
 A. Insects B. Bacteria
 C. Rodents D. Weeds

40. Identify the abiotic factors responsible for the loss of stored grains.
 (i) Insects
 (ii) Fungi
 (iii) Unsuitable moisture
 (iv) Inappropriate temperature
 A. (i) and (ii) only
 B. (i) and (iii) only
 C. (iii) and (iv) only
 D. (ii) and (iv) only

41. When does the lactation period start for a cattle?
 A. Before the birth of calf
 B. After the birth of calf
 C. After the maturation of the cattle
 D. Soon after the breeding of the cattle

42. Identify the breed of cattle which has excellent resistance towards diseases in India.
   A. Ayrshire
   B. Jersey
   C. Brown Swiss
   D. Red Sindhi

43. How can the production of milk in cattles be increased?
   A. By increasing the lactation period of the cattle
   B. By providing more food to the cattle
   C. By increasing the breeding period of the cattle
   D. By providing more rest to the cattle

44. Identify the fish with high economic value that is farmed in seawater.
   A. Tuna  B. Pomfret
   C. Prawn  D. Mackerel

45. Identify the correct ways of rearing fish.
   (i) Apiculture
   (ii) Fish farming
   (iii) Pisciculture
   (iv) Horticulture
   A. (i) and (ii) are correct.
   B. (ii) and (iii) are correct.
   C. (i) and (iii) are correct.
   D. (iii) and (iv) are correct.

46. Identify the freshwater source of fish.
   A. Rain  B. Sea
   C. Mountain  D. River

47. Identify the problem related to composite fish culture.
   A. Frequent death
   B. Migration to other places
   C. Breeding only during monsoon
   D. Less amount of water to survive

48. What can be done for intensive fish farming?
   A. Composite fish culture systems
   B. Cloud farming
   C. Change the direction of wind on waterbody
   D. Decrease the temperature

49. Identify the local varieties of bees used for commercial honey production.
   A. Bumble bee
   B. *Apis indica*
   C. *Apis mellifera*
   D. *Lebah kelulut*

50. Identify the purpose of beekeeping.
   A. To obtain leather
   B. To obtain manure
   C. To obtain honey and wax
   D. To pollinate flowers in horticulture

# PART 2

## SUBJECTIVE TYPE QUESTIONS

# SELF-ASSESSMENT 3

## A. Short Answer Type Questions

**1. Give reasons for the following questions.**

i. Yaangba wipes his room's floor with water twice a day in summer.

---

ii. Bose-Einstein condensate is considered as a state of matter.

---

iii. Liquids and gases behave like fluids.

---

iv. Solidification is the reverse process of fusion.

---

v. Osmosis is used to increase the shelf life of food items.

---

**2. Answer the following questions in brief.**

i. Describe melting point.

---

---

ii. Arrange the given items in the order of their increasing density.

Atmospheric air, exhaust from kitchen chimneys, honey, ice cube, milk, cotton boll and steel magnet.

---

---

iii. What is meant by the latent heat of fusion?

---

---

iv. Harpreet found a sample of water that would boil at 120 °C at normal temperature and pressure. Comment on the purity of the sample and its freezing temperature.

v. Aquatic animals live even at freezing temperatures.

## B. Long Answer Type Questions

**1. Answer the following questions in detail.**

i. Explain the process of diffusion by using the example of blowing balloons with helium gas.

ii. Explain the use of compressed gas in our daily life.

iii. Differentiate between the arrangements of states of matter in solids, liquids and gases.

iv. Define the terms P, Q, R and S in the given diagram.

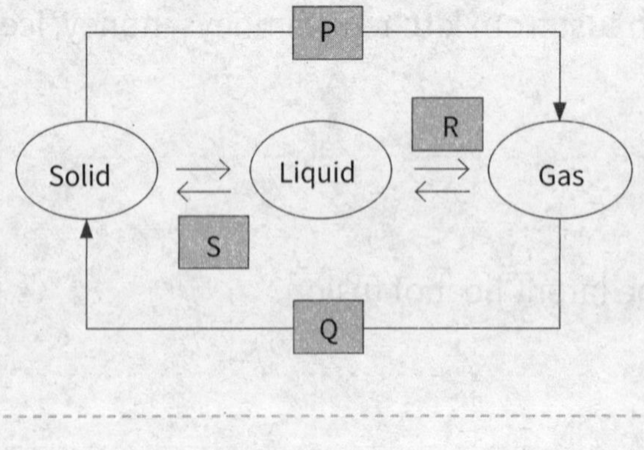

v. Explain the factors on which the rate of evaporation depends.

2. **Life skills questions**

i. Dibaang helped his mother by spreading clothes to dry. Half of the clothesline was in shade. So, he shifted the positions of clothes every hour.

a. Why did he shuffle the clothes every hour?

b. Would all the clothes dry at the same time if left at the same position after spreading them initially?

c. What did you learn from Dibaang?

ii. Arsalan was getting late for school. When mother served him milk, he sipped the hot milk from the glass and got his tongue burnt. His mother took the glass from him, poured some of the milk into a plate, and then asked him to sip milk from the plate. Now, Arsalan could comfortably drink the milk.

a. Why did Arsalan's tongue get burned when he sipped milk from the glass?

b. How could Arsalan comfortably drink milk from the plate?

c. What is the life skill associated with it?

# SELF-ASSESSMENT 3

## A. Short Answer Type Questions

**1. Give reasons for the following questions.**

i. Crystallisation is a better technique of separation than evaporation.

ii. Blood is considered as a heterogeneous substance.

iii. The burning of kerosene in a lantern is an example of a chemical change.

iv. Graphite, though a non-metal, is used as electrodes in dry cells.

v. Hydrogen and oxygen are considered elements while water is not.

**2. Answer the following questions in brief.**

i. How is smoke different from fog?

ii. What is the Tyndall effect?

iii. Name any five techniques used to separate the components of a mixture.

iv. What method will you use to separate iron nails from sawdust?

v. What is chromatography? Write any two applications of it.

## B. Long Answer Type Questions

**1. Answer the following questions in detail.**

i. List the properties of a solution.

ii. With a neat diagrammatic representation, explain the method of distillation and its application.

iii. During an experiment, students were asked to prepare 15% (mass/mass) solution of salt in water. Rahul dissolved 15 g of salt in 100 g of water, while Anjali prepared it by dissolving 15 g of salt in water to make 100 g of solution. Compare the mass percentage of the two solutions.

iv. Outline the separation technique and complete the diagram.

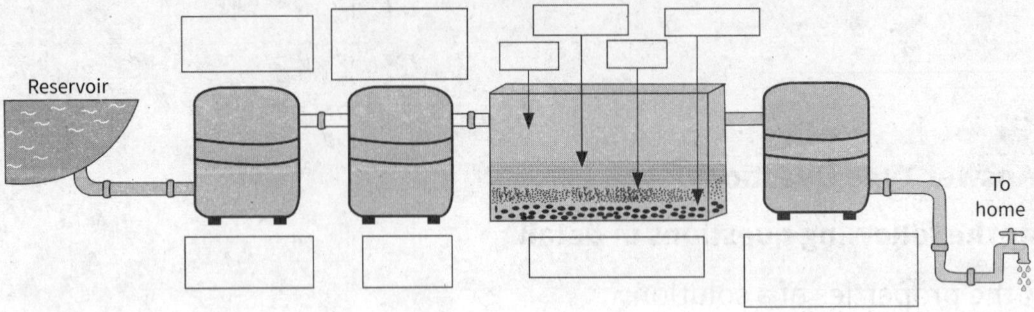


v. Tina added cubes of sugar to a glass of water. Now, she has to label the solution as homogeneous or heterogeneous. Which label would she put on the solution and why?

## 2. Life skills questions

i. Sam and his friends planned to visit a hill station for a short trip in a jeep. The driver of the jeep was constantly wiping his front window as he had an obstruction to his view.

a. Why was there an obstruction to his view?

b. What is the type of colloid formed here?

c. Write any two properties of it.

# SELF-ASSESSMENT 3

## A. Short Answer Type Questions

**1. Give reasons for the following questions.**

i. The atomic mass of an element does not represent the actual mass of its atom.

---

ii. Avogadro's number is $6.022 \times 10^{23}$ and not any other number.

---

iii. A change in the physical state can be brought about when energy is either given to or taken out of a system.

---

iv. The atomicity of ozone and oxygen molecule differs even though they are made of only oxygen atoms.

---

v. Dalton's symbols are not used in modern chemistry.

---

**2. Answer the following questions in brief.**

i. Define atomicity. Write the atomicity of the following elements—phosphorus, nitrogen, sulphur and copper.

---

ii. How is molecular mass different from molar mass?

---

iii. Calculate the formula mass of sodium bicarbonate.

---

iv. Explain how the solubility of a substance changes with the help of an example.

v. A group of students were provided with a fine white-coloured powder which can be either sugar or salt. Students were instructed not to taste the same. What would be the possible ways through which they can find the difference between the two?

**B. Long Answer Type Questions**

**1. Answer the following questions in detail.**

i. State the postulates of Dalton's atomic theory.

ii. What is a mole? What is its significance?

iii. Calculate the number of ions present in 5.85 g of sodium chloride.

iv. Calculate the ratio between the mass of one atom of silver and mass of one atom of gold. (Atomic mass of silver is 108 g and atomic mass of gold is 197 g.)

v. Identify the experimental setup and what it explains. Explain the procedure and give an example each for the solutions X and Y.

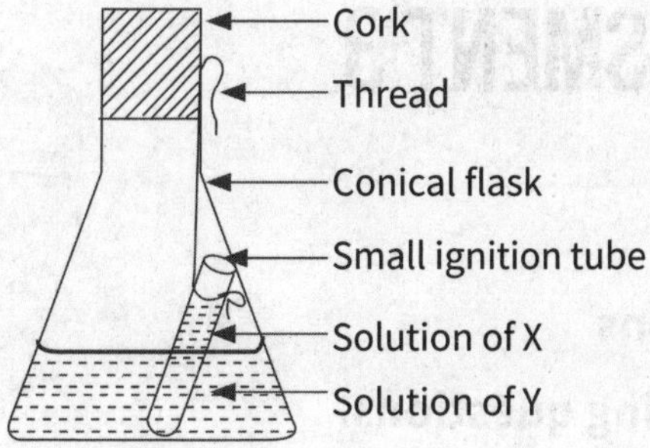


---

---

---

**2. Life skills questions**

i. Nitika, wanted to verify the law of conservation of mass. She mixed 7.2 g of sodium carbonate and 18 g of ethanoic acid in a flask. She weighed the flask before and after the experiment. The weight of the residue in the flask was only 20.0 g. On further research, she repeated the experiment in a closed flask with a cork. The flask weight remained constant before and after the experiment.

a. What was the flaw in the first part of the experiment?

b. Write the balanced chemical equation of the reaction occurring in the flask.

c. Why did the weight not match earlier?

d. What was her learning from the two sets of experiments?

---

---

---

---

# SELF-ASSESSMENT 3

## A. Short Answer Type Questions

**1. Give reasons for the following questions.**

i. Dalton's atomic theory was a failure.

ii. Thomson's atomic model is compared with a Christmas pudding or a watermelon.

iii. The mass of a hydrogen atom is equal to the mass of a proton.

iv. The maximum number of electrons that can be accommodated in different shells vary.

v. The valency of noble gasses is always zero.

**2. Answer the following questions in brief.**

i. Rutherford is called the 'Father' of nuclear physics.

ii. What are isotopes? Give an example.

iii. Calculate the mass number of an atom that contains 11 electrons, 11 protons and 12 neutrons.

iv. Define the valency of an atom.

v. The chemical symbol of an element 'X' is written as shown alongside. What does Z represent here?

$^{A}_{Z}X$

**B. Long Answer Type Questions**

**1. Answer the following questions in detail.**

i. Write three applications of isotopes.

ii. Differentiate between isotopes and isobars.

iii. Draw the electron-dot structure of fluorine and neon and explain the distribution of electrons in their shells.

iv. State the postulates of Rutherford's nuclear model of the atom.

v. Explain J. J. Thomson's model of atom with the help of a diagram.

**2. fe skills questions**

. Bankei made a Bohr's model for calcium using three rings of different sizes for the various energy levels, 20 tennis balls to represent electrons and a cricket ball to represent the nucleus. He arranged all the items as shown in the first picture. Before showing this model to the teacher, he showed it to his friend Jenny. Jenny gave him one more ring that she had with her and asked him to arrange the tennis balls as shown in the second image.

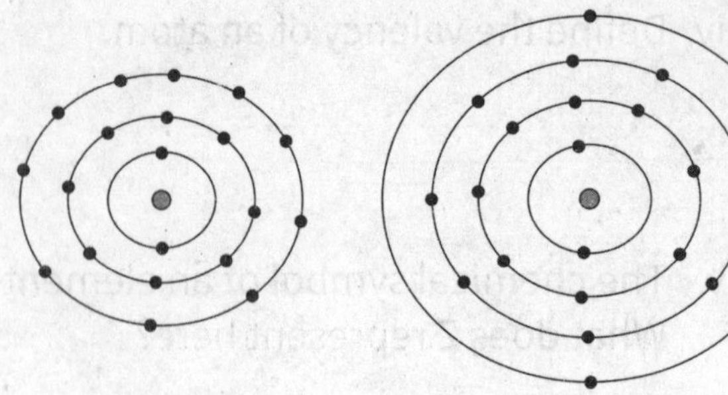

Bankei's model  Jenny's model

a. What was wrong with the model made by Bankei?

b. How did Jenny help Bankei?

c. What life skill is associated with this?

ii. Shourya knows the electron number of an atom X as 8 but does not know how to deduce the valency, atomic number and mass number from this information. His mother, who is a science graduate, explained to him the atomic and mass number as well as the relation between the two.

a. Can Shourya now predict the valency of the atom?

b. What would be the atomic number of this atom?

c. How can he calculate the mass number of the atom?

d. What is the associated life skill?

# SELF-ASSESSMENT 3

## A. Short Answer Type Questions

**1. Give reasons for the following questions.**

i. Plasma membrane is also known as selectively permeable membrane.

ii. Mitochondria are referred to as the powerhouse of a cell.

iii. A de-shelled egg swells in water.

iv. Different cell organelles stain differently while dying.

v. All multicellular organisms originated from a single cell.

**2. Answer the following questions in brief.**

i. What is the function of the protoplasm?

ii. Give one difference between multicellular and unicellular organisms.

iii. Name two unicellular and two multicellular organisms.

iv. Define hypotonic solution.

. What is the importance of a cover slip?

------------------------------------------------------------------------

------------------------------------------------------------------------

**3. Long Answer Type Questions**

**1. Answer the following questions in detail.**

i. What are the steps involved in preparing and observing a human cheek cell under a microscope?

------------------------------------------------------------------------

------------------------------------------------------------------------

------------------------------------------------------------------------

ii. Explain plasmolysis with an example.

------------------------------------------------------------------------

------------------------------------------------------------------------

------------------------------------------------------------------------

iii. Identify the cell given here and explain its structure.

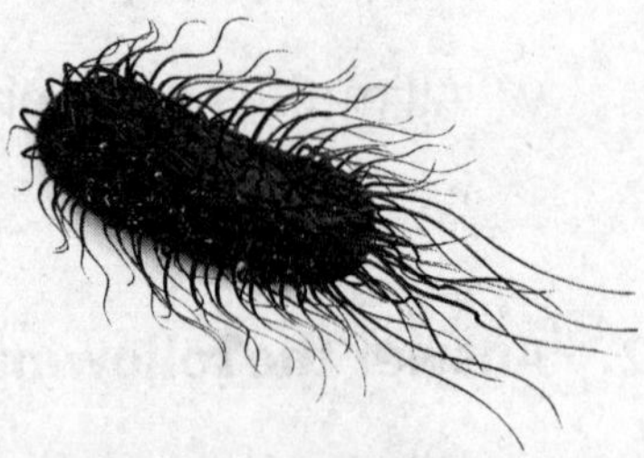

------------------------------------------------------------------------

------------------------------------------------------------------------

------------------------------------------------------------------------

iv. Describe the contribution of Robert Hooke in the discovery of a cell.

------------------------------------------------------------------------

------------------------------------------------------------------------

------------------------------------------------------------------------

v. Differentiate between a prokaryotic and a eukaryotic cell.

------------------------------------------------------------------------

------------------------------------------------------------------------

------------------------------------------------------------------------

2. **Life skills questions**

i. Seema observed some plant cells under a compound microscope.

a. Would the cells of root, stem and leaf look alike?

b. What would be the differences and similarities in the cells observed?

c. What could Seema learn from her observation?

---

---

---

---

ii. Lucky's father is a pathologist. He told Lucky that he uses a microscope in his pathology lab too.

a. Why do you think microscopes are used in a pathology lab?

b. List some of the cells that could be observed in a pathology lab.

c. How can a pathologist predict if a person is infected by a malarial parasite?

---

---

---

---

# SELF-ASSESSMENT 3

## A. Short Answer Type Questions

**1. Give reasons for the following questions.**

i. Sclerenchyma tissues lack intercellular space.

---

ii. When we chew a pear fruit, it gives a crunchy and granular feeling in our mouth.

---

iii. A glass jar that is inverted and used to cover a potted plant will have water droplets inside.

---

iv. Voluntary muscles are also called skeletal muscles.

---

v. Meristematic cells lack vacuole.

---

**2. Answer the following questions in brief.**

i. List some of the economically important plant fibres derived from sclerenchyma.

---

---

ii. What are the functions of smooth muscles?

---

---

iii. What are the functions of stomata?

---

---

iv. Differentiate between tendons and ligaments.

---

---

v. Draw a labelled diagram of a neuron.

## B. Long Answer Type Questions

**1. Answer the following questions in detail.**

i. Describe the different types of meristems.

ii. How is a cork formed? What are its characteristics?

iii. Write a short note on complex permanent tissues.

iv. What are the major functions of conducting tissues in a human body?

v. What are the different types of epithelial cells found in a human body? Where are they located? Draw well-labelled diagrams to show all the different types of epithelial cells.

**2. Life skills questions**

i. One of Isha's friends fell down during their school morning assembly. Her friend recovered after some time. However, she looked very pale and tired. The school doctor asked her to get a complete blood test done. Isha was curious about what a blood test is. Help her find the answers.

   a. What is a blood test?

   b. Why was her friend asked to get the test done?

   c. What kind of food enriches the blood in our body?

ii. Adarsh is playing with his brother and making funny faces. He is twisting his ears and the tip of his nose.

   a. Which type of tissue is Adarsh twisting and playing with?

   b. Which characteristic of the tissue allows it to be flexible?

   c. What is the life skill learned from this act?

# SELF-ASSESSMENT 3

## A. Short Answer Type Questions

**1. Give reasons for the following questions.**

i. Habitat plays a major role in the classification of living organisms.

ii. Cell structure and function are the basis for the classification of cells.

iii. The region between the Tropic of Cancer and the Tropic of Capricorn is called the megadiversity region.

iv. Only the fittest organisms survive and evolve.

v. Bryophytes are the amphibians of the plant kingdom.

**2. Answer the following questions in brief.**

i. What are the hierarchy and the levels of biological classification?

ii. Which organisms belong to the kingdom Monera?

iii. Name two characteristics of kingdom Plantae.

iv. Write two differences between kingdom Animalia and Plantae.

v. What are lichens?

**B. Long Answer Type Questions**

**1. Answer the following questions in detail.**

i. Name the pteridophyte shown in the image. Describe its characteristics.

ii. Explain the division of angiosperms based on the number of their cotyledons.

iii. Differentiate between angiosperms and gymnosperms.

iv. Porifera are usually called sponges. Why?

v. Liver fluke and tapeworm are called flatworms. Write a note on them.

2. **Life skills questions**

i. Manoj collected some seashells and dead starfishes from a beach on a holiday.

   a. Do *Unio* and starfish belong to the same Phylum?

   b. What are the differences and similarities between these animals?

   c. What would Manoj learn from his findings?

--------------------------------------------------------------------------------

--------------------------------------------------------------------------------

--------------------------------------------------------------------------------

--------------------------------------------------------------------------------

ii. Pranathi wants to donate some animals to a local zoo.

   a. When she enquired with the authority of the zoo, she was asked to donate a pair of animals of the same species. Why?

   b. What would happen if the animals are not pairs but both of the same gender?

   c. What role does reproduction play in ecology?

--------------------------------------------------------------------------------

--------------------------------------------------------------------------------

--------------------------------------------------------------------------------

--------------------------------------------------------------------------------

# SELF-ASSESSMENT 3

## A. Short Answer Type Questions

**1. Give reasons for the following questions.**

i. The magnitude of the displacement cannot be greater than the distance travelled.

---

ii. An object moving through a certain distance can have zero displacement.

---

iii. Uniform circular motion is considered to be an accelerated motion.

---

iv. The average velocity of a body can be zero.

---

v. Speed and velocity are not always equal in magnitude.

---

**2. Answer the following questions in brief.**

i. What can we infer about the motion of an object whose distance-time graph is a straight line parallel to the time-axis?

---

---

ii. Differentiate between speed and velocity.

---

---

iii. A bike covers first 70 km in 2 hours and then another 70 km in the next 3 hours. What is the average speed of the bike?

---

---

iv. An object starting from rest accelerates in a straight line at a constant rate of 5 $m/s^2$ for 10 seconds. Calculate the magnitude of displacement of the object during this time.

v. A fast-moving body accelerates uniformly from 12 m/s to 20 m/s in 2 seconds. Find the acceleration of the body and the distance travelled.

**B. Long Answer Type Questions**

**1. Answer the following questions in detail.**

i. Observe the given graph and answer the following questions.

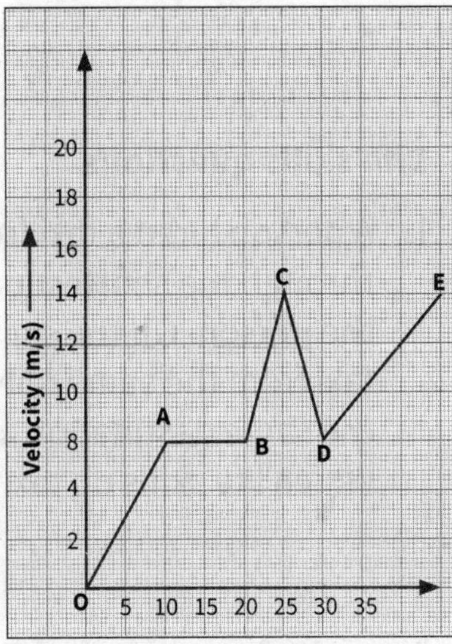


a. Calculate the displacement of the body between O and A.

b. Which part of the graph represents deceleration of the body?

c. Which part of the graph represents constant speed of the body?

ii. Derive the equation of motion, $v = u + at$ through the graphical method.

iii. A bike, starting from rest, accelerates and attains a velocity of 10 m/s in 20 s. When brakes were applied, its velocity decreases uniformly to 5 m/s in the next 5 s. Calculate the acceleration and deceleration of the bike.

iv. When is a body said to have uniform acceleration or non-uniform acceleration? Give an example for both.

v. A racing car applies its brakes and decelerates by 10 $m/s^2$. If the car comes to rest in 5 s, then what is the distance covered by it after applying the brakes.

**2. Life skills questions**

i. A person hired a taxi from the railway station to his house. The driver X travelled through the shortest path and reached the destination in 1 hour. X charged ₹ 750 from the person. On the same day, his brother also came to his house after travelling in a taxi from the same railway station. The driver of the taxi Y took 90 minutes to reach the same destination and charged ₹ 1000. Is the displacement of both the taxis same? Which life skills do taxi driver X show here?

ii. Harmeet and Irfaan were going to attend their friend's marriage function and they travelled on their own bikes. While travelling, they saw a signboard showing "SPEED LIMIT 50 km/h". Irfaan applied brakes and started driving at 40 km/h, but Harmeet continued to move at a speed of 60 km/h. A traffic police stopped Harmeet's vehicle and charged ₹ 1000 for over-speeding. Here, what is the life skill demonstrated by Irfaan through his behaviour?

# SELF-ASSESSMENT 3

**A. Short Answer Type Questions**

**1. Give reasons for the following questions.**

i. A cyclist continues to apply force in order to move a cycle with a constant speed.

ii. It is advised to tie the luggage with a rope on the roof of buses.

iii. When a bullet is fired from a gun, the gun jerks towards the backward direction.

iv. An athlete presses the ground with his feet before he sprints.

v. A bullet when fired against a glass win dowpane makes a hole in it but a stone shatters it.

**2. Answer the following questions in brief.**

i. A body of mass m is acted upon by a force *F*. If the mass of the object is doubled and the applied force is halved, find the ratio of accelerations produced in the two cases.

ii. An object has a weight 49 N at a place where the acceleration due to gravity is 9.8 $m/s^2$. What are its mass and weight at a place where the acceleration due to gravity is 2.4 $m/s^2$?

iii. A metal box with a mass of 5 kg falls to the ground from a height of 20 m. What is the momentum with which the metal box hits the ground if it falls from the given height? (Given $g = 10$ $m/s^2$)

iv. State the law of conservation of momentum.

v. An object of mass 10 g moving at a speed of 700 m/s strikes a wooden block with mass of 3 kg and gets embedded in it. What would be the speed with which the block moves along with the object?

**B. Long Answer Type Questions**

**1. Answer the following questions in detail.**

i. Give an example of Newton's first law of motion from your daily life.

ii. Differentiate between mass and weight.

iii. Calculate the speed with which an object should be thrown vertically upwards to reach a height of 20 m. How long will the object to return to the starting point? (Given $g = 10\ m/s^2$)

iv. State Newton's second law of motion and derive it mathematically.

v. The velocity-time graph of an object with mass of 100 g which is moving along a ground is given below. What is the acceleration and frictional force applied by the ground on the object?

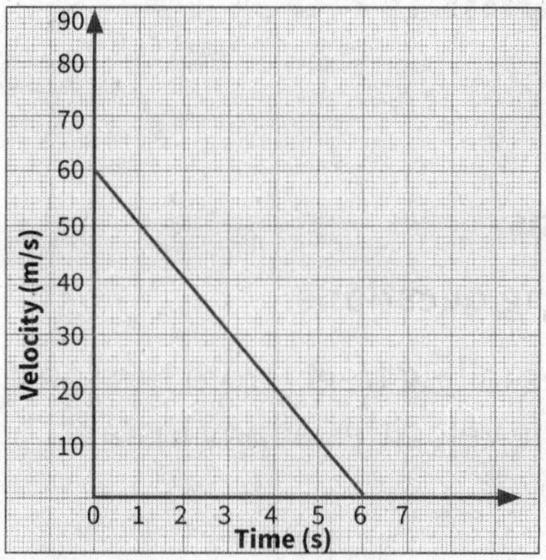


## 2. Life skills questions

i. In a football match, the goalkeeper, Sreekant, hurts his hand while catching the ball. Thereafter, he remained worried about stopping the ball from hitting the goalpost with his hands. During the match, his teammate, Ajay understood the difficulty faced by Sreekant and advised him to catch the ball by lowering the hands backward. Next time, when the ball came, Sreekant followed Ajay's advice and caught the ball cleanly without getting hurt. Which life skills do Ajay show here?

ii. Boy A was trying to jump from a slow-moving bus. His friend B asked him not to do because it would injure him. A was not ready to listen to B. Then, B told A to run towards the direction of the moving bus as soon as his feet touched the road. This time, A listened to B and landed safely. Why did B ask A to run in the direction of the moving bus as soon as his feet touches the road? Which life skills do B show and why did he ask A not to do such an act?

# SELF-ASSESSMENT 3

## A. Short Answer Type Questions

**1. Give reasons for the following questions.**

i. Objects of different masses falling freely from the same height near the surface of the moon would have the same velocities at any instant.

ii. The weight of an object on the moon is one-sixth its weight on the Earth.

iii. A body experiences loss of weight when immersed in a liquid.

iv. A stone and a feather were dropped from a certain height but both of these objects did not reach the ground at the same time.

v. The acceleration of a freely falling body does not depend on its mass.

**2. Answer the following questions in brief.**

i. Write the conditions for an object to sink or float in a fluid.

ii. What is meant by buoyancy?

iii. If the weight of a person on the Earth is 500 N and on a certain planet is 250 N, then find the acceleration due to gravity on the planet. (Given $g = 10 \text{ m/s}^2$ on the Earth)

iv. Differentiate between thrust and pressure.

v. What is centripetal force? Give one example.

## B. Long Answer Type Questions

**1. Answer the following questions in detail.**

i. State the universal law of gravitation and mention its importance.

ii. How is the acceleration due to gravity at North Pole and South Pole different from that at equator?

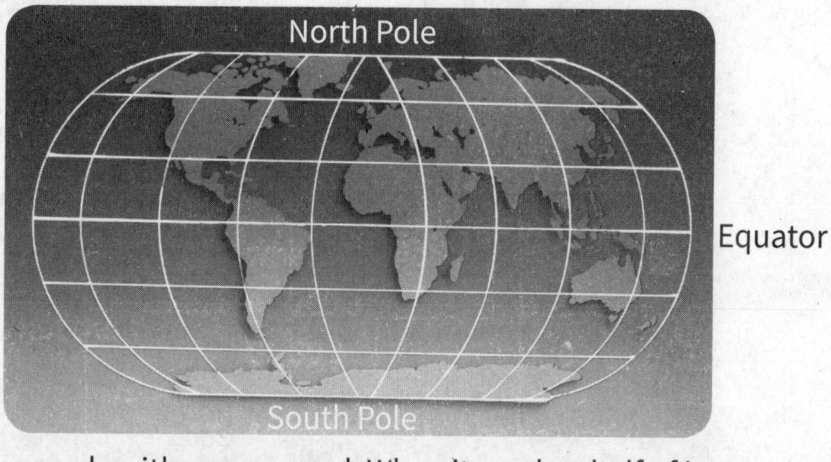


iii. An object is thrown vertically upwards with some speed. When it reaches half of its maximum height, it has a speed of 5 m/s. Calculate the maximum height reached by the object. (Given $g = 10\ m/s^2$)

iv. An object A is dropped from a building of height 50 m. At the same time, another object B is projected vertically upwards from the ground with a velocity of 5 m/s. When will the two objects A and B meet?

v. State Archimedes' principle and write its applications.

**2. Life skills questions**

i. A and B were walking along the shores of a lake. They saw a drowning person in the lake screaming for help. They immediately took an inflated rubber tube and swam towards the person. The person was saved.

a. Why did they use the inflated rubber tube to help the person?

b. Which life skills do A and B show in the given scenario?

ii. In a society, a milkman started carrying a lactometer. His move of carrying a lactometer was appreciated by the society members. On what principle does the lactometer work? Which life skills do milkman show here?

# SELF-ASSESSMENT 2

**A. Short Answer Type Questions**

**1. Give reasons for the following questions.**

i. An object can get displaced even when no force is applied on it.

ii. The total energy of a freely falling body remains constant.

iii. A racing car is moving along a straight-levelled track. Even when it attains a velocity of 5 times its initial velocity, the potential energy of the car does not change.

iv. If an object possess energy, it is not necessary that it will do work.

v. It is possible for a body to have zero momentum and a non-zero mechanical energy.

**2. Answer the following questions in brief.**

i. An object is moving with a velocity *v*. If the velocity of this object is doubled, what will be the ratio of the two kinetic energies?

ii. What is the power of an engine which does 25,000 J of work in 10 s?

iii. What is the difference between kinetic energy and potential energy? Give one example of each.

iv. It is possible for an object to be in the state of accelerated motion due to external force acting on it but no work is being done by the force. Justify.

v. State the law of conservation of energy.

**B. Long Answer Type Questions**

**1. Answer the following questions in detail.**

i. Calculate the amount of water that can be raised per minute to a height of 5 m by a pump having the power 1 kW. (Given $g = 10\ m/s^2$)

ii. Work can either be positive or negative. Comment. Observe the given diagrams and state whether the work done is positive or negative.

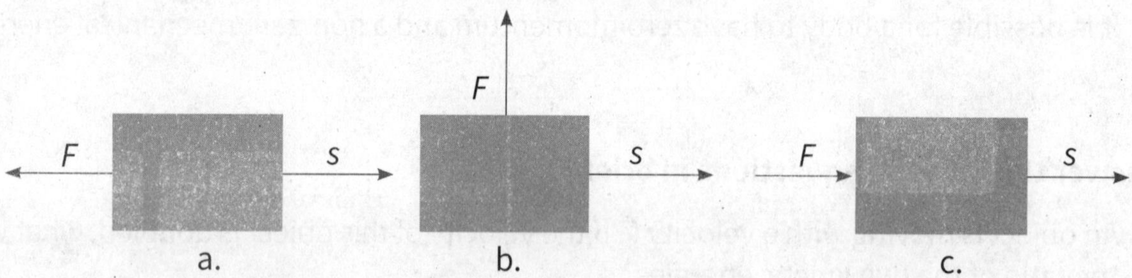


iii. The mass of a lighter body is $m_1$ and that of a heavier body is $m_2$. If both the bodies have the same momentum, which one has higher a kinetic energy?

iv. An object is dropped from a building of height 10 m. If the energy of the ball reduces by 30% after striking the ground, how high can the ball bounce back?
(Given $g = 10 \text{ m/s}^2$)

v. The weight of a man on a certain planet is 1/4th of his weight on the Earth. If he can jump to a height of 50 cm on the surface of the Earth, to what height can he jump on the planet with the same potential energy ?

**2. Life skills questions**

i. Abdul saw an old man trying to keep a big box on the top of a bus. The old man was unable to do so. Abdul helped him by lifting and placing the box on top of the bus.

a. Is the work done by the gravity on the box, positive or negative?

b. Which life skills do Abdul show in the given situation?

ii. Smitha saw an old man lying on the roadside. She touched the old man's body, and it felt cold. When Smitha rubbed the old man's hands and feet, they became warm. The old man opened his eyes and Smitha helped him to reach his home.

a. Why did the hands of the old man become warm when rubbed?

b. Which life skills do Smitha show here?

# SELF-ASSESSMENT 3

## A. Short Answer Type Questions

**1. Give reasons for the following questions.**

i. We hear sound produced by humming bees while the sound of vibration of a pendulum is not heard.

---

ii. Sound produced by a thunderstorm is heard a few seconds after lightning is seen.

---

iii. The ceiling and wall behind the stage of a good conference hall or a concert hall is curved.

---

iv. A sound wave is a longitudinal wave.

---

v. Sound requires a medium to travel.

---

**2. Answer the following questions in brief.**

i. What is meant by high-pitched sound and low-pitched sound?

---

---

ii. What is an echo? Write any two areas of its application.

---

---

iii. Differentiate between loudness of a sound and intensity of sound.

---

---

iv. If an underwater device directs the sound of frequency of 5000 Hz towards the water surface, find the wavelength of the sound in air above the water surface. (Given speed of sound = 340 m/s)

v. If an echo returns in 2 seconds, then what is the distance between the reflecting surface and the source of sound? (Given speed of sound = 340 m/s)

## B. Life skills questions

**1. Answer the following questions in detail.**

i. When Neena threw a ball in a pond, 16 full ripples were produced in 2 seconds. If the distance between its crest and trough is 5 cm, find the velocity of the wave.

ii. An explosion takes place at the bottom of a waterbody. Explain the type of shock waves taking place in the water.

iii. A sound wave travelling in a medium is shown below. Label the amplitude and wavelength of the wave. Find the frequency and time period of the source of sound if the vibrating source of sound makes 180 oscillations in 3 minutes.

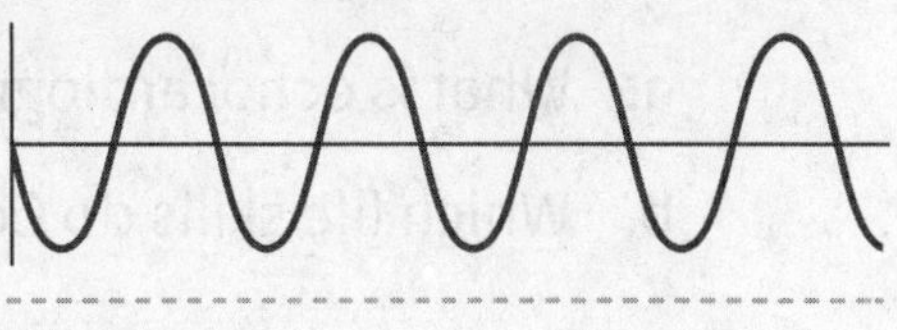

iv. What are the practical applications of the reflection of sound?

v. If the sound produced by a thunderstorm is heard 10 s after the lightning is seen, then find the approximate distance of the thundercloud. (Given speed of sound = 340 m/s)

**2. Value-based questions**

i. While watching a television programme, Lisa saw a device attached to a ship through which a man on the ship located the enemy and sent a message to the higher authorities at the headquarters. Lisa goes through the details of the device on the internet and shared the information with her friends.

a. Name the device fitted in the ship. What is the principle behind the working of that device?

b. Which life skills do Lisa show in the given situation?

ii. Chitra read an article about echocardiography. She used various media to know more about it. Her uncle is a heart patient and the doctor has advised him to have an echocardiography. Chitra convinced her uncle by explaining the advantages of echocardiography and finally her uncle got ready to have it done.

a. What is echocardiography?

b. Which life skills do Chitra show here?

# SELF-ASSESSMENT 3

## A. Short Answer Type Questions

**1. Give reasons for the following questions.**

i. A person can be in poor health and yet disease-free.

---

ii. Acute and chronic diseases have different effects on our health.

---

iii. Some diseases do not spread by contact with the sick, but some people get infected with such diseases.

---

iv. Regular physical exercise is very important.

---

v. Penicillin is given to people suffering from pneumonia, strep throat, meningitis, syphilis and gonorrhoea.

---

**2. Answer the following questions in brief.**

i. How are peptic ulcers caused?

---

---

ii. What is meant by infectious agents?

---

---

iii. Describe immunization with an example.

---

---

iv. Write a brief note on hygiene.

v. Why should we consume sufficient food and a well-balanced diet?

**B. Long Answer Type Questions**

**1. Answer the following questions in detail.**

i. From which epidemic disease is the boy suffering? Write a note on the symptoms and prevention of the disease.

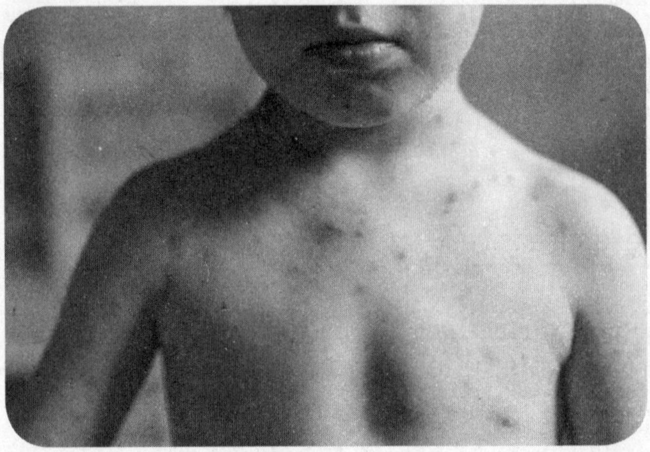

ii. Prevention is better than cure. Explain.

iii. Which disease is caused by the hepatitis virus? How does the disease spread and how can it be prevented?

iv. What are the diseases spread by mosquitoes as vectors?

v. Describe the causes of AIDS.

**2. Life skills questions**

i. Tanu was infected with an unknown viral infection that caused cold, sore throat and fever. She has overcome the infection.

a. What precautionary measures do you think she would have followed initially?

b. Does social distancing help to prevent the spread of the disease?

c. Which life skills do Tanu show?

ii. Pranathi was gifted with a puppy on her birthday. She took it to the veterinary doctor the next day.

a. Why do you think Pranathi took her pet to a veterinary doctor?

b. What would happen if the animal is not vaccinated against rabies?

c. Which other animals can spread the rabies virus?

# SELF-ASSESSMENT 3

## A. Short Answer Type Questions

**1. Give reasons for the following questions.**

i. During the day time, the air above the land starts rising.

ii. The levels of oxides of nitrogen and sulphur in the air are increasing.

iii. All organisms require water for their survival.

iv. Removal of desirable substances from water bodies leads to water pollution.

v. Living organisms influence the formation of soil.

**2. Answer the following questions in brief.**

i. State the relationship between the available amount of water and the number and variety of plants and animals in a given area.

ii. What role does water play in the formation of soil?

iii. How is soil affected when pesticides and fertilizers are used for a longer period of time?

iv. What does the greenhouse effect mean?

v. How does oxygen maintain its level in the atmosphere?

## B. Long Answer Type Questions

**1. Answer the following questions in detail.**

i. Depict the conditions that affect aquatic life during water pollution.

ii. Explain the processes involved in a nitrogen cycle.

iii. Describe the activities involved in a carbon cycle.

iv. Explain the factors and processes involved in the formation of soil.

v. Observe the digram given below and explain the processes involved in a water cycle. Also, label the diagram.

2. **Life skills questions**

   i. Diljit found that the river in his neighbourhood is very polluted. He informed the authorities about the condition of the river and suggested measures for its revival.

      a. State the possible causes for the pollution of the river.

      b. How did life in the river get affected due to pollution?

      c. What made Diljit inform about the situation and suggest measures for the revival of the river?

   ---

   ii. Anuradha is the daughter of a farmer who usually suffers great loss in his farms due to less fertility in the soil. She advises her father to leave the land uncultivated for the next two seasons.

      a. State the possible causes for the reduction in the fertility of the soil.

      b. How important is soil as a resource?

      c. Which life skills enabled Anuradha to advise her father to leave the land uncultivated for the next two seasons?

# SELF-ASSESSMENT 3

## A. Short Answer Type Questions

**1. Give reasons for the following questions.**

i. Varieties of crops that can be grown in diverse climatic conditions are useful.

ii. Two or three crops can be grown in a year with good harvest.

iii. Fields are ploughed deep in the summers.

iv. The floor of the cattle shed needs to be sloppy.

v. Fertilizers should be applied carefully for their complete utilization.

**2. Answer the following questions in brief.**

i. How are the major group of activities for improving the yield of crops classified?

ii. What are the various requirements of different crops for their growth and completion of their life cycle?

iii. What do you mean by hybridization?

iv. How can manure be classified based on the biological material used?

v. What do you mean by organic farming?

## B. Long Answer Type Questions

**1. Answer the following questions in detail.**

i. Explain the different cropping patterns with examples.

ii. How do marine fisheries and inland fisheries serve as a resource for fish production?

iii. Describe how bee-keeping has become an agricultural enterprise.

iv. How is poultry farming undertaken to raise domestic fowl for egg production and chicken meat?

v. Identify the animals given here based on their eating habits. Explain the food requirement of these animals.

2. **Life skills questions**

   i. Bijoy is a young farmer who incurred a great deal of loss due to heavy rains during crop harvest. Bijoy is unhappy and his family is facing shortage of food supply. Bijoy wants to restart farming so that he can solve the problem of shortage of food supply. Maybe, in the future he would be able to help the society if his farming become successful.

      a. Suggest measures that can be undertaken by Bijoy to combat the problem of hunger and sustain his livelihood.

      b. What are the different crop production management practices that can be adopted by Bijoy?

      c. What made Bijoy restart farming in spite of the loss incurred by him?

   ii. Rani has completed her studies in horticulture and wants to start organic farming. How much do you know about organic farming? Answer the following questions to find out.

      a. State the advantages of organic farming.

      b. How are nutrients provided to crops in organic farming?

      c. What could be the reason for selecting organic farming as a career by Rani?

# PISA-based Questions

## Chapter 1 Matter in Our Surroundings

**Choose the correct option.**

1. Concentrated Dettol solution is diluted ten times and used to disinfect various surfaces. Which of the following is used as a solvent to dilute Dettol?

   A. Water  B. Kerosene

   C. Petrol  D. Absolute alcohol

2. Which of the following tests is performed to detect the presence of Dettol in water?

   A. pH test  B. Flame test

   C. Odour test  D. Density test

3. **Assertion (A):** Dettol particles got evenly distributed in the universal solvent.

   **Reason (R):** Particles of matter have space between them.

   A. Both A and R are true and R is the correct explanation of A.

   B. Both A and R are true but R is the not correct explanation of A.

   C. A is true but R is false.

   D. R is true but A is false.

## Chapter 2 Is Matter Around Us Pure?

The chromatography technique of separation was initially developed in 1903 by Mikhail Tsvet, a Russian botanist.

Mikhail used the difference in the polarity of different molecules in a mixture as the criteria for the separation of these molecules. He extracted the different colour pigments from plants by using liquid-adsorption column chromatography. He used calcium carbonate as the adsorbent (stationary phase) and petroleum ether/ethanol mixtures (mobile phase) as the solvent to separate the plant pigments (chlorophylls and carotenoids).

Ever since its discovery, chromatography has evolved into a powerful tool in the lab for the separation and identification of different compounds in a mixture. Today, there are several types of chromatography that are being used in different labs across the world. Paper, liquid, thin layer, gas, high performance liquid, and ion exchange chromatography are some of its types.

**Choose the correct option.**

1. According to the text given on the previous page, what is the principle used for the separation of the sample?

   A. Adsorption of the solutes of a solution through a stationary phase.

   B. Adsorption of the solutes of a solution through a mobile phase.

   C. Affinity of the mobile and the stationary phase with each other.

   D. Affinity of the sample towards the stationary phase.

2. If multiple samples are to be separated, which method of chromatography separation is best suited?

   A. Gas chromatography

   B. Paper chromatography

   C. High-performance liquid chromatography

   D. Ion exchange chromatography

3. What was the criterion used for the separation of different molecules in a mixture in the Mikhail technique?

   A. Difference in polarity

   B. Affinity between the molecules

   C. Retention mechanism

   D. Absorption of light

## Chapter 3 Atoms and Molecules

Chemists need to measure the quantities of substances for many purposes. They cannot weigh individual atoms and molecules, but the average atomic mass provided in the periodic table gives a convenient way of obtaining an equal number of different kinds of atoms. The number of atoms, N, present in exactly 12 grams of carbon-12 isotope has been chosen as the standard, as its chemical atomic weight was almost identical to the atomic weight based on the natural mix of oxygen. This constant is called Avogadro's (*Lorenzo Romano Amedeo Carlo Avogadro di Quaregna e di Cerretois* the full name) number. One can use Avogadro's number to convert between mass and the number of molecules of any pure substance.

Avogadro's number is a sort of a bridge between chemistry and atomic physics. In chemistry, we measure things based on their bulk properties such as mass, pressure, volume and temperature. In physics, we consider things from an atomic perspective and look at individual atoms and its momentum and the velocity of these particles. Avogadro's number connects these two ideas and allows us to explore atomic-level things by measuring their macroscopic-level quantities.

**Choose the correct option.**

1. According to the text given above which of the following is connected in the Avogadro's number?

   A. Chemistry and atomic physics

   B. Mass and pressure

   C. Momentum and velocity of the particles

   D. Atomic and microscopic measurement

2. How many $H_2O$ molecules are there in a snowflake weighing 1 mg? (Given: 1 mole of $H_2O$ is 18.02 g) (Hint: Determine the number of $H_2O$ molecules in one gram of water.)

   A. $3.35 \times 10^{19}$ B. $6.023 \times 10^{23}$

   C. $3.35 \times 10^{22}$ D. $6.023 \times 10^{19}$

## Chapter 4 Structure of the Atom

**Choose the correct option.**

1. An isotope of an element has the same atomic number. Carbon atom has the atomic number 6. Which of the following is true with respect to its neutron numbers?

   A. Neutron number of isotopes is 6.

   B. Neutron numbers are 6, 7 and 8.

   C. Neutron numbers are 12, 13 and 14.

   D. Neutron numbers are 5, 6 and 7.

2. Mass of an atom is determined by the mass of the nucleus of an atom. Identify the correct statement related to the electrons of an atom.

   A. In an atom, the number of electrons keeps changing.

   B. They contribute to the mass of the atom.

   C. They are positively charged.

   D. They do not contribute to the mass of the atom.

3. **Assertion (A):** Electrons do not radiate energy in discrete orbits.

   **Reason (R):** Discrete electronic orbits are allowed to revolve inside an atom.

   A. Both A and R are true and R is the correct explanation of A.

   B. Both A and R are true but R is not the correct explanation of A.

   C. A is true but R is false.

   D. R is true but A is false.

## Chapter 5 Fundamental Unit of Life

### Choose the correct option.

1. Farheen observed a transverse section of a stem and root cell of the same plant under a microscope. Which of the following could be common in the root cells and stem cells in green plants?

   A. Guard cells
   B. Chloroplast
   C. Cell wall
   D. Stomata

2. If Farheen compared a leaf cell with a muscle cell, which of the following would be present in the plant cell but absent in the animal cell?

   A. Chloroplasts
   B. Vacuoles
   C. Mitochondria
   D. Cell membrane

3. Many plant cell structures have more than one internal membrane. Which of the following structures consists of many internal membrane layers?

   A. Cisterns
   B. Stroma
   C. Endoplasmic reticulum
   D. Ribosomes

## Chapter 6 Tissues

### Muscle tissues

Who does not know Arnold Schwarzenegger? He is one of the greatest body builders of all times. A good muscle pump is what all body builders aim for. This indicates the effectiveness of training, and ultimately, muscle hypertrophy (growth). During these exercises, there are a lot of chemical and physical changes occurring in the body. Muscle cells contract and relax during such rigorous activities.

Muscle contraction is the activation of tension-generating sites within muscle fibres. For example, holding a heavy book or a dumbbell at the same position. When you are pushing a door to open, muscles are actually pulling your elbow and shoulder against the door.

Muscle contraction can be described with two variables: force and length. There are two main types of muscle contraction:

(a) Isometric contraction: muscle contracts and force is generated without changing the length of the muscle.

(b) Isotonic contraction: muscle generates force by changing the length of the muscle; two types: concentric and eccentric.

- Concentric contraction: muscle generates force by shortening the length of the muscle.
- Eccentric contractions: muscle generates force by elongating the length of the muscle.

**Choose the correct option.**

1. According to the text given on the previous page, holding a dumbbell at the same position is a/an ______ kind of contraction.

   A. isometric  B. voluntary

   C. concentric  D. eccentric

2. No matter what we are doing, we have muscles at work. However, to keep them healthy, they need exercise. Even our heart needs a workout to stay strong. What type of exercise is best suited for cardiac muscles?

   A. Flexibility  B. Balance

   C. Strength  D. Endurance

3. Which of the following terms does not refer to the ability to receive and respond to a stimulus of a muscle cell?

   A. Contractility  B. Excitability

   C. Responsiveness  D. Irritability

## Chapter 7 Diversity in Living Organisms

**Choose the correct option.**

1. The environment where a pre-existing organism lived would have changed drastically over the generations. Which of the following aids in the evolution and survival of an organism?

   A. The fittest of the species

   B. The weakest of the species

   C. Similar species living in different habitats

   D. The species that do not adapt

2. A great scientist had described evolution and its origin in one of his books. This book is referred to as one of the early books on the classification and the evolution of living organisms. Which of the following is the book being described here?

   A. The Origin of Family  B. The Origin of Species

   C. The Origin of Genus  D. The Origin of Phylum

3. Some characteristics are acquired during a generation and are passed on to the next generation. Which of the following describes the characteristics that have have been acquired and are passed on to the next generation?

   A. Accumulation  B. Assimilation

   C. Adaptation  D. Assertion

4. Some species do not evolve. Which of the following is still a primitive organism?

   A. Algae B. *Aspergillus*

   C. *Agaricus* D. *Amoeba*

## Chapter 8 Motion

**Choose the correct option.**

1. A bus starts from a place P at 10 am with a constant speed. At 4 pm, a car starts from the same place P, and follows the bus at a uniform speed of 60 km/h. The car catches up with the bus in 4 hours. Find the speed of the bus.

   A. 6 km/h B. 24 km/h

   C. 15 km/h D. 240 km/h

2. The distance between two towns P and Q is 50 km. A motorbike going from P to Q travels half the distance with a speed of 50 km/h and covered the next half distance with a speed of 25 km/h. What is the total time taken by the motorbike to travel from P to Q?

   A. 30 minutes B. 1 hour 30 minutes

   C. 1 hour 10 minutes D. 1 hour

3. If the relationship between velocity and time for a body can be expressed by the equation $v = 10 - 0.5t$, then it indicates the object undergoes a ______________.

   A. uniform acceleration of 0.5 $m/s^2$

   B. uniform retardation of 0.5 $m/s^2$

   C. uniform acceleration of 0.25 $m/s^2$

   D. uniform acceleration of 0.25 $m/s^2$

## Chapter 9 Force and Laws of Motion

**Choose the correct option.**

1. Two balls X and Y have same radii. X is made up of wood and Y is made up of iron. Equal forces are applied on them and they move on a horizontal frictionless surface. If the acceleration of X is 10 times that of the Y, what is the ratio of the mass of Y to X?

   A. 1:2 B. 10:1

   C. 2:1 D. 1:5

2. A metal ball of mass 200 g moving with a velocity of 30 m/s collides with a stationery rubber ball of mass 100 g . After the collision, both the balls stick together and move with a velocity $v$. What is the value of $v$?

   A. 10 m/s B. 15 m/s

   C. 20 m/s D. 30 m/s

3. P, Q and R are three moving trucks having same mass. P is loaded with a mass of 450 kg, Q is loaded with a mass of 750 kg while no load is added to R. If they all have same momentum, arrange them in increasing order of their speeds.

A. P < Q < R

B. R < Q < P

C. R < P < Q

D. Q < P < R

## Chapter 10 Gravitation

**Choose the correct option.**

1. Anant is a space voyager who researches about the weight of objects in space. He collects an object from the surface of the moon. When weighed with the help of a spring balance, its weight was found to be 6 N. He notices that when the same object is brought to the surface of the Earth, it weighs different. Which of the following observations is correct?

   A. Weight of the object on the Earth is 1 N.

   B. Weight of the object on the Earth is 3 N.

   C. Weight of the object on the Earth is 12 N.

   D. Weight of the object on the Earth is 36 N.

2. A rubber ball has a mass of 250 g and a radius of 12 cm. When it is placed in a bucket of water, it floats on the water surface. What is the volume of water displaced by the ball? (Density of water = $10^3$ kg $m^{-3}$)

   A. 0.125 litre  B. 0.250 litre

   C. 0.500 litre  D. 1.00 litre

3. If we drop a stone and a feather from a height, they do not reach the Earth's surface at the same time. But if we repeat the same experiment on the moon, they reach the surface at the same time. Why?

   A. Acceleration due to the gravity of the Earth is more than that of the moon.

   B. Acceleration due to the gravity of the Earth is less than that of the moon.

   C. Moon has no atmosphere, but the Earth has an atmosphere which resists the motion of the objects.

   D. Time of fall is more on the surface of moon than that of the Earth.

## Chapter 11 Work and Energy

**Choose the correct option.**

1. An object of mass 10 kg is projected upwards with a kinetic energy of 500 J. At what height will the potential energy of the object be equal to its initial kinetic energy?

   A. 0.5 m    B. 2.5 m

   C. 250 m    D. 25 m

2. An object of mass m is moving with a velocity *v*. If the velocity of the object becomes 4 times, then its new kinetic energy will be____________.

   A. 20 times its initial kinetic energy    B. 5 times its initial kinetic energy

   C. 250 times its initial kinetic energy    D. 16 times its initial kinetic energy

3. If an object of a certain mass is moved along a straight line by a machine producing constant power, then the velocity of the object at time *t* is proportional to ______________.

   A. $t^{1/2}$    B. $t^2$

   C. $t^{3/2}$    D. $t^{1/4}$

## Chapter 12 Sound

**Choose the correct option.**

1. The distance between the two walls, X and Y, of an auditorium is 100 m. A person standing 30 m away from wall X claps his hands once. If the speed of sound in air is 330 m/s, what is the time interval between the first and the second echo that he hears?

   A. $\frac{6}{33}$ s    B. $\frac{14}{33}$ s

   C. $\frac{8}{33}$ s    D. 1 s

2. At a certain position of a radio wave, there is a trough at $t = 0$. If the time period of the radio wave is 0.6 seconds, then identify the value of $t$ at which the next crest appear at this position.

   A. 0.6 s    B. 1.2 s

   C. 0.3 s    D. 1 s

3. The distance between the bed of an ocean and the surface of the ocean is found to be 15 km by using a sonar signal. Calculate the time taken for an echo of the signal to reach the surface of the ocean after reflection from the ocean bed. (Take the speed of sound in sea water as 1,500 m/s).

   A. 30 s    B. 0.2 s

   C. 20 s    D. 15 s

## Chapter 13 Why Do We Fall Ill?

**Choose the correct option.**

1. Which of the following is necessary for the general health of a body?

   A. All metabolic and non-metabolic functions of the body

   B. Only a healthy heart

   C. Only a healthy stomach and intestine

   D. Only a healthy brain

2. Which of the following does not affect the general health of a body?

   A. Mental disease  B. Acute disease

   C. Chronic disease  D. Community issues

3. Which of the following affects the health of a body for a long time?

   A. Tuberculosis  B. Common cold

   C. Burn injury  D. Diarrhoea

4. Which of the following is the mode for the spread of tuberculosis?

   A. Droplets in the air  B. Contaminated water

   C. Contaminated food  D. Unhygienic clothing

## Chapter 14 Natural Resources

**Choose the correct option.**

1. A motor car is parked directly under the sun with its glasses fully closed. What will be the temperature inside the car when compared to the temperature outside?

   A. Less than the outside temperature

   B. More than the outside temperature

   C. Both temperatures will be equal

   D. There will be no effect of temperature

2. In spite of being a useful gas for plants, why is carbon dioxide considered to be a pollutant?

   A. It is a greenhouse gas.

   B. It increases the pressure in the atmosphere.

   C. It can exist in solid and liquid form.

   D. Its density is more.

3. A weather report on newspaper and television says, 'Depression in the Bay of Bengal'. Which of the following can be used to collect information for weather forecast?

A. Beam balance, multimeter, odometer and potentiometer

B. Ammeter, audiometer, electrometer and speedometer

C. Thermometer, barometer, rain gauge and anemometer

D. Hydrometer, lactometer, pH meter and spirometer

## Chapter 15 Improvement In Food Resources

**Choose the correct option.**

1. Rohit has decided to undertake poultry farming. Suggest him the poultry feed suitable for broilers.

A. Poultry feeds that are high in vitamins C and E.

B. Poultry feeds that are high in vitamins A and K.

C. Poultry feeds containing less protein and more fat.

D. Poultry feeds containing neither protein nor fat.

2. Poultry birds used for farming purpose are larger in size but they have less adaptability to summer. Identify what can be done for getting variety of birds which are smaller in size and can adapt well in summer.

A. Crossbreed between Indian and foreign breeds

B. Buy foreign breeds

C. Provide summer adaptation vaccines to breeds

D. Change physical conditions to help the breed to adapt

3. Rohit's friend visited his livestock farmhouse and stated that the animals he found in the farmhouse are healthy. What made his friend comment that the animals are healthy?

A. Location of the farmhouse

B. Availability of rain in the region

C. Use of healthy feeds and healthy posture of animals

D. Space provided for animals in the cattle shed

# General Tips

Science is something that is seen in and around us. If you can connect almost everything about you and around you with science, it will be easy for you to understand and enjoy studying science as a subject.

*Here are some tips to ease the process of learning different areas of science.*

1. **GET HOLD OF THE SYLLABUS**

   Have a soft or hard copy of the current syllabus.

2. **MAKE A STUDY PLAN**

   Make a tabular column of the chapter-wise weightage according to an exam's blueprint.

3. **MAKE NOTES FOR IMPORTANT POINTS**

   For quick reference, note down important points while listening to the class or reading texts. Make a note of SI units and their conversions and formulae. Don't skip the sample problems.

4. **MAKE CONNECTIONS**

   Try and relate the learning from science to the day to day activities and events.

5. **ASK RELEVANT QUESTIONS**

   The only questions one should have while learning something is ''why" and "how". Why is it like this? How can this be altered? Read the reference documents from different sources.

6. **KEEP YOUR BASICS STRONG**

   Test your understanding of the concepts frequently by taking some assessments and exams.

7. **BE AND STAY ORGANIZED**

   Have all the tools or equipment and stationary handy and clean.

8. **FIND A MENTOR OR A STUDY GROUP**

   Choose a mentor or group of similar interest to discuss, clear doubts, and revise at regular intervals.

9. **STAY HEALTHY**

   Eat healthy food, keep yourself hydrated, exercise, meditate, do yoga, get enough sleep, and keep your mind motivated.

10. **MAINTAIN FOCUS**

    Complete concentration and dedication towards learning a concept leads to faster understanding and comprehension. Put away gadgets so that you can focus.

# Quick Tips

## 1. STUDY SMART

Always keep the syllabus copy handy. The best method of learning is to teach others.

## 2. BE ATTENTIVE AND ALERT

While performing an experiment, make sure that the right indicators are used. Be careful about calibration errors in the instruments.

## 3. SKILL UP

Learn the scientific notations.

## 4. PRACTISE

Do a good practise of all chemical structures, chemical formulae, writing and balancing chemical equations.

## 5. BE YOUR OWN COMPETITOR

Formulate all possible questions for each concept learned and answer them. Attempt all the questions during assessments.

# Answer Keys

## PRE-TEST

| Chapter 1 | Chapter 2 | Chapter 3 | Chapter 4 | Chapter 5 | Chapter 6 | Chapter 7 | Chapter 8 |
|---|---|---|---|---|---|---|---|
| 1. B | 1. C | 1. D | 1. A | 1. C | 1. A | 1. D | 1. A |
| 2. C | 2. B | 2. A | 2. B | 2. B | 2. B | 2. A | 2. A |
| 3. A | 3. C | 3. D | 3. D | 3. A | 3. B | 3. A | 3. D |
| 4. D | 4. C | 4. B | 4. B | 4. A | 4. C | 4. B | 4. B |
| 5. A | 5. D | 5. A | 5. C | 5. A | 5. B | 5. A | 5. A |

| Chapter 9 | Chapter 10 | Chapter 11 | Chapter 12 | Chapter 13 | Chapter 14 | Chapter 15 |
|---|---|---|---|---|---|---|
| 1. A | 1. D | 1. C | 1. C | 1. A | 1. B | 1. B |
| 2. C | 2. A | 2. B | 2. C | 2. B | 2. A | 2. A |
| 3. B | 3. B | 3. B | 3. B | 3. A | 3. B | 3. C |
| 4. C | 4. C | 4. B | 4. B | 4. B | 4. C | 4. D |
| 5. B | 5. C | 5. C | 5. A | 5. D | 5. D | 5. C |

## PART 1

| Chapter 1 | | Chapter 2 | | Chapter 3 | | Chapter 4 | | Chapter 5 | | Chapter 6 | | Chapter 7 | | Chapter 8 | |
|---|---|---|---|---|---|---|---|---|---|---|---|---|---|---|---|
| SA 1 | SA 2 | SA 1 | SA 2 | SA 1 | SA 2 | SA 1 | SA 2 | SA 1 | SA 2 | SA 1 | SA 2 | SA 1 | SA 2 | SA 1 | SA 2 |
| 1. A | 26. D | 1. D | 26. B | 1. C | 26. B | 1. B | 26. B | 1. C | 26. D | 1. C | 26. A | 1. A | 26. A | 1. C | 26. D |
| 2. B | 27. A | 2. B | 27. C | 2. A | 27. C | 2. C | 27. C | 2. A | 27. A | 2. C | 27. B | 2. A | 27. A | 2. C | 27. B |
| 3. A | 28. A | 3. A | 28. B | 3. C | 28. B | 3. A | 28. A | 3. A | 28. C | 3. C | 28. C | 3. C | 28. A | 3. D | 28. A |
| 4. D | 29. A | 4. C | 29. C | 4. B | 29. A | 4. B | 29. D | 4. B | 29. A | 4. A | 29. C | 4. D | 29. A | 4. D | 29. C |
| 5. A | 30. A | 5. C | 30. C | 5. A | 30. D | 5. D | 30. B | 5. B | 30. A | 5. B | 30. B | 5. C | 30. C | 5. C | 30. B |
| 6. B | 31. A | 6. D | 31. B | 6. A | 31. C | 6. A | 31. B | 6. A | 31. A | 6. B | 31. C | 6. D | 31. C | 6. C | 31. B |
| 7. A | 32. B | 7. A | 32. C | 7. D | 32. B | 7. C | 32. C | 7. B | 32. B | 7. C | 32. B | 7. A | 32. B | 7. C | 32. C |
| 8. A | 33. D | 8. D | 33. D | 8. B | 33. D | 8. B | 33. A | 8. C | 33. C | 8. C | 33. A | 8. B | 33. B | 8. D | 33. A |
| 9. A | 34. B | 9. D | 34. C | 9. B | 34. A | 9. A | 34. D | 9. A | 34. A | 9. C | 34. C | 9. B | 34. C | 9. C | 34. D |
| 10. B | 35. A | 10. A | 35. A | 10. B | 35. A | 10. C | 35. B | 10. B | 35. D | 10. B | 35. C | 10. C | 35. B | 10. A | 35. D |
| 11. A | 36. D | 11. A | 36. B | 11. A | 36. A | 11. D | 36. C | 11. C | 36. B | 11. B | 36. B | 11. B | 36. D | 11. B | 36. C |
| 12. B | 37. A | 12. D | 37. B | 12. C | 37. B | 12. A | 37. D | 12. C | 37. B | 12. B | 37. D | 12. B | 37. B | 12. B | 37. C |
| 13. B | 38. B | 13. A | 38. D | 13. A | 38. A | 13. B | 38. B | 13. A | 38. D | 13. A | 38. C | 13. D | 38. D | 13. A | 38. B |
| 14. C | 39. A | 14. B | 39. A | 14. B | 39. D | 14. A | 39. D | 14. B | 39. A | 14. D | 39. B | 14. A | 39. A | 14. C | 39. D |
| 15. C | 40. A | 15. A | 40. B | 15. D | 40. C | 15. D | 40. D | 15. B | 40. B | 15. B | 40. B | 15. C | 40. A | 15. D | 40. A |
| 16.D | 41. A | 16. D | 41. B | 16. A | 41. D | 16. C | 41. B | 16. A | 41. B | 16. A | 41. C | 16. A | 41. A | 16. B | 41. D |
| 17. A | 42. B | 17. A | 42. D | 17. D | 42. B | 17. B | 42. B | 17. A | 42. A | 17. A | 42. B | 17. A | 42. D | 17. B | 42. B |
| 18. B | 43. D | 18. C | 43. A | 18. D | 43. C | 18. A | 43. B | 18. D | 43. B | 18. A | 43. B | 18. C | 43. D | 18. B | 43. C |
| 19. A | 44. C | 19. B | 44. D | 19. A | 44. B | 19. A | 44. B | 19. A | 44. C | 19. B | 44. C | 19. A | 44. D | 19. A | 44. D |
| 20. A | 45. D | 20. D | 45. D | 20. C | 45. D | 20. B | 45. D | 20. B | 45. D | 20. A | 45. B | 20. A | 45. D | 20. A | 45. C |
| 21. B | 46. A | 21. A | 46. A | 21. A | 46. B | 21. D | 46. C | 21. A | 46. D | 21. C | 46. C | 21. A | 46. A | 21. C | 46. D |
| 22. A | 47. A | 22. B | 47. C | 22. B | 47. A | 22. C | 47. C | 22. B | 47. D | 22. B | 47. B | 22. C | 47. B | 22. D | 47. A |
| 23. C | 48. B | 23. B | 48. A | 23. B | 48. C | 23. A | 48. D | 23. C | 48. D | 23. C | 48. B | 23. C | 48. D | 23. C | 48. A |
| 24. A | 49. B | 24. D | 49. D | 24. B | 49. A | 24. C | 49. C | 24. A | 49. B | 24. A | 49. A | 24. B | 49. A | 24. D | 49. C |
| 25.D | 50. A | 25. B | 50. A | 25. B | 50. B | 25. A | 50. D | 25. A | 50. C | 25. B | 50. A | 25. A | 50. A | 25. B | 50. C |

| Chapter 9 | | Chapter 10 | | Chapter 11 | Chapter 12 | | Chapter 13 | | Chapter 14 | | Chapter 15 | |
|---|---|---|---|---|---|---|---|---|---|---|---|---|
| SA 1 | SA 2 | SA 1 | SA 2 | SA 1 | SA 1 | SA 2 | SA 1 | SA 2 | SA 1 | SA 2 | SA 1 | SA 2 |
| 1. D | 26. B | 1. C | 26. B | 1. C | 1. C | 26. C | 1. A | 26. B | 1. B | 26. B | 1. B | 26. B |
| 2. A | 27. B | 2. D | 27. B | 2. A | 2. C | 27. D | 2. B | 27. B | 2. B | 27. A | 2. A | 27. A |
| 3. A | 28. B | 3. B | 28. B | 3. B | 3. D | 28. D | 3. B | 28. A | 3. A | 28. C | 3. D | 28. C |
| 4. D | 29. D | 4. B | 29. D | 4. C | 4. B | 29. D | 4. A | 29. D | 4. A | 29. C | 4. B | 29. B |
| 5. C | 30. B | 5. C | 30. C | 5. D | 5. D | 30. C | 5. C | 30. D | 5. D | 30. B | 5. A | 30. C |
| 6. B | 31. C | 6. A | 31. D | 6. A | 6. A | 31. A | 6. B | 31. C | 6. C | 31. D | 6. C | 31. B |
| 7. A | 32. C | 7. D | 32. C | 7. A | 7. C | 32. C | 7. B | 32. C | 7. A | 32. A | 7. D | 32. D |
| 8. B | 33. A | 8. B | 33. A | 8. C | 8. A | 33. C | 8. B | 33. A | 8. C | 33. C | 8. A | 33. C |
| 9. C | 34. C | 9. C | 34. A | 9. C | 9. B | 34. D | 9. C | 34. A | 9. B | 34. A | 9. B | 34. D |
| 10. A | 35. A | 10. C | 35. D | 10. D | 10. D | 35. B | 10. D | 35. C | 10. C | 35. D | 10. C | 35. A |
| 11. D | 36. C | 11. B | 36. D | 11. A | 11. C | 36. D | 11. B | 36. B | 11. B | 36. B | 11. B | 36. B |
| 12. C | 37. D | 12. D | 37. C | 12. B | 12. A | 37. D | 12. C | 37. C | 12. D | 37. A | 12. A | 37. B |
| 13. C | 38. B | 13. D | 38. B | 13. C | 13. D | 38. B | 13. D | 38. C | 13. A | 38. D | 13. D | 38. A |
| 14. C | 39. C | 14. B | 39. B | 14. C | 14. D | 39. A | 14. D | 39. A | 14. C | 39. C | 14. B | 39. D |
| 15. B | 40. A | 15. D | 40. B | 15. B | 15. C | 40. B | 15. D | 40. A | 15. A | 40. A | 15. A | 40. C |
| 16. B | 41. B | 16. D | 41. D | 16. A | 16. C | 41. D | 16. D | 41. D | 16. B | 41. B | 16. D | 41. B |
| 17. D | 42. C | 17. C | 42. A | 17. B | 17. B | 42. C | 17. D | 42. A | 17. D | 42. D | 17. B | 42. D |
| 18. D | 43. B | 18. D | 43. A | 18. D | 18. B | 43. C | 18. A | 43. B | 18. D | 43. B | 18. D | 43. A |
| 19. C | 44. D | 19. B | 44. C | 19. C | 19. C | 44. B | 19. B | 44. A | 19. C | 44. A | 19. C | 44. C |
| 20. D | 45. A | 20. A | 45. A | 20. B | 20. C | 45. A | 20. D | 45. B | 20. C | 45. C | 20. D | 45. B |
| 21. B | 46. B | 21. C | 46. C | 21. B | 21. C | 46. A | 21. A | 46. B | 21. C | 46. D | 21. B | 46. D |
| 22. D | 47. D | 22. B | 47. A | 22. D | 22. C | 47. B | 22. A | 47. C | 22. A | 47. A | 22. C | 47. C |
| 23. B | 48. B | 23. D | 48. C | 23. C | 23. B | 48. C | 23. D | 48. A | 23. B | 48. C | 23. A | 48. A |
| 24. A | 49. A | 24. B | 49. A | 24. A | 24. C | 49. B | 24. B | 49. C | 24. D | 49. B | 24. B | 49. B |
| 25. A | 50. C | 25. A | 50. D | 25. D | 25. C | 50. A | 25. D | 50. A | 25. A | 50. C | 25. C | 50. C |

# PART 2

**Chapter 1: Matter in Our Surroundings**

A. 1. i. Evaporation of water from the wet wiped floor keeps the surface cool.

ii. The BEC or Bose-Einstein condensate is a state of matter formed by cooling a gas at extremely low density.

iii. Gases and liquids behave like fluids as they do not have a fixed shape and the particles in a fluid slide past each other.

iv. Solidification is the conversion of liquid to solid where as in fusion solid turns into a liquid.

v. Osmosis removes the excess water present in the food items increasing their shelf-life.

2. i. Recall what melting point is.

ii. atmospheric air < smoke < cotton boll < ice cube < milk < honey <steel magnet

iii. The amount of heat energy required to change 1 kg of a solid into liquid at its melting point is called latent heat of fusion.

iv. Recall how impurities increase boiling point and decrease freezing point of water.

v. Ice being less dense than water floats on its surface. Ice is a poor conductor of heat, therefore, it keeps the water below warm enough for the survival of aquatic animals.

B. 1. i. Recall how helium particles diffuse from the helium cylinder into the balloon.

ii. Many gases can be compressed and used in various domains of life such as: Liquefied petroleum gas or LPG is used as cooking fuel.; Compressed gases such as oxygen are used in hospitals.; The liquefied and compressed gases are stored in cylinders.; Cylinders are easy to seal, store and transport.

iii. Recall arrangement of particles in solids, liquids and gases.

iv. P and Q—Sublimation is the process in which solids get converted into gases with increased temperature and decreased pressure and vice versa.; R—Vaporization is the process in which liquids get converted to their gaseous state when heated or under high temperature and pressure.; S—Solidification is the process in which liquids get converted to solids under decreased temperature and increased pressure.

v. Recall the various factors that affect the rate of evaporation such as surface area, humidity in the air, wind speed and temperature.

2. i. a. Dibaang shuffled the clothes so that all the clothes could dry in the sun evenly.

b. No, because all clothes would not receive the same amount of sunlight.

c. We should help our parents in household chores and get ready for school in time.

ii. a. As the surface area of the glass was not enough to let the milk cool. Thus, the hot milk burned Arsalan's tongue.

b. Plate had a larger surface area which allowed more evaporation leading to faster cooling of milk. Thus, Arslan could drink milk comfortably from the plate.

c. We should never try to drink or eat anything when it is hot. This can burn our tongue and cause injury to our throat.

**Chapter 2: Is Matter Around Us Pure?**

A. 1. i. Solvent evaporates leaving behind the component to be separated along with the impurities. Prolonged heating during evaporation, may also degrade the component to be separated.

ii. Recall the various components present in blood.

iii. Recall what burning is.

iv. Graphite is a good conductor of electricity.

v. Hydrogen and oxygen are considered as elements as these cannot be split further into simpler substances by any chemical method while water can be split into hydrogen and oxygen by chemical process.

2. i. Recall the dispersion medium and dispersed phase in smoke and fog.

ii. Recall the Tyndall effect.

iii. Evaporation, Centrifugation, Sublimation, Chromatography and Distillation

iv. Magnetic separation Students may answer handpicking or sieving also as response

v. Recall what chromatography is and where is it used.

B. 1. i. Recall the properties of true solutions.

ii.

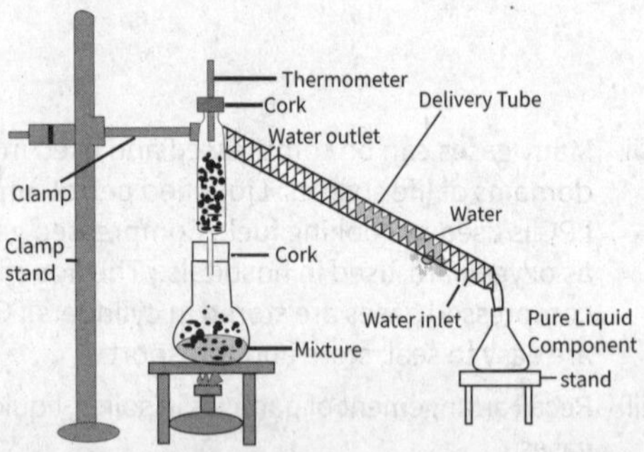


Look at the above diagram and write the procedure. Recall the applications of distillation.

iii. We know; Mass percentage of solution = (Mass of solute/Mass of solution) x 100

| *For Rahul's solution* | *For Anjali's solution* |
|---|---|
| Mass of solute = 15 g<br>Mass of solution = 100 g + 15 g = 115 g; Mass % of solution = (15/115 )× 100 = 13.04% | Mass of solute = 15 g;<br>Mass of solution = 100 g;<br>Mass % of solution<br>= (15/100) × 100 = 15% |

iv.

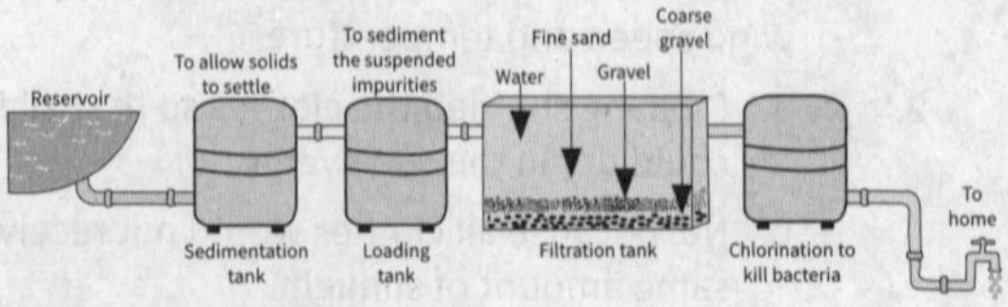


Observe the above diagram carefully to write down the steps.

v. Homogeneous solution.

2. i. a. Obstruction to the driver's view was because of the formation of smog. Smog is a combination of smoke and fog.

b. Smog is an aerosol type of colloid.

c. The particle size of smog ranges between $10^{-3}$ cm to $10^{-5}$ cm. These particles do not pass through filter paper.

**Chapter 3: Atoms and Molecules**

A. 1. i. The atom size of different elements is very small and its mass is extremely less. Therefore, the relative mass of the elements is considered rather than the atomic mass.

ii. Avogadro's number represents the number of atoms in one-gram atom of an element or number of molecules in one-gram mole of a compound. It has been calculated and confirmed that one mole of an element always contains $6.022 \times 10^{23}$ atoms and one mole of a compound always contains $6.022 \times 10^{23}$ molecules. If the atomic mass of an element is divided by actual mass of its atom or the molecular mass of a compound is divided by the actual mass of its molecule, the value is same, that is, $6.022 \times 10^{23}$.

iii. Adding or removing of energy helps in changing the magnitude of the forces of attraction between the particles. This helps in changing the physical state of a matter.

iv. Recall the molecular formula of ozone and oxygen gas.

v. Dalton's symbols were difficult to memorise and draw thus, these are not used in modern chemistry.

2. i. The number of atoms in a molecule of a single element is known as its atomicity. Atomicity of phosphorus is 4, nitrogen is 2, sulphur is 8 and copper is 1.

ii. Molecular mass is the mass of one molecule of an element or a compound. It is expressed in amu or u. Mass of one mole of a molecule is called its molar mass. Its is expressed in grams per mole.

iii. 84.01 g/mol

iv. Recall how temperature affects solubility.

v. *Method 1:* Heat the powder. If it chars, it is sugar.
*Method 2:* Dissolve in water and check for the conduction of electricity. If it is conducting, it is salt.

B. 1. i. Recall the postulates of the Dalton's atomic theory.

ii. The collection of $6.023 \times 10^{23}$ particles is called a mole.
Its significance is:

- In a substance, one mole represents $6.022 \times 10^{23}$ entities.
- In an element, one mole contains $6.022 \times 10^{23}$ atoms.

iii. $1.2044 \times 10^{23}$ ions (Hint: One formula unit of NaCl contains 1 $Na^+$ and 1 $Cl^-$ i.e., 2 ions)

iv. Mass of 1 mole, $6.022 \times 10^{23}$ silver atoms = 108 g
So, mass of one atom of silver = $(108/6.022 \times 10^{23})$ g = $1.793 \times 10^{-22}$ g
Similarly, mass of one gold atom = $3.2707 \times 10^{-22}$ g
Ratio between masses of silver and gold atoms = $3.2707 \times 10^{-22}$ g/$1.793 \times 10^{-22}$ g = 1.8241

v. Image shows the experimental setup explaining the law of conservation of mass. Observe the diagram carefully to write down the steps.

2. i. a. The experiment had to be conducted in the closed environment for the results to be in coherent to the law.

b. $2CH_3COOH + Na_2CO_3 \rightarrow 2CH_3COONa + H_2O + CO_2$

c. Carbon dioxide gas evolved would have escaped from the flask thus affecting the total weight of the residue in the flask.

d. Experiments relating to the law of conservation of mass always have to be conducted in the closed container.

**Chapter 4: Structure of the Atom**

A. 1. i. According to Dalton, atom was indivisible. This proved to be the biggest drawback of the Dalton's atomic theory.

ii. Recall how does Thomson's atomic model looks like.

iii. Hydrogen atom consists of only one proton in its nucleus and hence its mass is equal to the mass of a proton.

iv. Different shells have different energy levels which gives them ability to accommodate different number of electrons. The electrons that can be accommodated in different shells are given by $2n^2$; n is the number of electron orbit. In the first shell, K-shell $2n^2 = 2$, L-shell = $2 \times 2^2 = 8$, M-shell = $2 \times 3^2 = 18$ and for N-shell = $2 \times 4^2 = 32$.

v. Noble gases have stable outer electronic configuration.

2. i. Rutherford is considered as the 'Father' of nuclear physics for his discovery of nucleus of an atom and for his work on radioactivity.

ii. Atoms of the same element having the same atomic number but different atomic mass are called isotopes. Example: ${}_6C^{12}$ and ${}_6C^{14}$ are isotopes of carbon.

iii. 23

iv. The combining capacity of an element is called valency.

v. Z represents atomic number.

B. 1. i. Recall applications of isotopes in different fields.

ii.

| Isotopes | Isobars |
|---|---|
| • Atoms of same elements with different mass number form isotopes.<br>• Isotopes have same atomic number but different mass number. | • Atoms of different elements with same mass number form isobars.<br>• Isobars have the same mass number but different electron number and proton number. |

iii.

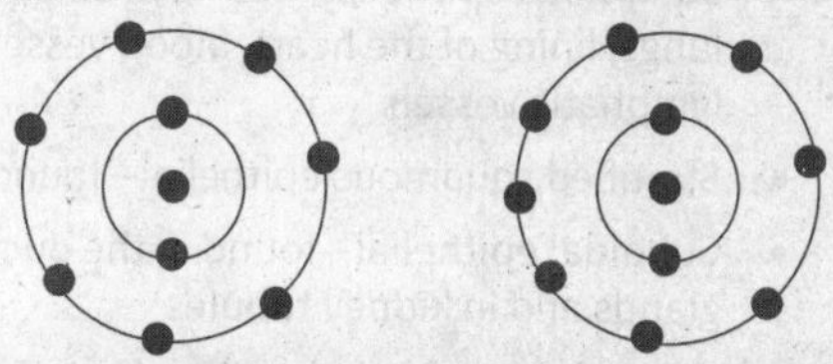

Electron dot structure of fluorine   Electron dot structure of neon

iv. Recall the postulates of Rutherford's model.

v. Thomson's model of atom is similar to a Christmas pudding or a watermelon. It has a positively charged sphere of protons and scattered electrons like seed or dry fruits in a pudding.

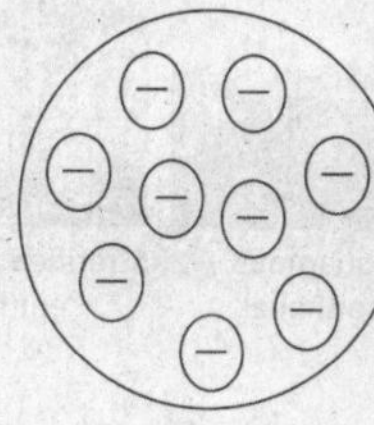

2. i. a. The outermost shell cannot have more than 8 electrons, however Bankei put 10 electrons.

b. Jenny helped Bankei in making the correct model by proper placement of the electrons in various shells of the calcium atom.

c. Bankei learned that the outermost shell can not have more than 8 electrons and the correct electronic configuration of calcium is 2, 8, 8, 2 and not 2, 8, 10.

ii. An atom X with electron number 8 is oxygen.

a. Yes, the valency of the atom is 2 as the electrons filled in K-shell will be 2 and L-shell will be 6.

b. Atomic number of the atom would be 8.

c. Mass of the atom = Number of protons + Number of neutrons = 8 + 8 = 16 u

d. Shaurya learned that an atom is electrically neutral and possesses equal number of protons and electrons.

**Chapter 5: The Fundamental Unit of Life**

A. 1. i. Plasma membrane does not allow all the substances to pass through it.

ii. The energy required for various metabolic and physical activities of the cell is released as a result of reactions in mitochondria.

iii. A de-shelled egg contains only plasma membrane which is semi-permeable.

iv. There are different organelles in a cell. Based on the components they are made up of and their densities, cells allow absorption of stain differently.

v. The unicellular or single cell divides to form multi-cellular tissues, organs and organ system.

2. i. The protoplasm is the jelly-like substance that holds all the organelles in place.

ii. All the metabolic functions are carried out within a single cell in a unicellular organism while different types of cells perform different set of functions in a multi-cellular organism.

iii. *Amoeba* and bacteria are unicellular organisms. Human and mint plant are examples of multi-cellular organisms.

iv. Out of two solutions having different concentrations, the solution having lower concentration is said to be hypotonic solution.

v. A cover slip is used to cover a specimen or a sample on a microscopic slide. It slip protects the mounting liquid from evaporation and keeps the sample moist and protects from dehydrating.

B. 1. i. Recall the steps involved in mounting human cheek cells.

ii. The loss of water from living plant cells through osmosis leading to the shrinkage or contraction of the contents of the cell away from the cell wall is called plasmolysis. For example, grapes shrink when put in sugar syrup.

iii. The given cell is of bacteria which is a prokaryote. Prokaryotes have poorly designed nucleus without nuclear membrane. The nucleic acid is suspended in the cell and is called nucleoid. It consists of a plasma membrane and a cell wall. Whip-like flagella or many flagellum help in their movement.

iv. Recall how Robert Hooke discovered cell.

v. The differences between a prokaryotic and eukaryotic cell are:

| Prokaryotic cell | Eukaryotic cell |
|---|---|
| • Nucleus is free without a nuclear membrane in prokaryotes.<br>• Cytoplasm is poorly developed.<br>• It lacks plastids. | • Nucleus is highly developed with a well-defined nuclear membrane in eukaryotes.<br>• Cytoplasm is highly developed.<br>• There is presence of plastids |

2. i. a. The cells of root, stem and leaf look different as they are different types of cells with different structures and functions.

b. The leaf cells contain stomata, guard cells besides other cells such as cell membrane and cell wall. The root and stem cells lack chloroplasts but contain cell wall and cell membrane.

c. Seema learnt that multi-cellular organisms such as plants are made up of different types of cells in their different parts. Each cell has a special structure and function to perform.

ii. a. Microscope is used to observe samples and screen for abnormalities.

b. Blood cell, skin cell, tissues like muscle, lining or organelles etc., and hair cell are some of the cells that could be observed under the microscope.

c. The blood sample smear can be observed for the evidence of *Plasmodium* parasite for the detection of malaria.

**Chapter 6: Tissues**

A. 1. i. Sclerenchyma tissues do not have inter-cellular space because they are made of thick lignified walls.

ii. Pear fruits are rich in sclereids (also referred as stone cells or grit cells) which give the pear fruits its characteristic crunchy and granular texture.

iii. Recall transpiration.

iv. Voluntary muscles are attached to the bones of the body and aid in the movement of the body.

v. Meristematic cells divide continuously and do not store food material or any waste material. Therefore, these cells lack vacuoles.

2. i. Flax, coconut, hemp, ramie and jute

ii. Smooth muscles are also called involuntary muscles and help in the movement of food in the alimentary canal and in contraction and relaxation of blood vessels.

iii. Recall the functions of stomata.

iv. Ligaments are the tissues that connect bone to bone. These tissues are strong, elastic and consist of yellow fibres.

Tendons are the tissues that connect muscles to bone. These tissues are tough, non-elastic and consist of white fibres.

v.

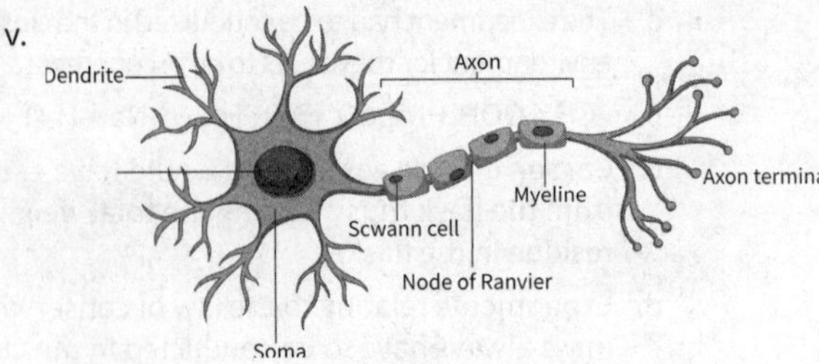


B. 1. i. There are three types of meristems based on their location in the plant body.

- Apical meristems: These occur at the tips of roots and shoots of the plant. This increases the length of the plant.
- Lateral meristems: These occur parallel to the long axis of the stem, branches and roots of the plant. This increases the girth of the plant organs.
- Intercalary meristems: These occur at the base of the internodes. This increases the length of the internodes. It is mostly seen in monocot plants.

ii. With the aging of the plant, epidermis of the stem is replaced by a strip of secondary meristem. The outer layer of the cells is now separated from the inner cells. This forms the cork or the bark of the tree. The characteristics of cork are:

- Cork cells are dead at maturity
- These cells are arranged compactly
- They lack intercellular spaces
- It has suberin in their walls
- They are thick and made of several layers

iii. Recall what permanent tissues are.

iv. Blood is a type of conducting tissue in the human body. Its functions are:

- Transport of respiratory gases – carbon dioxide and oxygen
- Transport of food materials
- Transport of waste products in the body to the kidneys
- Regulate the body temperature
- Protect from the pathogens and heal wounds

v. The four different types of epithelial tissues based on the part of the body where they are located.

- Squamous epithelial—found in air sacs of the lungs, lining of the heart, blood vessels and lymphatic vessels
- Stratified squamous epithelial—found in skin
- Cuboidal epithelial—found in the ducts of small glands and in kidney tubules
- Ciliated columnar epithelial—found in bronchi, uterine tubes and uterus

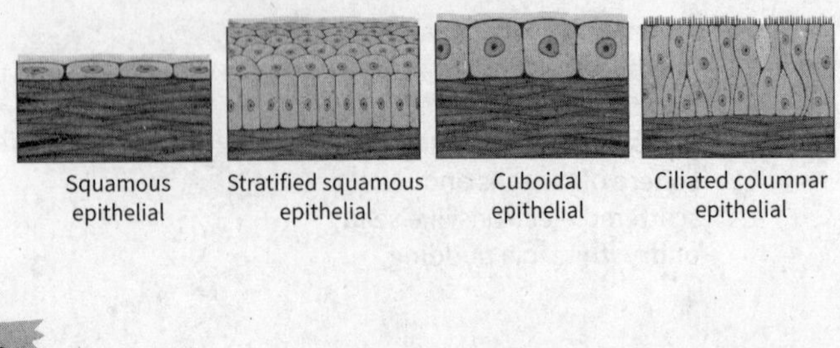

2. i. a. A blood test is the scientific examination of a blood sample for the detection of illness and measurement of other substances in the blood.

b. Isha's friend looked pale and tired. This could be because of the varied levels of haemoglobin in the blood. A blood test would reveal the cause why she fainted during assembly.

c. Iron-rich foods like green leafy vegetables, tofu, spinach, eggs, whole grains, pulses and beans, meat, fish and dry fruits enrich the blood in us.

ii. a. Connective tissue (cartilage) which is present in the ear lobes and nose tip.

b. Connective tissue is made up of proteins and sugar matrix. It smoothens the bone surfaces and joints and is flexible as it does not contain any bony material.

c. From this act, Adarsh learned that he could bend the cartilages and not bones.

**Chapter 7: Diversity in Living Organisms**

A. 1 i. Living organisms are classified based on the basis of the habitat as terrestrial, aquatic and arboreal and hence habitat plays a major role in classifying living organisms.

ii. The structure of the cell decides the function of the cells which is the main characteristic to classify them into groups.

iii. The region between Tropic of Cancer and Tropic of Capricorn has dense pollution of various diverse living organisms. The pleasant climate allows the diversity of living organisms to flourish in this region. Most of the world's diverse organisms are concentrated in this region and hence the region is called mega diversity.

iv. Fittest organisms survive and reproduce better by acclimatizing to the changes in their surroundings, hence they evolve. The origin of life is possible by adaptation and survival.

v. Bryophytes are called amphibians of the plant because these plants live in soil but they require water for their reproduction.

2. i. Kingdom, Phylum or Division, Class, Order, Family, Genus and Species.

ii. The Kingdom Monera consists of bacteria such as *Cyanobacteria* and blue-green algae like *Nostoc*.

iii. The main characteristics of Kingdom Plantae are:

- They are multi-cellular eukaryotes with a cell wall.
- They are autotrophs which photosynthesize with the pigment chlorophyll.

iv. Organisms of Kingdom Animalia do not have cell wall like organisms which belong to Kingdom Plantae. Most of the organisms of Kingdom Plantae are autotrophs while all the organisms of Kingdom Animalia are heterotrophs.

v. Lichens are symbionts of Algae and fungi. They live on the bark of trees and also are the biological indicators of pollution.

B. 1. i. The pteridophyte shown in the image is Fern and its characteristics are:

- They have well-differentiated root, stem and leaves.
- They have special tissues to conduct water.
- They have naked embryos called spores.
- As their reproductive organs are inconspicuous, they are called cryptogamae.

ii. The angiosperms are classified into monocotyledons and dicotyledons based on the number of cotyledons.

- Monocots have single cotyledons.
- Plants with seeds having two cotyledons are called dicots or dicotyledons.
- Monocots have fibrous root system.
- Dicots have tap root system.

iii. The differences between angiosperms and gymnosperms are:

- Gymnosperms bear naked seeds.
- Angiosperms bear seeds inside fruits.
- Angiosperms are flowering plants like *Ipomoea* and *Paphiopedilum.*
- The flowers of gymnosperms are woody and evergreen. Example: Pine and deodar

iv. The body of the organism belonging to Kingdom Porifera consists of pores all over.

v. Liver fluke and tapeworm are called flatworms as their body is dorsiventrally flat with bilateral symmetry.

- They have no true body cavity.
- They are parasitic and live in the intestine of animals.

2. i. a. *Unio* belongs to Phylum Mollusca and starfish belongs to Echinodermata.

b. The similarity is that both have exoskeleton made up of calcium carbonate and the difference is that Mollusca use muscular foot for movement, whereas Echinoderms use water-driven tube system for their movement.

c. Manoj learned that though *Unio* and starfish belong to the same habitat, there are similarities and differences in them. It is easy to identify the kingdom, family and group of organisms based on the characteristics of the organisms and vice versa.

ii. a. Only species of the same kind interbreed.

b. Only a male and a female animal can breed but not of the same gender. So, the next generation would be produced.

c. Reproduction ensures that the generations continue to balance ecology in nature.

**Chapter 8: Motion**

A. 1. i. Recall the difference between distance and displacement.

ii. If an object reaches the original position from where it started, the displacement would be zero.

iii. Uniform circular motion is accelerated because the velocity changes due to continuous change in the direction of motion.

iv. If a body starts its motion from a point and comes back to the same point after some time, the displacement is zero. So, the average velocity is also zero.

v. Magnitude of displacement is the shortest distance. Speed of a body is the distance travelled by it per unit time. On the other hand, velocity of a body is the displacement covered by it per unit time in a given direction.

2. i. The object is at rest.

ii. Recall what speed and velocity are.

iii. 28 km/h

iv. 250 m

v. Acceleration = 4 m/s²; Distance = 32 m

B. 1. i. Area under a velocity-time graph gives the displacement.

a. The magnitude of displacement = ½ × 10 × 8 = 40 m

b. The path represents that the deceleration is CD.

c. The path that represents constant speed is AB

ii. Recall the steps to derive the equation.

iii. **Case I:** $u = 0$ m/s and $v = 10$ m/s; $a = (v - u)/t = (10 - 0)/20 = 0.5$ m/s²

**Case II:** $u = 10$ m/s and $v = 5$ m/s; $a = (v - u)/t = (5 - 10)/5 = -1$ m/s²

iv. Recall what uniform and non-uniform acceleration are.

v. 125 m

2. i. Displacement of both the taxis is same. Driver X is honest and sincere, he values time and he is concerned about others.

ii. Irfaan is a responsible citizen as he did not violate the traffic rules.

## Chapter 9: Force and Laws of Motion

A. 1. i. To overcome the force of friction offered by the road

ii. When a moving bus suddenly stops, the luggage on its roof still tends to continue in the state of motion due to inertia of motion.

iii. To every action there is an equal and opposite reaction.

iv. Pressing the ground with feet in backward direction exerts and equal and opposite force in forward direction that helps the athlete to sprint.

v. When a bullet strikes a windowpane, only the part of the windowpane which is struck by the bullet comes in motion while the rest of windowpane won't get enough time to move with bullet and remains at rest due to very high velocity of the bullet. While in the case of stone, the momentum and hence the velocity is less and the whole glass window comes in motion, thus smashing it.

2. i. $a_1 = F/m$; $a_2 = (F/2)/2m = F/4m = ¼\ (F/m) = (¼)\ a_1$

This implies that the acceleration will be reduced to one-fourth.

ii. Mass = 5 kg; Weight = 12 N

iii. 100 kg m/s

iv. The sum of momenta of the two objects before collision is equal to the sum of momenta after the collision provided there is no external unbalanced force acting on them.

v. 2.32 m/s

B. 1. i. When a bus stops suddenly, we fall in the forward direction.

ii. Mass is the total matter contained in a body while weight is the force exerted on a body by the Earth.

iii. **Case I:**

$v^2 = u^2 + 2as \rightarrow u^2 = 2 \times (-10\text{ m/s}^2) \times 20\text{ m} = 400$ m/s $\rightarrow u = 20$ m/s

**Case II:**

$v = u + at \rightarrow 0 = 20\text{ m/s} + (-10\text{ m/s}^2) \times t \rightarrow t = 2$ s

The object takes 2 s to go up and 2 s to come down. Hence, the total time of flight is 4 s.

iv. Recall the steps to derive Newton's second law of motion.

v. From the graph, it is clear that, $u = 60$ m/s, $v = 0$ m/s and $t = 6$ s

$a = v - u/t = (0 - 60)/6 = -10$ m/s²

Force of friction, $F = ma = 0.1\text{ kg} \times (-10\text{ m/s}^2) = -1$ N

2. i. Ajay helped his teammate to overcome a difficulty. Ajay showed a high degree of awareness and team spirit.

ii. B told A to run in the direction of the moving bus as soon as his feet touches the road as the feet of A comes to rest as soon as it touches the ground but the upper part of the body remains in motion due to inertia of motion. Hence, A will fall down.

B is concerned about A. B has the social awareness that getting down from a moving bus is a serious act.

## Chapter 10: Gravitation

A. 1. i. Freely falling objects will have same acceleration due to gravity.

ii. The gravitational attraction on the moon is about one-sixth of the Earth's gravitational attraction.

iii. Buoyant forces acting in the upward direction reduces the weight of an object immersed in a liquid.

iv. Feather experiences more buoyant force due to air drag and thus stone reaches the ground before feather.

v. Acceleration acting on freely falling objects is independent of their mass.

2. i. When the density of the object is higher than the density of liquid, then it would sink. When the density of the object is less than the density of liquid, then it would float.

ii. Buoyancy is the upward force offered by a liquid on an object immersed in it.

iii. 5 m/s²

iv.

| Thrust | Pressure |
|---|---|
| The force exerted by the body perpendicular to the surface is known as thrust. | Thrust acting on unit area is called pressure, i.e. Pressure = Force/ Area |
| SI unit of thrust is newton (N). | SI unit of pressure is Pa (pascal). |

v. It is a force acting on a body moving in a circular path towards the centre and makes the body follow the circular or curved path. Example: The force of gravity acting on a satellite in an orbit.

B. 1. i. Recall what universal law of gravitation is and what its importance is.

ii. $g = GM/R^2 \Rightarrow g$ is more at poles because of lesser radius

iii. 2.5 m

iv. The two objects A and B will meet after 10 seconds.

v. Recall Archimedes' principle and its applications.

2. i. a. The average density of the inflated rubber tube is less than the density of water, so it floats on the water.

b. A and B are helping and have the caring attitude towards the nature. They have the presence of mind that helps them to save the man.

ii. Lactometer works on the basis of Archimedes principle. The move shows the honesty and sincerity of the milkman.

**Chapter 11: Work and Energy**

A. 1. i. In the absence of any force on the object, i.e. $F = 0$, ma = 0 (as $F = ma$). In such a case, the object is either at rest or in a state of uniform motion in a straight line. In the latter case, there is a displacement of the object without any force acting on it.

ii. Body falling freely towards the Earth possess the same kinetic and potential energy and it follows the Law of conservation of energy; hence its total energy remains constant.

iii. Potential energy, $E_p = mgh$

Potential energy is independent of velocity. For a levelled track, height remains constant and hence potential energy of the car does not change.

iv. A stone placed on a table has potential energy but it is not performing any work

v. Momentum, $p = mv$; If $p = 0 \Rightarrow v = 0$ as $m \neq 0$

Mechanical energy = K.E. + P.E. = $\frac{1}{2} mv^2 + mgh$

$= 0 + mgh$ (using $v = 0$)

Thus, mechanical energy = $mgh \neq 0$

2. i. Kinetic energy becomes four times.

ii. $P$ = Work done/time taken = 25000/10 = 2500 W

iii. Kinetic energy is the energy possessed by a body by virtue of its motion. Example: A moving car possesses kinetic energy.

Potential energy is the energy possessed by a body by virtue of its position. Example: Water stored in an overhead tank.

iv. In case of vertically projected body, it has acceleration but after some time, it will come back again to the initial position.

We know that displacement = final position-initial position: in this case, displacement is zero. So, work done is zero in case of vertically projected body on the Earth.

v. The law of conservation of energy states that, energy can only be converted from one form to another; it can neither be created nor destroyed. The total energy before and after the transformation remains the same.

B. 1. i. 1200 kg

ii. If the force is in the same direction as the displacement of the object, the force is doing positive work. If the force is in the direction opposite to the displacement, the force does negative work.

a. In this case, displacement is in the opposite direction of force; hence the work done is negative.

b. In this case, displacement is perpendicular to the direction of force; hence the work done is zero.

c. In this case, displacement is in the direction of force; hence the work done is positive.

iii. Lighter body will have more kinetic energy.

iv. 7 m

v. The man can jump on the planet up to a height of 2 m.

2. i. a. Negative

b. Abdul has concern for others and he has helping nature.

ii. a. When hands are rubbed against each other, mechanical energy is converted into heat energy, and the hands become warm.

b. Smitha has a very good presence of mind and social awareness. She is helpful and feels concerned for others.

**Chapter 12: Sound**

A. 1. i. Humming bees produce the sound of higher frequency while a pendulum produces lower frequency sounds and we can hear only audible frequency range of sound i.e., between 20 Hz to 20 kHz.

ii. The speed of light ($3 \times 10^8$ m/s) in air is more than the speed of sound (340 m/s) in air. Hence the light reaches us first.

iii. The sound after multiple reflections reaches to all parts of the hall uniformly.

iv. In a sound wave, the particles of the medium vibrate in the direction parallel to the direction of propagation of the disturbance.

v. Sound is a mechanical wave and hence needs a material medium for its propagation such as solid, liquid or gas to travel.

2. i. High-pitch sounds are those sounds which have higher frequency. Low-pitch sounds are those sounds which have lesser frequency.

ii. Recall what an echo is and what its importance is.

iii. Loudness is a measure of response of our ear to sound. The unit of loudness is decibel. It depends on amplitude. If the amplitude is high, the loudness also will be high. Sound intensity is the sound power per unit area. The sound intensity is directly proportional to the square of the amplitude of sound wave.

iv. 0.068 m

v. 340 m

B. 1. i. 0.8 m/ s

ii. If any explosion takes place at the bottom of a lake or river, longitudinal waves are formed in the water. Longitudinal waves are the waves in which the displacement of the particles in the medium is parallel to the direction of propagation of the wave. Mechanical longitudinal waves are also called compression waves because they produce compression and rarefaction when travelling through a medium.

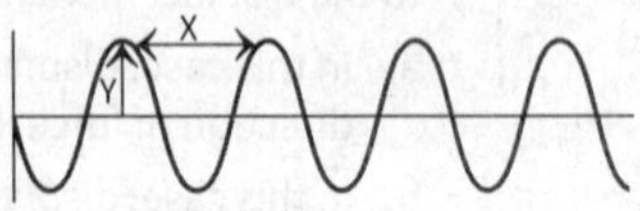


iii. x—Wavelength

y—Amplitude

Frequency = Number of oscillation/ Time

= 180/(3 × 60) = 1 Hz

Time period = 1/1 Hz = 1 s

iv. Recall the applications of sound.

v. 3.4 km

2. i. a. SONAR which works on the principle of reflection of sound waves.

b. Lisa is inquisitive and takes interest in understanding scientific phenomena. He had shown the willingness to share the knowledge.

ii. a. Echocardiography is a test that uses sound waves to produce live images of our heart. The image is an echocardiogram. This test allows your doctor to monitor how your heart and its valves are functioning.

b. Chitra has high degree of general awareness, she is helpful and she has concern for her uncle.

**Chapter 13: Why Do We Fall Ill?**

A. 1. i. A person can be in poor health without any identifiable disease because health is a mental, physical as well as social aspect whereas when we talk about a disease, we only consider the physical aspect. A person is said to be in poor health if he is in poor state of mental or physical or social health.

ii. Acute diseases have short-term effect while chronic diseases have long-term effect on our health.

iii. Recall what communicable and non-communicable diseases are.

iv. Recall the importance of regular exercise.

v. Penicillin antibiotic blocks the biochemical and metabolic pathway of bacteria preventing it from further developing in a host.

2. i. The bacteria *Helicobacter pylori* causes peptic ulcer.

ii. The organisms such as bacteria, virus, fungi and protozoa that can cause a disease are called infectious agents.

iii. The immune system of a healthy person is triggered by harmless infectious agent by administering an inactive/ dead or weakened microbe in the body in the form of a vaccine. The immune response will be stored in the memory of the person's immune system. When the same infectious agent comes in contact with the immunized person, his immune system attacks them and prevents the disease.

iv. Recall the importance of hygiene.

v. Proper, sufficient food and a well-balanced diet keep us healthy. The right amount of nutrients in our food is essential for the proper functioning of all parts of the body like growth, repair and immunity against diseases.

B. 1. i. The boy is suffering from "chicken pox". The symptoms are pimple like structures or rashes all over the body and fever. The prevention of this disease is through vaccination.

ii. The prevention of any disease is better than cure for the following reasons:

- Diseases and their cure may consume time, money and effort.
- It is always better to prevent any disease than curing and avoid distress to body and mind.
- Once a disease is contracted, it may leave some post effects too.

iii. Jaundice is caused by hepatitis virus.

- The disease is spread through contaminated water.
- Hepatitis A vaccine prevents the disease.
- Consuming clean filtered and boiled water prevents waterborne diseases.

iv. The mosquitoes are vectors and are the transmitters of many diseases.

- Female mosquitoes feed on the blood of animals.
- Some mosquitoes carry parasites in them which transmit diseases like malaria, dengue, yellow fever and chikungunya.
- Mosquito transmits parasitic infection from an infected person to a healthy person.

v. AIDS is caused by the infection of HIV.

- There are many means of getting infected with the virus by direct physical contact;
- Through blood transfusions and
- Could spread from an infected mother to her baby.

2. i. a. Tanu washed her hands frequently and sanitized her body regularly. She kept to herself and maintained distance from others and covered her mouth while coughing, sneezing until she was completely cured. She also must have seen a doctor and followed his instructions without fail.

b. Social distancing prevents the spread of droplet nuclei and further infections from an infected to a non-infected person.

c. Tanu must be appreciated for her rightful thought of social distancing and taking aid of a doctor and following the instructions faithfully.

ii. a. Pranathi took her new pet to a veterinary doctor so that it could be vaccinated against rabies and other diseases the dog might get infected with.

b. The animal could get infected with rabies and also spread it to healthy human beings .

c. Rodents like bat, rat and bandicoots spread rabies infection.

**Chapter 14: Natural resources**

A. 1. i. The air above the land gets heated up faster and so starts rising.

ii. Burning of fossil fuels such as coal and petroleum release nitrogen and oxygen to the atmosphere.

iii. All cellular processes occur in water medium.

iv. The reduction in the amount of dissolved oxygen in water deteriorates the quality of water.

v. Living organisms like lichens and mosses help in breaking down of rocks leading to the formation of soil.

2. i. The availability of water decides the number and the variety of species that can survive in a particular area.

ii. Water gets into cracks of rocks and gets frozen and expands and then breaks the rocks to form the soil. Fast-flowing water makes the big rocks rub against each other and form small particles to form soil.

iii. The usage of pesticides and insecticides over a longer period of time destroy the soil structure by killing the microorganisms in the soil; reducing the porosity and changing the pH of the soil.

iv. An increase in the percentage of greenhouse gases leads to average increase in temperature worldwide.

v. Oxygen maintains its level in the atmosphere through oxygen cycle which involves respiration and photosynthesis.

B. 1. i. Following are the conditions that affect the life in water bodies due to water pollution:

- The addition of undesirable substances to the water bodies like fertilizers, pesticides or poisonous substances;
- Removal of desirable substances that decrease the quality of water and reduces the lifespan of aquatic organisms;
- A change in temperature adversely effects breeding of aquatic species.

ii. Recall how interconversion of nitrogen and its compounds occurs in the environment and living beings.

iii. Recall how carbon compounds are incorporated in the living beings through processes such as photosynthesis and its return to the environment through respiration, oxidation of fossil fuels and decay of dead organisms.

iv. Recall how factors like the sun, water and living things lead to the formation of soil.

v. Given image depicts water cycle. Observe the image carefully to write the various steps involved in the cycle.

2. i. a. The causes of pollution of the river could be fertilizers or pesticides dissolved in it, reduction of the amount of dissolved oxygen in the river water due to the growth of weeds and increase in temperature due to exposure to sunlight.

b. It will be hard for the aquatic animals to survive due to reduced amount of oxygen in the river water. Further, the increase in temperature hinders the breeding of aquatic animals.

c. Diljit values the importance of rivers as a natural resource. Further, he thinks it is the responsibility of each citizen to protect the natural resources especially in his surroundings.

ii. a. Use of large amount of fertilizers and pesticides in the soil, flowing water and wind that takes away the top soil and fertility and continuous use of soil for crop cultivation also reduces the fertility of the soil.

b. Soil is a valuable resource that needs to be protected from pollution. Fertile soil aids in the cultivation and also in providing more yield of crops.

c. Anuradha values the importance of agriculture as a livelihood. Moreover, she values land as a natural resource that can aid for the sustainable development through its effective management.

**Chapter 15: Improvement in Food Resources**

A. 1. i. Since weather conditions such as drought and flood situations are unpredictable, varieties that can be grown in diverse climatic conditions are useful.

ii. Depending upon the duration, availability of moisture and irrigation facilities, farmers make the choice of the crop. If crop rotation is done properly then two or three crops can be grown in a year with good harvest.

iii. To destroy weeds and pests present in the soil, the fields are ploughed deep.

iv. To stay dry and facilitate cleaning, the floor of the cattle shed needs to be sloppy.

v. Excess fertilizers get washed away due to excessive irrigation, polluting the water bodies.

2. i. Crop variety improvement; Crop production improvement; Crop production management

ii. Different climatic conditions; Temperature; Photoperiods; Water and nutrition

iii. Crossing between genetically dissimilar crops

iv. Compost and vermicompost; Green manure

v. It is a farming system with minimal or no use of chemicals as fertilizers, herbicides, pesticides, etc.

B. 1. i. Different cropping patterns are:

- Mixed cropping: Growing two or more crops on the same piece of land; Examples: wheat + gram or wheat + mustard
- Inter-cropping: Growing two or more crops simultaneously on the same piece of land in some pattern; Examples: soya bean + maize or finger millet + cow pea

ii. Recall how fish is captured in both types of fisheries.

iii. The wide use and demand for honey opens the scope of beekeeping as an agricultural enterprise for the following causes:

- In addition to honey, beehives provide wax which can be used for various medicinal preparations.
- The availability of varieties of local honeybees for the production of honey.
- The scope of commercial production of honey.

iv. Poultry farming has undertaken various steps to raise the overall production:

- Improved poultry breeds are developed.
- Crossbreeding programs between Indian and foreign breeds for variety improvement are focused.
- Broiler chickens are fed with vitamin-rich supplementary feed for better growth and feed efficiency.
- Maintenance of temperature and hygienic condition in housing and appropriate vaccination for control and prevention of diseases and pests.

v. These animals belong to the category of ' dairy animals'. The food requirements of dairy animals fall under two categories: maintenance requirement and milk production requirement. Maintenance requirement stands for food that support the animals to lead a healthy life whereas milk production requirement means food required during lactation period. Animal feed include roughage which contains largely fibre and concentrates which have high proteins and other nutrients. Cattle need all nutrients in balanced proportions.

2. i. a. Scientific management practices like mixed farming and integrated farming should be undertaken to increase the yield from farming. He can opt for growing crops which are more feasible to be grown as per the climate of his region.

b. Bijoy needs to adopt a crop production management strategy based on the land, available money and access to information and technologies. He needs to choose from production practices that include no-cost, low cost and high cost.

c. Bijoy values the importance of agriculture to solve the problems of hunger and obtain a sustained livelihood. Further, he is ready to learn from his past experiences and ready to adapt to new farming practices.

ii. a. Healthy cropping system which is beneficial for insect and pest control; An eco-friendly culture using minimal or no fertilizers.

b. Replenishing of organic matter in the soil by the action of microorganisms; Organic manure, recycled farm wastes and bio fertilizers together with bio-agents make soil nutrient-rich for the crops in organic farming.

c. Rani values the importance of agriculture as a livelihood. By selecting organic farming, Rani promotes eco-friendly model of farming. Moreover, she believes in natural ways of replenishing the soil for cultivation.

## PISA-based Questions Answer Key

### Chapter 1: Matter in Our Surroundings

1. A; Water is used to dilute Dettol and used as a surface cleaner. It is used to disinfect metal, ceramic, glass as well as surface of the skin.
2. C; Dettol has a distinctive strong odour which can be detected even after many dilutions. If the smell is not detectable, such dilution does not act as a disinfectant.
3. A; Particles of matter have space between them and the solute such as Dettol gets evenly distributed between the particles of water molecules or universal solvent.

### Chapter 2: Is Matter Around Us Pure?

1. A; The main principle involved in column chromatography is the adsorption of the solutes of a solution through a stationary phase and separating the mixture into individual components.
2. B; Simple paper chromatography can be used to separate multiple different samples, before which the samples have to be examined to check and group them to run in different affinity medium for separation. The type of paper that can be used to separate also varies with the sample to be used.
3. A; Difference in polarity was the criterion used for the separation of plant pigments in the Mikhail's method of chromatography.

### Chapter 3: Atoms and Molecules

1. A; Chemistry and atomic physics
2. A; 18.02 g $H_2O$ contain $6.023 \times 10^{23}$ molecules => 1 mg $H_2O$ contain $(6.023 \times 10^{23})/(1000 \times 18.02)$ i.e., $3.35 \times 10^{19}$ molecules

### Chapter 4: Structure of the Atom

1. B; Isotopes of an element differ in their neutron number. Neutron numbers of carbon isotopes are 6, 7 and 8 respectively.
2. D; Electrons are negatively charged. They do not contribute to the mass of the atom as they revolve around the nucleus in electronic shells and orbits.
3. B; Only certain special orbits known as discrete electron orbits are allowed inside the atom. While revolving in discrete orbits, the electrons do not radiate energy. These are Bohr's postulates.

### Chapter 5: The Fundamental Unit of Life

1. C; All the cells of a plant have a cell wall.
2. A; Plastids are present in plant cells but are absent in animal cells. Chlorophyll containing plastids are called chloroplasts.
3. B; Numerous membranous layers are embedded in a material called stroma inside a plastid.

### Chapter 6: Tissues

1. A; Holding a heavy weight at the same position for a long time shows isometric contraction of the muscles.
2. D; Endurance activities include aerobic exercises. This increases the breathing and heart rates of an individual.
3. A; Contractility is a muscle's capacity to actively shorten when appropriately stimulated.

### Chapter 7: Diversity in Living Organisms

1. A; Life evolves when the fittest of the species accumulates necessary changes in its body and adapts to survive in an environment.

2. B; Charles Darwin's book titled 'The origin of species' is based on the evolution of life.
3. C; The adapted feature is passed from one generation to the next generation through evolution.
4. A; Alga, which is an aquatic living organism, has a primitive body design.

**Chapter 8: Motion**

1. B; Let the speed of the bus be $x$ km/h

   Distance covered by the bus in 10 hours = Distance covered by the car in 4 hours; $10x = 4 \times 60 \Rightarrow x = 24$ km/h
2. B; For the first 25 km, $25 = 50 \times t_1 \Rightarrow t_1 = ½$ h = 30 minutes

   For the next 25 km, $25 = 25 \times t_2 \Rightarrow t_2 = 1$ h = 60 minutes

   $t_1 + t_2 = 90$ minutes (1 hour 30 minutes)
3. B; Comparing the given expression with the equation with $v = u + at$. The negative sign indicates retardation.

**Chapter 9: Force and Laws of Motion**

1. B; (Acceleration of X, $a_1$)/ (Acceleration of Y, $a_2$) = 10/ 1
   Applied forces on X and Y are equal,
   therefore, $F = m_1 a_1 = m_2 a_2 \Rightarrow a_1/a_2 = m_2/m_1 = 10/1$
2. C; Law of conservation of momentum

   Momentum before collision = momentum after collision.
   Here, $m_1 \times u = (m_1 + m_2)v$
3. C; Q has highest momentum, P lesser and R least.

**Chapter 10: Gravitation**

1. D; Acceleration due to gravity on the surface of the moon is 1/6th of that of the Earth.
2. B; Buoyant force, $F_B = mg = \rho g V_{displaced} \Rightarrow V_{displaced} = m/\rho$
   $= 0.25$ kg/(1000 kg m$^{-3}$) = 0.00025 m$^3$. Since, 1 m$^3$ = 1000 ℓ
   $\Rightarrow V_{displaced} = 0.250$ ℓ
3. C; If the same objects are dropped on moon surface from a height in vacuum they reach at same time. Atmosphere offers resistive force to the motion of objects falling down and moon does not have atmosphere.

**Chapter 11: Work and Energy**

1. B.; When kinetic energy becomes half of its original value, the other half is converted into potential energy.

   $250 \text{ J} = 10 \times 10 \times h \Rightarrow h = 2.5$ m
2. D; When velocity increases 4 times, the increase in kinetic energy is 16 times.
3. A; Power, $Pt = ½ mv^2$ = constant: So, $v^2$ is proportional to $t$

   $\Rightarrow v$ is proportional to $t^{1/2}$

**Chapter 12: Sound**

1. C; The time taken between the clap and the first echo from wall X, $t_1 = (2 \times 30)/330 = 6/33$; $t_2 = (2 \times 70)/ 330 = 14/33 \Rightarrow t_2 - t_1 = 8/33$
2. C; The time period of a periodic wave i.e., the time difference between two consecutive crests/trough is 0.6 s. The time difference between a trough and the next crest will be half the time period, i.e. 0.3 s.
3. C; Total distance travelled by the sonar beam = 15 × 2 = 30 km
   Speed of the wave = 30000 m/1500 m/s = 20 s

**Chapter 13: Why Do We Fall Ill?**

1. A; For the general health of a body, all metabolic and non-metabolic functions of the body are required.
2. B; The duration of an acute disease is minimal when compared to chronic, mental and community issues and hence does not affect the general health of a body.
3. A; Tuberculosis of the lungs is one of the chronic diseases. It affects the health of a body for a long duration.
4. A; Tuberculosis spreads through air and through droplets from sneeze, cough and spits of an infected person.

**Chapter 14: Natural Resources**

1. B; The sun emits infrared radiation that can pass the transparent glass and it increases the temperature inside the car. Due to smaller wavelength of the infrared radiations, the glass of the car remains opaque, further increasing the temperature.
2. A; Carbon dioxide is a greenhouse gas that is responsible for global warming.
3. C; The instruments used for weather forecast are thermometer for measuring atmospheric temperature, barometer for measuring atmospheric pressure, rain gauge for measuring the amount of rainfall and anemometer for measuring wind speed.

**Chapter 15: Improvement in Food Resources**

1. B; The poultry feed suitable for broilers are those rich in vitamin A and K.
2. A; The method of crossbreeding between Indian and foreign breeds is used to get the breeds that are small in size and have summer adaptability.
3. C; Rohit's friend has observed the feeds that are rich in proteins and vitamins. He also observed the posture of animals to comment on their health status.

# Hints for Difficult Questions

## Chapter 1: Matter in Our Surroundings

### Assessment 1

6. The fluorescent tubes and neon sign bulbs have ionised gases which are in the state of plasma.
9. Smell from the hot food diffuses to the air around it when kept open.
15. Ice is less dense than its liquid form (water) and hence water displaces ice and lets it float on it.
16. Particles of a gas move randomly. They hit the wall of their container by the force exerted by the gas per unit area.
24. The water vapour moves faster from the surroundings with the increased speed of wind. Thus, clothes dry faster during windy days.

### Assessment 2

27. The neon signboards have ionised gases which are in the state of plasma. Plasma is the fourth state of matter.
33. The more surface area exposed, the higher will be the rate of evaporation. Hence the spread wet cloth will dry faster.
34. The water vapour in the atmosphere condenses when it comes in contact with the cold surface of the juice bottle and forms water droplets.
35. The cooling of water in the earthen pot is due to evaporation and regaining of energy by the particles of water remaining in the pot.
37. Hot tea when served in a saucer has more surface area exposed for evaporation and hence it is easier to sip in it.

## Chapter 2: Is Matter Around Us Pure

### Assessment 1

21. Mixtures do not give out energy while being prepared.
22. Alcohol can be separated from a mixture of alcohol and water by distillation. Salt can be recovered from an aqueous salt solution by evaporation.
23. A is Sulphur, B is Copper sulphate, C is Carbon disulphide and D is water.
24. Substance C sublimates in room temperature and is separated. Dissolution of substance A and B separates substance B by filtration. Substance A can be recovered from filtrate by crystallization.
25. Sublimation→Separation of iodine and sand; Distillation→Separation of benzene and aniline; Separating funnel→Separation of water and carbon tetrachloride; Magnetic separation→Separation of iron and sand

### Assessment 2

46. Element can be a metal, non-metal or a metalloid.
47. A suspension has its insoluble solid particles suspended in a liquid and is visible to the naked eyes but in colloidal solution, the particle size is small and cannot be seen with naked eyes.; The suspended particles and colloidal particles (though small in size) can scatter a beam of light passing through them and make the path of the light visible.
48. 'Y' is the iodine crystals that can sublimate on slight heating.
49. Process A is burning of candle (chemical change), process B is melting of candle wax (physical change).
50. Different techniques are used to separate elements from different mixtures. Filtration is one of the techniques.

## Chapter 3: Atoms and Molecules

### Assessment 1

21. Mole weight of an isotope is different from that of its element as the isotope is charged.
22. Sodium oxide—$Na_2O$; Aluminium chloride—$AlCl_3$; Sodium sulphide—$Na_2S$; Magnesium hydroxide—$Mg(OH)_2$
23. In 1961, for a universally accepted atomic mass unit, carbon-12 isotope was chosen as the standard reference for measuring the atomic masses.
24. Law of definite proportion was stated by Proust as "In a chemical substance, the elements are always present in definite proportions by mass".
25. Two elements combine with each other to form more than one compound. The weights of one element that combine with a fixed weight of the other are in a ratio of small whole numbers.

### Assessment 2

46. Some of the elements in the periodic table are derived from the Latin names.
47. Valence of X in $XCl_3$ is +3 and valence of $PO_4$ is –3. Therefore, it will be $XPO_4$.
48. The molecular weights of $H_2O$, $H_2S$, $CO_2$ and $SO_2$ are 18, 34, 44 and 64 respectively.
49. $Al_2(SO_4)_3$—Aluminium sulphate; $K_2SO_4$—Potassium sulphate; $NaHCO_3$—Sodium bicarbonate; $Cu(NO_3)_2$—Copper nitrate
50. Atomic theory was proposed by John Dalton. Maharishi Kanad postulated that if we go on dividing matter (*padarth*), we shall get a smallest particle called *paramanu* that cannot be further divided.

## Chapter 4: Structure of the Atom

### Assessment 1

12. There will be a total of 17 electrons in chlorine with 7 electrons in its M-shell and valency 1.
13. There will be a total of 14 electrons in silicon with 4 electrons in its M-shell and valency 4.
14. The mass numbers of Protium, deuterium and hydrogen are all equal to 1 as they are isotopes of hydrogen.
15. The mass number of tritium, an isotope of hydrogen, is 3 and hence has atomic number 1 and neutron number.
22. The number of electrons of an atom is the same as the atomic number (Z).

### Assessment 2

38. The atomic number of hydrogen is one (1) and contains only one electron which is occupied in its K-shell, whereas helium, fluorine and chlorine elements contain two electrons in their K-shell.
39. Based on Bohr-Bury theory, the maximum number of electrons present in a particular energy shell of an atom is represented by the formula $2n^2$, where 'n' is the orbit number or energy level index 1, 2, 3, or K, L, M ----. As per this, the element with atomic number 17 contains 7 (seven) electrons in its M-shell or third orbit.
40. Recall the electron arrangement of the elements. As per the Bohr-Bury theory, the maximum number of electrons that can be accommodated in a given shell adhere to the formula $2n^2$.
41. The maximum number of electrons that can be accommodated in a given shell adhere to the formula $2n^2$ based on Bohr-Bury theory. Unless the inner shells are filled, the electrons cannot be accommodated in a new shell. Thus, the below order is followed: $K < L < M < N$.
43. The atomic number of chlorine is 17 and its electronic distribution is: K=2, L=8, M=7.; The atomic number of nitrogen is 7 & its electronic distribution is: K= 2, L=5.

## Chapter 5: The Fundamental Unit of Life

### Assessment 1

12. The cell theory of Schleiden and Schwann states that all the living things are made up of cells and cell is the basic unit of life.
14. The cells are collected, mounted on the glass slide containing a few drops of water, stained and then observed under the microscope.
16. The cytoplasm stains less as it is less dense than the organelles.
17. Viruses lack cell membrane and cell wall and hence do not exhibit the characteristics of life until they enter the host.
18. *Hydrilla* is an aquatic plant and is a eukaryote and hence has more than one chromosome when compared to the prokaryotes; *Paramoecium, Chlamydomonas* and bacteria.

### Assessment 2

27. Nucleus protects the DNA from chemical reactions of the cytoplasm, selectively allows certain substances in and out of the nucleus and controls the biochemical reactions of the cell.
42. Mitochondria are also called as powerhouses of the cell as the energy required by the cell is generated and released by it in the form of ATP.
43. Plastids are classified as three types based on their contents as: (i) leucoplasts that store starch or lipids and hence are colourless, (ii) chromoplast which store yellow or orange coloured pigments (iii) chloroplast that stores the green coloured chlorophyll.
44. Mitochondria have their own DNA called as mDNA and aids in the synthesis of their proteins for internal processes.
45. Golgi apparatus synthesizes lysosomes. Endoplasmic reticulum provides the skeletal support with their network of passageway and lysosomes contain hydrolytic enzymes that degrade foreign substances and food materials.

## Chapter 6: Tissues

### Assessment 1

21. Cardiac muscles are involuntary and have branched network. They have their nucleus centrally located and have intercalated discs at the intervals in the fibres.
22. Sieve tube: Conduction of food; Companion cells: Conduction of food through sieve tube; Phloem parenchyma: Storage; Phloem fibres: Mechanical support.
23. Ligaments connect bone to bone in a skeletal system. Dislocation of bone would be due to the breakage of ligament between the bones.
24. Lateral meristem is responsible for increase in the girth of the plant.
25. The Inner lining of the mouth is made of many layers to prevent wear and tear. Since they are arranged in a pattern of layers, the epithelium is called stratified squamous epithelium.

### Assessment 2

46. Under a compound microscope, striated muscles or voluntary muscles show light and dark bands and involuntary muscles do not show light and dark bands.
47. Meristematic tissue: Undifferentiated actively dividing cells; Permanent tissue: Differentiated cells without the ability to divide; Xylem: Conducts water from roots to all parts of the plant; Phloem: Conducts food from leaves to all parts of the plant
48. Collenchyma cells of this tissue are living, elongated and irregularly thickened at the corners. The cells have very little intercellular space.
49. Any plant grows from the tips of the shoot and the hammered nail in between the plant will not show any change in its height with respect to the growth in plant.
50. Areolar tissue is present in the hump of a camel and blubbers in whale. In camel, it helps in regulating the body temperature with its climate. Blubbers in whale act as insulators and help maintain the energy and warmth in cold water.

**Chapter 7: Diversity in Living Organisms**

**Assessment 1**

21. Arthropoda have jointed legs. Prawn or *Palaemon* is an arthropod.
22. The annelids are bilaterally symmetrical, triploblastic, have segmented body and possess a body cavity.
23. Plants that belong to the division Bryophyta live in the soil but need water for reproduction. Therefore, these are called amphibians of plant kingdom.
24. The body cavity of Annelida helps to pack the body organs into a structure and thus there is extensive organ differentiation.
25. Angiosperms are divided into two groups as monocots bearing one seed leaf and dicots bearing two seed leaves. They have differentiated plant body with vascular tissues.

**Assessment 2**

46. The organisms that belong to kingdom Animalia are multicellular eukaryotes and do not have a cell wall.
47. Nematodes have bilaterally symmetrical body, pseudocoelom, triploblastic and cylindrical body.
48. Porifera has pores throughout their body to take oxygen and food dissolved in water.
49. The body of Platyhelminthes does not have a coelom, but have a flattened body dorsiventrally.
50. Amphibians have a mucus gland in their skin, three-chambered heart and live both on land and in water.

**Chapter 8: Motion**

**Assessment 1**

1. $a = (v - u)/t = (20 - 0) / 60 = 1/3 \text{ m/s}^2$

   $s = (v^2 - u^2) / 2a = (20^2 - 0^2)/ (2 \times 1/3) = 600 \text{ m}$
4. PR is the required displacement.

   $(PR)^2 = (PQ)^2 + (QR)^2 = 25$, Therefore, PR = 5 km
6. Distance travelled by a freely-falling body, $s \propto t^2$ $(s = ½ gt^2)$

   Here, $s_1/ s_2 = H_1/H_2 = t_1^2/t_2^2 \Rightarrow t_1/t_2 = (H_1/H_2)^{1/2}$
12. The average velocity of the object = Displacement/time = 0/ 100 s = 0
14. Average velocity = $(u + v)/2 = (30 + 70)/2 = 50$ km/h

**Assessment 2**

26. Average speed $v_{av} = s/t = (1800 \text{ km})/30 \text{ h} = 60 \text{ km/ h}$
27. Average speed = 2 m/s = Total distance travelled/ total time taken; 2 m/s= (30 + 40) m/ $(10 + t_2)$ s; $t_2 = (70 - 20)$ s/ 2 = 25 s
28. Required distance travelled = Area under the horizontal line in the graph = 15 × 2 = 30 m
30. Compare the given equation with $v = u + at$, we get $u = 6$ m/s;

    $a = -0.02 \text{m/s}^{-2}$ The '–' sign indicates negative acceleration.
31. Radius (r) = 1 cm: Distance covered in half revolution = $2\pi r/2 = \pi r = \pi$; Displacement in half revolution = $2r = 2$; Required ratio = π: 2

**Chapter 9: Force and Laws of Motion**

**Assessment 1**

10 While shaking the branches of a tree, due to inertia of rest, the leaves tend to remain its position hence detaches from the tree.

15. $F_1 = 5 \text{ kg} \times 2 \text{ m/s}^2 = 10 \text{ N}$; $F_2 = 3 \text{ kg} \times 5 \text{ m/s}^2 = 15 \text{ N}$;

    $F_3 = 2 \text{ kg} \times 4 \text{ m/s}^2 = 8 \text{ N}$
16. The box exerts a force of 50 N on the head of John and this is action. The head of John exerts a force of 50 N on the suitcase. This is the reaction.
17. $s = ut + (½)\, at^2$ ; 500 cm = 5 m = 0 + (½) × a × 1²; $a = 10 \text{ m/s}^2$;

    $F = ma = 0.1 \times 10 = 1$ N
18. Gain in momentum = $m\,(v - u)$;$v = u + at = 0 + 2.5 \times 4$ = 10 m/s

    Gain in momentum = $[m\,(v - u)] = [3 \times (10)] = 30$ kg m/s

**Assessment 2**

27. Only unbalanced force acting on an object can bring it to motion.
30. The upper part of our body continues to be in motion and hence we fall in the forward direction due to inertia of motion.
31. Inertia of motion and inertia of direction are responsible for the movement of the stone.
40. $F = 50 \text{ N} = [m\,(v - u)]/t = [20 \times (v - 0)]/10 = 2v$; $v = 50/2$ = 25 m/s
45. $F = 6000 \text{ N} = ma = \{m \times [54 \times (5/18)]/5\} = 2000$ kg

**Chapter 10: Gravitation**

**Assessment 1**

3. The Earth attracts objects towards it. This is due to the gravitational force.
6. Distance travelled, $s = ut + (½\,)at^2 = [0 + (½\,) + 10 \text{ m/s}^2 \times (2.5 \text{ s})^2] = 62.5$ m
7. $v^2 = u^2 + 2as$

   $0 = u^2 + 2 \times (-\,10 \text{ m/s}^2) \times 20 \text{ m} = u^2 + 400 \text{ (m/s)}^2$ : ($g$ is acting in the opposite direction of motion); hence, $u = 20$ m/s
16. $v^2 - (-u)^2 = 2as \Rightarrow (5u)^2 - u^2 = 2 \times g \times s \Rightarrow s = (12u^2)/g$
17. $F = mg$ = volume × density × $g$ = (5 m × 5 m × 8 m) × (10³ kg/m³) × (10 m/s²) = 20 × 10⁵ N

**Assessment 2**

29. $v^2 = u^2 + 2as \Rightarrow 0 = u^2 + 2 \times (-\,10 \text{ m/s}^2) \times 2 \text{ m} = u^2 + 400 \text{ (m/s)}^2$ : ($g$ is acting in the opposite direction of motion); hence, $u = 20$ m/s

    $v = u + at \Rightarrow 0 = 20 \text{ m/s} + (-10 \text{ m/s}^2) \times t \Rightarrow t = 2s$
37. When the gravitational force becomes zero, then the centripetal force on the satellite also becomes zero. Therefore, the satellite moves tangentially and escapes away from its orbit.
42. $F_{AB} = Gm_A\, m_B/(d_{AB})^2 = Gm_A\, m_B/d^2$; $F_{CD} = Gm_C\, m_D/(d_{CD})^2 = Gm_C m_D/d^2 = F_{AB}$, (Since; $m_A = m_B = m_C = m_D$)

43. The acceleration due to gravity is same for both the objects.

44. **Case 1:** $F_1 = Gm_x m_y/d^2$;
**Case 2:** $F_2 = G2m_x 2m_y/d^2$
$= 4 \times (Gm_x m_y/d^2) = 4F_1$

**Chapter 11: Work and Energy**

**Assessment 1**

7. $W = F \times s = (2 \times 9.8)$ N $\times$ 1 m = 19.6 J ($F = mg = 2$ kg $\times$ 9.8 m/s$^2$)

8. $W$ =3920 J = $F \times s$ = (200 kg $\times$ 9.8 m/s$^2$) $\times$ s => $s = W/F$ = 2 m

13. The kinetic energy of a body moving with a certain velocity is equal to the work done on it to make it acquire that velocity.

15. $E_k$ = 250 J = $(1/2)mv^2 = (1/2) \times m \times (36 \times 5/18)^2 \Rightarrow m = 5$ kg

16. $E_k$ = 50 J = $(1/2)mv^2 = (1/2) \times m \times 10^2 \Rightarrow m = 1$ kg: If its velocity is doubled, then $E_k = (1/2) \times 1 \times 20^2 = 200$ J

**Chapter 12: Sound**

**Assessment 1**

12. $v = \lambda v$ = 0.5 m × 800 Hz = 400 m/ s

The time taken by the wave to travel a distance of 400 m = 1 second

Therefore, the time taken by the wave to travel 2 km (2000 m) = 5 seconds

13. v = 1/ $T \rightarrow T$ = 1/ v = 1/ 200 = 0.005 s

14. Sound travels most slowly in gases (Air); it travels faster in liquids (Water); and fastest in solids (Iron).

17. Distance travelled by the sound = $v \times t$ = (342 m/s) × 1 s = 342 m

In 1 s sound has to travel twice the distance between the rock and Reena. Hence, the distance = 342 m/ 2 = 171 m

20. Distance travelled by the ultrasound (2 times the depth of the ocean) = $v \times t$ = 1500 m/s × 4 s = 6000 m. Therefore, the distance of the ocean floor from the ship = 6000 m/ 2 = 3000 m

**Assessment 2**

27. The amplitude of the wave determines its loudness and the pitch is determined by the frequency of it.

29. Distance travelled by the sound = $v \times t$ = (342m/ s) × 5 s = 1710 m

In 5 s sound has to travel twice the distance between the reflecting surface and Raj. Hence, the distance = 1710 m/ 2 = 855 m

30. Distance travelled by the ultrasound (2 times the depth of the ocean) = $v \times t$ = 1500 m/s × 2.5 s = 3750 m; Therefore, the distance of the ocean floor from the ship = 3750 m/ 2 = 1875 m

31. v = 1/ $T$ = 40 oscillations/ 0.5 seconds = 80 Hz

34. Time period = 4 s; Frequency = 1/ $T$ = 1/ 4 s = 0.25 Hz

**Chapter 13: Why Do We Fall Ill?**

**Assessment 1**

21. The severity of chronic disease is very high, and it affects the health for a long term. All diseases have symptoms.

22. Only antibiotics interfere with the biological pathways of the bacteria as their metabolism is blocked.

23. Poverty leads to poor supply of basic necessities which lead to many infectious diseases and poor immunity.

24. Cancer of any type is caused by genetic abnormalities. It can also be inherited, but it does not spread from an infected person to a healthy person.

25. High blood pressure is caused by non-infectious agents like stress, obesity and lifestyle disorders.

**Assessment 2**

46. Insulin is the medicine prescribed to the patients suffering from diabetes.

47. An individual might be a carrier of some disease or there might be some disease of that country to which we are not immune. Therefore, all visitors to a foreign country are vaccinated.

48. Saline expand intravascular volume without disturbing ion concentration in the blood or causing significant fluid shifts between intravascular, intracellular, and interstitial spaces.

49. Immobilizing the injured and inflamed part of the body and relaxing with an anti-inflammatory drug consumed orally or applied physically reduces it.

50. Kala-azar is caused by a protozoan infection of the genus *Leishmania.*

**Chapter 14: Natural Resources**

**Assessment 1**

21. All organisms require water to perform cellular processes and ultimately for their survival.

22. If suspended particles are more during cold weather, the vision will be affected.

23. Since industrial revolution, burning of fossil fuels is the cause for doubling of carbon dioxide concentration in the atmosphere.

24. Lightning, rain, nitrogen-fixing bacteria and roots of plants have a role to play in the nitrogen cycle.

25. The direction of air at night in the coastal region will be towards sea due to the low-pressure area developing above the sea.

**Assessment 2**

27. The factors that affect the wind in an area are rotation of the Earth and the presence of mountain ranges.

30. The quality of top soil is the major factor that determines biodiversity in that area.

31. Nitrogen-fixing bacteria cannot survive in the presence of oxygen and gets poisoned, thereby preventing nitrogen fixation in the soil.

33. Carbon is found in combined state in carbohydrates, proteins, fats and vitamins.

50. All the rainwater that falls on the ground does not reach the sea. Some of the water seeps down to the ground.

**Chapter 15: Improvement in Food Resources**

**Assessment 1**

8. Excess use of fertilizers lead to water pollution as they get washed away by irrigation and not being fully absorbed by the plants.
11. The elaborately and extensively used irrigation system is the canals.
13. The three ways in which the insects generally attack the plants are: they cut the root, stem and leaf, bore the cell sap from various parts of the plant and bore the stem and fruits.
17. The main purposes of cattle husbandry are milk and draught labour for agricultural work.
23. Cross breeding of Indian and foreign breeds help to reduce the size of egg-laying bird.

**Assessment 2**

34. The fertilizers provide nitrogen, potassium and phosphorus to ensure good vegetative growth to bring up healthy plants.
37. Crops are grown in rows in intercropping because their nutrient requirement is different.
43. The milk production can be increased by increasing the lactation period of the cattle.
47. The problem related to composite fish culture is that the fishes only breed during monsoon.
48. Fish farming can be done intensively using composite fish culture system.

# Collins Perfect Science Assessments 9

## CHAPTER 1

## SAMPLE OMR ANSWER SHEET

***IMPORTANT:*** *PLEASE FILL IN NAME, SCHOOL CODE, CLASS, SECTION & ROLL NO. CORRECTLY*

### PERSONAL DETAILS

**1. STUDENT NAME (IN ENGLISH CAPITAL LETTERS ONLY)**

**2. SCHOOL CODE**

| | | | | | |
|---|---|---|---|---|---|
| Ⓐ | Ⓐ | ⓪ | ⓪ | ⓪ | ⓪ |
| Ⓑ | Ⓑ | ① | ① | ① | ① |
| Ⓒ | Ⓒ | ② | ② | ② | ② |
| Ⓓ | Ⓓ | ③ | ③ | ③ | ③ |
| Ⓔ | Ⓔ | ④ | ④ | ④ | ④ |
| Ⓕ | Ⓕ | ⑤ | ⑤ | ⑤ | ⑤ |
| Ⓖ | Ⓖ | ⑥ | ⑥ | ⑥ | ⑥ |
| Ⓗ | Ⓗ | ⑦ | ⑦ | ⑦ | ⑦ |
| Ⓘ | Ⓘ | ⑧ | ⑧ | ⑧ | ⑧ |
| Ⓙ | Ⓙ | ⑨ | ⑨ | ⑨ | ⑨ |
| Ⓚ | Ⓚ | | | | |
| Ⓛ | Ⓛ | | | | |
| Ⓜ | Ⓜ | | | | |
| Ⓝ | Ⓝ | | | | |
| Ⓞ | Ⓞ | | | | |
| Ⓟ | Ⓟ | | | | |
| Ⓠ | Ⓠ | | | | |
| Ⓡ | Ⓡ | | | | |
| Ⓢ | Ⓢ | | | | |
| Ⓣ | Ⓣ | | | | |
| Ⓤ | Ⓤ | | | | |
| Ⓥ | Ⓥ | | | | |
| Ⓦ | Ⓦ | | | | |
| Ⓧ | Ⓧ | | | | |
| Ⓨ | Ⓨ | | | | |
| Ⓩ | Ⓩ | | | | |

**3. CLASS**

| | |
|---|---|
| ⓪ | ⓪ |
| ① | ① |
| | ② |
| | ③ |
| | ④ |
| | ⑤ |
| | ⑥ |
| | ⑦ |
| | ⑧ |
| | ⑨ |

**4. SECTION**

| | | |
|---|---|---|
| Ⓐ | Ⓙ | Ⓢ |
| Ⓑ | Ⓚ | Ⓣ |
| Ⓒ | Ⓛ | Ⓤ |
| Ⓓ | Ⓜ | Ⓥ |
| Ⓔ | Ⓝ | Ⓦ |
| Ⓕ | Ⓞ | Ⓧ |
| Ⓖ | Ⓟ | Ⓨ |
| Ⓗ | Ⓠ | Ⓩ |
| Ⓘ | Ⓡ | |

**5. ROLL NO.**

| | | | | |
|---|---|---|---|---|
| ⓪ | ⓪ | ⓪ | ⓪ | ⓪ |
| ① | ① | ① | ① | ① |
| ② | ② | ② | ② | ② |
| ③ | ③ | ③ | ③ | ③ |
| ④ | ④ | ④ | ④ | ④ |
| ⑤ | ⑤ | ⑤ | ⑤ | ⑤ |
| ⑥ | ⑥ | ⑥ | ⑥ | ⑥ |
| ⑦ | ⑦ | ⑦ | ⑦ | ⑦ |
| ⑧ | ⑧ | ⑧ | ⑧ | ⑧ |
| ⑨ | ⑨ | ⑨ | ⑨ | ⑨ |

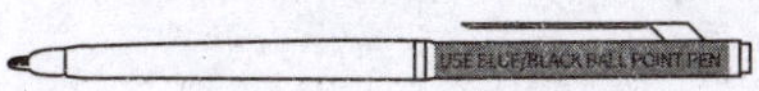


### MARK YOUR ANSWERS

| | | | | | | | | | |
|---|---|---|---|---|---|---|---|---|---|
| **1.** | Ⓐ | Ⓑ | Ⓒ | Ⓓ | **26.** | Ⓐ | Ⓑ | Ⓒ | Ⓓ |
| **2.** | Ⓐ | Ⓑ | Ⓒ | Ⓓ | **27.** | Ⓐ | Ⓑ | Ⓒ | Ⓓ |
| **3.** | Ⓐ | Ⓑ | Ⓒ | Ⓓ | **28.** | Ⓐ | Ⓑ | Ⓒ | Ⓓ |
| **4.** | Ⓐ | Ⓑ | Ⓒ | Ⓓ | **29.** | Ⓐ | Ⓑ | Ⓒ | Ⓓ |
| **5.** | Ⓐ | Ⓑ | Ⓒ | Ⓓ | **30.** | Ⓐ | Ⓑ | Ⓒ | Ⓓ |
| **6.** | Ⓐ | Ⓑ | Ⓒ | Ⓓ | **31.** | Ⓐ | Ⓑ | Ⓒ | Ⓓ |
| **7.** | Ⓐ | Ⓑ | Ⓒ | Ⓓ | **32.** | Ⓐ | Ⓑ | Ⓒ | Ⓓ |
| **8.** | Ⓐ | Ⓑ | Ⓒ | Ⓓ | **33.** | Ⓐ | Ⓑ | Ⓒ | Ⓓ |
| **9.** | Ⓐ | Ⓑ | Ⓒ | Ⓓ | **34.** | Ⓐ | Ⓑ | Ⓒ | Ⓓ |
| **10.** | Ⓐ | Ⓑ | Ⓒ | Ⓓ | **35.** | Ⓐ | Ⓑ | Ⓒ | Ⓓ |
| **11.** | Ⓐ | Ⓑ | Ⓒ | Ⓓ | **36.** | Ⓐ | Ⓑ | Ⓒ | Ⓓ |
| **12.** | Ⓐ | Ⓑ | Ⓒ | Ⓓ | **37.** | Ⓐ | Ⓑ | Ⓒ | Ⓓ |
| **13.** | Ⓐ | Ⓑ | Ⓒ | Ⓓ | **38.** | Ⓐ | Ⓑ | Ⓒ | Ⓓ |
| **14.** | Ⓐ | Ⓑ | Ⓒ | Ⓓ | **39.** | Ⓐ | Ⓑ | Ⓒ | Ⓓ |
| **15.** | Ⓐ | Ⓑ | Ⓒ | Ⓓ | **40.** | Ⓐ | Ⓑ | Ⓒ | Ⓓ |
| **16.** | Ⓐ | Ⓑ | Ⓒ | Ⓓ | **41.** | Ⓐ | Ⓑ | Ⓒ | Ⓓ |
| **17.** | Ⓐ | Ⓑ | Ⓒ | Ⓓ | **42.** | Ⓐ | Ⓑ | Ⓒ | Ⓓ |
| **18.** | Ⓐ | Ⓑ | Ⓒ | Ⓓ | **43.** | Ⓐ | Ⓑ | Ⓒ | Ⓓ |
| **19.** | Ⓐ | Ⓑ | Ⓒ | Ⓓ | **44.** | Ⓐ | Ⓑ | Ⓒ | Ⓓ |
| **20.** | Ⓐ | Ⓑ | Ⓒ | Ⓓ | **45.** | Ⓐ | Ⓑ | Ⓒ | Ⓓ |
| **21.** | Ⓐ | Ⓑ | Ⓒ | Ⓓ | **46.** | Ⓐ | Ⓑ | Ⓒ | Ⓓ |
| **22.** | Ⓐ | Ⓑ | Ⓒ | Ⓓ | **47.** | Ⓐ | Ⓑ | Ⓒ | Ⓓ |
| **23.** | Ⓐ | Ⓑ | Ⓒ | Ⓓ | **48.** | Ⓐ | Ⓑ | Ⓒ | Ⓓ |
| **24.** | Ⓐ | Ⓑ | Ⓒ | Ⓓ | **49.** | Ⓐ | Ⓑ | Ⓒ | Ⓓ |
| **25.** | Ⓐ | Ⓑ | Ⓒ | Ⓓ | **50.** | Ⓐ | Ⓑ | Ⓒ | Ⓓ |

# CHAPTER 2

## SAMPLE OMR ANSWER SHEET

***IMPORTANT:*** *PLEASE FILL IN NAME, SCHOOL CODE, CLASS, SECTION & ROLL NO. CORRECTLY*

### PERSONAL DETAILS

**1. STUDENT NAME (IN ENGLISH CAPITAL LETTERS ONLY)**

**2. SCHOOL CODE**

| | | | | | |
|---|---|---|---|---|---|
| A–Z | A–Z | 0–9 | 0–9 | 0–9 | 0–9 |

**3. CLASS**

| | |
|---|---|
| 0–1 | 0–9 |

**4. SECTION**

| | | |
|---|---|---|
| A–I | J–R | S–Z |

**5. ROLL NO.**

| | | | | |
|---|---|---|---|---|
| 0–9 | 0–9 | 0–9 | 0–9 | 0–9 |

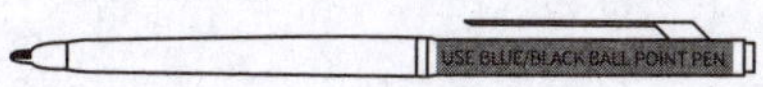


### MARK YOUR ANSWERS

| | | | | | | | | | |
|---|---|---|---|---|---|---|---|---|---|
| 1. | A | B | C | D | 26. | A | B | C | D |
| 2. | A | B | C | D | 27. | A | B | C | D |
| 3. | A | B | C | D | 28. | A | B | C | D |
| 4. | A | B | C | D | 29. | A | B | C | D |
| 5. | A | B | C | D | 30. | A | B | C | D |
| 6. | A | B | C | D | 31. | A | B | C | D |
| 7. | A | B | C | D | 32. | A | B | C | D |
| 8. | A | B | C | D | 33. | A | B | C | D |
| 9. | A | B | C | D | 34. | A | B | C | D |
| 10. | A | B | C | D | 35. | A | B | C | D |
| 11. | A | B | C | D | 36. | A | B | C | D |
| 12. | A | B | C | D | 37. | A | B | C | D |
| 13. | A | B | C | D | 38. | A | B | C | D |
| 14. | A | B | C | D | 39. | A | B | C | D |
| 15. | A | B | C | D | 40. | A | B | C | D |
| 16. | A | B | C | D | 41. | A | B | C | D |
| 17. | A | B | C | D | 42. | A | B | C | D |
| 18. | A | B | C | D | 43. | A | B | C | D |
| 19. | A | B | C | D | 44. | A | B | C | D |
| 20. | A | B | C | D | 45. | A | B | C | D |
| 21. | A | B | C | D | 46. | A | B | C | D |
| 22. | A | B | C | D | 47. | A | B | C | D |
| 23. | A | B | C | D | 48. | A | B | C | D |
| 24. | A | B | C | D | 49. | A | B | C | D |
| 25. | A | B | C | D | 50. | A | B | C | D |

## CHAPTER 3

# SAMPLE OMR ANSWER SHEET

***IMPORTANT:*** *PLEASE FILL IN NAME, SCHOOL CODE, CLASS, SECTION & ROLL NO. CORRECTLY*

**PERSONAL DETAILS**

**1. STUDENT NAME (IN ENGLISH CAPITAL LETTERS ONLY)**

**2. SCHOOL CODE**

Columns 1–2: Ⓐ Ⓑ Ⓒ Ⓓ Ⓔ Ⓕ Ⓖ Ⓗ Ⓘ Ⓙ Ⓚ Ⓛ Ⓜ Ⓝ Ⓞ Ⓟ Ⓠ Ⓡ Ⓢ Ⓣ Ⓤ Ⓥ Ⓦ Ⓧ Ⓨ Ⓩ

Columns 3–6: ⓪ ① ② ③ ④ ⑤ ⑥ ⑦ ⑧ ⑨

**3. CLASS**

Column 1: ⓪ ①

Column 2: ⓪ ① ② ③ ④ ⑤ ⑥ ⑦ ⑧ ⑨

**4. SECTION**

Ⓐ Ⓑ Ⓒ Ⓓ Ⓔ Ⓕ Ⓖ Ⓗ Ⓘ Ⓙ Ⓚ Ⓛ Ⓜ Ⓝ Ⓞ Ⓟ Ⓠ Ⓡ Ⓢ Ⓣ Ⓤ Ⓥ Ⓦ Ⓧ Ⓨ Ⓩ

**5. ROLL NO.**

Columns 1–5: ⓪ ① ② ③ ④ ⑤ ⑥ ⑦ ⑧ ⑨

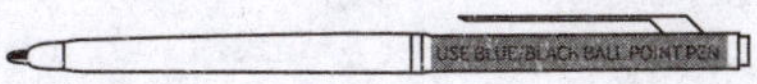


**MARK YOUR ANSWERS**

| Q. | | | | | Q. | | | | |
|---|---|---|---|---|---|---|---|---|---|
| 1. | Ⓐ | Ⓑ | Ⓒ | Ⓓ | 26. | Ⓐ | Ⓑ | Ⓒ | Ⓓ |
| 2. | Ⓐ | Ⓑ | Ⓒ | Ⓓ | 27. | Ⓐ | Ⓑ | Ⓒ | Ⓓ |
| 3. | Ⓐ | Ⓑ | Ⓒ | Ⓓ | 28. | Ⓐ | Ⓑ | Ⓒ | Ⓓ |
| 4. | Ⓐ | Ⓑ | Ⓒ | Ⓓ | 29. | Ⓐ | Ⓑ | Ⓒ | Ⓓ |
| 5. | Ⓐ | Ⓑ | Ⓒ | Ⓓ | 30. | Ⓐ | Ⓑ | Ⓒ | Ⓓ |
| 6. | Ⓐ | Ⓑ | Ⓒ | Ⓓ | 31. | Ⓐ | Ⓑ | Ⓒ | Ⓓ |
| 7. | Ⓐ | Ⓑ | Ⓒ | Ⓓ | 32. | Ⓐ | Ⓑ | Ⓒ | Ⓓ |
| 8. | Ⓐ | Ⓑ | Ⓒ | Ⓓ | 33. | Ⓐ | Ⓑ | Ⓒ | Ⓓ |
| 9. | Ⓐ | Ⓑ | Ⓒ | Ⓓ | 34. | Ⓐ | Ⓑ | Ⓒ | Ⓓ |
| 10. | Ⓐ | Ⓑ | Ⓒ | Ⓓ | 35. | Ⓐ | Ⓑ | Ⓒ | Ⓓ |
| 11. | Ⓐ | Ⓑ | Ⓒ | Ⓓ | 36. | Ⓐ | Ⓑ | Ⓒ | Ⓓ |
| 12. | Ⓐ | Ⓑ | Ⓒ | Ⓓ | 37. | Ⓐ | Ⓑ | Ⓒ | Ⓓ |
| 13. | Ⓐ | Ⓑ | Ⓒ | Ⓓ | 38. | Ⓐ | Ⓑ | Ⓒ | Ⓓ |
| 14. | Ⓐ | Ⓑ | Ⓒ | Ⓓ | 39. | Ⓐ | Ⓑ | Ⓒ | Ⓓ |
| 15. | Ⓐ | Ⓑ | Ⓒ | Ⓓ | 40. | Ⓐ | Ⓑ | Ⓒ | Ⓓ |
| 16. | Ⓐ | Ⓑ | Ⓒ | Ⓓ | 41. | Ⓐ | Ⓑ | Ⓒ | Ⓓ |
| 17. | Ⓐ | Ⓑ | Ⓒ | Ⓓ | 42. | Ⓐ | Ⓑ | Ⓒ | Ⓓ |
| 18. | Ⓐ | Ⓑ | Ⓒ | Ⓓ | 43. | Ⓐ | Ⓑ | Ⓒ | Ⓓ |
| 19. | Ⓐ | Ⓑ | Ⓒ | Ⓓ | 44. | Ⓐ | Ⓑ | Ⓒ | Ⓓ |
| 20. | Ⓐ | Ⓑ | Ⓒ | Ⓓ | 45. | Ⓐ | Ⓑ | Ⓒ | Ⓓ |
| 21. | Ⓐ | Ⓑ | Ⓒ | Ⓓ | 46. | Ⓐ | Ⓑ | Ⓒ | Ⓓ |
| 22. | Ⓐ | Ⓑ | Ⓒ | Ⓓ | 47. | Ⓐ | Ⓑ | Ⓒ | Ⓓ |
| 23. | Ⓐ | Ⓑ | Ⓒ | Ⓓ | 48. | Ⓐ | Ⓑ | Ⓒ | Ⓓ |
| 24. | Ⓐ | Ⓑ | Ⓒ | Ⓓ | 49. | Ⓐ | Ⓑ | Ⓒ | Ⓓ |
| 25. | Ⓐ | Ⓑ | Ⓒ | Ⓓ | 50. | Ⓐ | Ⓑ | Ⓒ | Ⓓ |

CHAPTER 4

## SAMPLE OMR ANSWER SHEET

***IMPORTANT:*** *PLEASE FILL IN NAME, SCHOOL CODE, CLASS, SECTION & ROLL NO. CORRECTLY*

### PERSONAL DETAILS

**1. STUDENT NAME (IN ENGLISH CAPITAL LETTERS ONLY)**

| | | | | | | | | | | | | | | |
|---|---|---|---|---|---|---|---|---|---|---|---|---|---|---|

**2. SCHOOL CODE**

| | | | | | |
|---|---|---|---|---|---|
| A–Z | A–Z | 0–9 | 0–9 | 0–9 | 0–9 |

**3. CLASS**

| | |
|---|---|
| 0–1 | 0–9 |

**4. SECTION**

A B C D E F G H I J K L M N O P Q R S T U V W X Y Z

**5. ROLL NO.**

| | | | | |
|---|---|---|---|---|
| 0–9 | 0–9 | 0–9 | 0–9 | 0–9 |

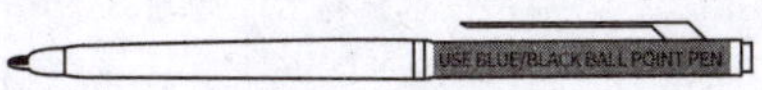


### MARK YOUR ANSWERS

| Q. | | | | | Q. | | | | |
|---|---|---|---|---|---|---|---|---|---|
| 1. | A | B | C | D | 26. | A | B | C | D |
| 2. | A | B | C | D | 27. | A | B | C | D |
| 3. | A | B | C | D | 28. | A | B | C | D |
| 4. | A | B | C | D | 29. | A | B | C | D |
| 5. | A | B | C | D | 30. | A | B | C | D |
| 6. | A | B | C | D | 31. | A | B | C | D |
| 7. | A | B | C | D | 32. | A | B | C | D |
| 8. | A | B | C | D | 33. | A | B | C | D |
| 9. | A | B | C | D | 34. | A | B | C | D |
| 10. | A | B | C | D | 35. | A | B | C | D |
| 11. | A | B | C | D | 36. | A | B | C | D |
| 12. | A | B | C | D | 37. | A | B | C | D |
| 13. | A | B | C | D | 38. | A | B | C | D |
| 14. | A | B | C | D | 39. | A | B | C | D |
| 15. | A | B | C | D | 40. | A | B | C | D |
| 16. | A | B | C | D | 41. | A | B | C | D |
| 17. | A | B | C | D | 42. | A | B | C | D |
| 18. | A | B | C | D | 43. | A | B | C | D |
| 19. | A | B | C | D | 44. | A | B | C | D |
| 20. | A | B | C | D | 45. | A | B | C | D |
| 21. | A | B | C | D | 46. | A | B | C | D |
| 22. | A | B | C | D | 47. | A | B | C | D |
| 23. | A | B | C | D | 48. | A | B | C | D |
| 24. | A | B | C | D | 49. | A | B | C | D |
| 25. | A | B | C | D | 50. | A | B | C | D |

CHAPTER 5

# SAMPLE OMR ANSWER SHEET

***IMPORTANT:*** *PLEASE FILL IN NAME, SCHOOL CODE, CLASS, SECTION & ROLL NO. CORRECTLY*

## PERSONAL DETAILS

**1. STUDENT NAME (IN ENGLISH CAPITAL LETTERS ONLY)**

**2. SCHOOL CODE**

Ⓐ–Ⓩ (two columns); ⓪–⑨ (four columns)

**3. CLASS**

⓪ ①; ⓪–⑨

**4. SECTION**

Ⓐ Ⓑ Ⓒ Ⓓ Ⓔ Ⓕ Ⓖ Ⓗ Ⓘ Ⓙ Ⓚ Ⓛ Ⓜ Ⓝ Ⓞ Ⓟ Ⓠ Ⓡ Ⓢ Ⓣ Ⓤ Ⓥ Ⓦ Ⓧ Ⓨ Ⓩ

**5. ROLL NO.**

⓪–⑨ (five columns)

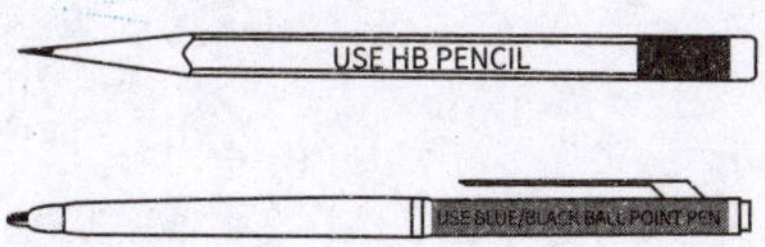


## MARK YOUR ANSWERS

| | | | | | | | | | |
|---|---|---|---|---|---|---|---|---|---|
| **1.** | Ⓐ | Ⓑ | Ⓒ | Ⓓ | **26.** | Ⓐ | Ⓑ | Ⓒ | Ⓓ |
| **2.** | Ⓐ | Ⓑ | Ⓒ | Ⓓ | **27.** | Ⓐ | Ⓑ | Ⓒ | Ⓓ |
| **3.** | Ⓐ | Ⓑ | Ⓒ | Ⓓ | **28.** | Ⓐ | Ⓑ | Ⓒ | Ⓓ |
| **4.** | Ⓐ | Ⓑ | Ⓒ | Ⓓ | **29.** | Ⓐ | Ⓑ | Ⓒ | Ⓓ |
| **5.** | Ⓐ | Ⓑ | Ⓒ | Ⓓ | **30.** | Ⓐ | Ⓑ | Ⓒ | Ⓓ |
| **6.** | Ⓐ | Ⓑ | Ⓒ | Ⓓ | **31.** | Ⓐ | Ⓑ | Ⓒ | Ⓓ |
| **7.** | Ⓐ | Ⓑ | Ⓒ | Ⓓ | **32.** | Ⓐ | Ⓑ | Ⓒ | Ⓓ |
| **8.** | Ⓐ | Ⓑ | Ⓒ | Ⓓ | **33.** | Ⓐ | Ⓑ | Ⓒ | Ⓓ |
| **9.** | Ⓐ | Ⓑ | Ⓒ | Ⓓ | **34.** | Ⓐ | Ⓑ | Ⓒ | Ⓓ |
| **10.** | Ⓐ | Ⓑ | Ⓒ | Ⓓ | **35.** | Ⓐ | Ⓑ | Ⓒ | Ⓓ |
| **11.** | Ⓐ | Ⓑ | Ⓒ | Ⓓ | **36.** | Ⓐ | Ⓑ | Ⓒ | Ⓓ |
| **12.** | Ⓐ | Ⓑ | Ⓒ | Ⓓ | **37.** | Ⓐ | Ⓑ | Ⓒ | Ⓓ |
| **13.** | Ⓐ | Ⓑ | Ⓒ | Ⓓ | **38.** | Ⓐ | Ⓑ | Ⓒ | Ⓓ |
| **14.** | Ⓐ | Ⓑ | Ⓒ | Ⓓ | **39.** | Ⓐ | Ⓑ | Ⓒ | Ⓓ |
| **15.** | Ⓐ | Ⓑ | Ⓒ | Ⓓ | **40.** | Ⓐ | Ⓑ | Ⓒ | Ⓓ |
| **16.** | Ⓐ | Ⓑ | Ⓒ | Ⓓ | **41.** | Ⓐ | Ⓑ | Ⓒ | Ⓓ |
| **17.** | Ⓐ | Ⓑ | Ⓒ | Ⓓ | **42.** | Ⓐ | Ⓑ | Ⓒ | Ⓓ |
| **18.** | Ⓐ | Ⓑ | Ⓒ | Ⓓ | **43.** | Ⓐ | Ⓑ | Ⓒ | Ⓓ |
| **19.** | Ⓐ | Ⓑ | Ⓒ | Ⓓ | **44.** | Ⓐ | Ⓑ | Ⓒ | Ⓓ |
| **20.** | Ⓐ | Ⓑ | Ⓒ | Ⓓ | **45.** | Ⓐ | Ⓑ | Ⓒ | Ⓓ |
| **21.** | Ⓐ | Ⓑ | Ⓒ | Ⓓ | **46.** | Ⓐ | Ⓑ | Ⓒ | Ⓓ |
| **22.** | Ⓐ | Ⓑ | Ⓒ | Ⓓ | **47.** | Ⓐ | Ⓑ | Ⓒ | Ⓓ |
| **23.** | Ⓐ | Ⓑ | Ⓒ | Ⓓ | **48.** | Ⓐ | Ⓑ | Ⓒ | Ⓓ |
| **24.** | Ⓐ | Ⓑ | Ⓒ | Ⓓ | **49.** | Ⓐ | Ⓑ | Ⓒ | Ⓓ |
| **25.** | Ⓐ | Ⓑ | Ⓒ | Ⓓ | **50.** | Ⓐ | Ⓑ | Ⓒ | Ⓓ |

CHAPTER 6

## SAMPLE OMR ANSWER SHEET

***IMPORTANT:*** *PLEASE FILL IN NAME, SCHOOL CODE, CLASS, SECTION & ROLL NO. CORRECTLY*

### PERSONAL DETAILS

**1. STUDENT NAME (IN ENGLISH CAPITAL LETTERS ONLY)**

**2. SCHOOL CODE**

| | | | | | |
|---|---|---|---|---|---|
| A–Z | A–Z | 0–9 | 0–9 | 0–9 | 0–9 |

**3. CLASS**

| | |
|---|---|
| 0–1 | 0–9 |

**4. SECTION**

A B C D E F G H I J K L M N O P Q R S T U V W X Y Z

**5. ROLL NO.**

| | | | | |
|---|---|---|---|---|
| 0–9 | 0–9 | 0–9 | 0–9 | 0–9 |

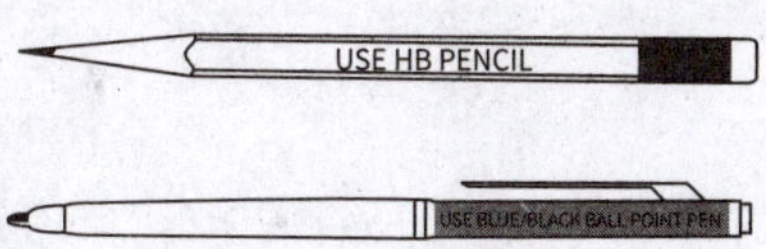


### MARK YOUR ANSWERS

| No. | | | | | No. | | | | |
|---|---|---|---|---|---|---|---|---|---|
| 1. | A | B | C | D | 26. | A | B | C | D |
| 2. | A | B | C | D | 27. | A | B | C | D |
| 3. | A | B | C | D | 28. | A | B | C | D |
| 4. | A | B | C | D | 29. | A | B | C | D |
| 5. | A | B | C | D | 30. | A | B | C | D |
| 6. | A | B | C | D | 31. | A | B | C | D |
| 7. | A | B | C | D | 32. | A | B | C | D |
| 8. | A | B | C | D | 33. | A | B | C | D |
| 9. | A | B | C | D | 34. | A | B | C | D |
| 10. | A | B | C | D | 35. | A | B | C | D |
| 11. | A | B | C | D | 36. | A | B | C | D |
| 12. | A | B | C | D | 37. | A | B | C | D |
| 13. | A | B | C | D | 38. | A | B | C | D |
| 14. | A | B | C | D | 39. | A | B | C | D |
| 15. | A | B | C | D | 40. | A | B | C | D |
| 16. | A | B | C | D | 41. | A | B | C | D |
| 17. | A | B | C | D | 42. | A | B | C | D |
| 18. | A | B | C | D | 43. | A | B | C | D |
| 19. | A | B | C | D | 44. | A | B | C | D |
| 20. | A | B | C | D | 45. | A | B | C | D |
| 21. | A | B | C | D | 46. | A | B | C | D |
| 22. | A | B | C | D | 47. | A | B | C | D |
| 23. | A | B | C | D | 48. | A | B | C | D |
| 24. | A | B | C | D | 49. | A | B | C | D |
| 25. | A | B | C | D | 50. | A | B | C | D |

## CHAPTER 7

# SAMPLE OMR ANSWER SHEET

***IMPORTANT:*** *PLEASE FILL IN NAME, SCHOOL CODE, CLASS, SECTION & ROLL NO. CORRECTLY*

### PERSONAL DETAILS

**1. STUDENT NAME (IN ENGLISH CAPITAL LETTERS ONLY)**

**2. SCHOOL CODE**

Columns 1–2: Ⓐ–Ⓩ (A B C D E F G H I J K L M N O P Q R S T U V W X Y Z)

Columns 3–6: 0 1 2 3 4 5 6 7 8 9

**3. CLASS**

Column 1: 0 1

Column 2: 0 1 2 3 4 5 6 7 8 9

**4. SECTION**

A B C D E F G H I / J K L M N O P Q R / S T U V W X Y Z

**5. ROLL NO.**

Columns 1–5: 0 1 2 3 4 5 6 7 8 9

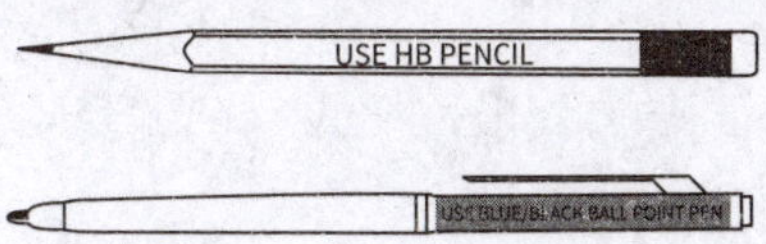


### MARK YOUR ANSWERS

| No. | | | | | No. | | | | |
|---|---|---|---|---|---|---|---|---|---|
| 1. | A | B | C | D | 26. | A | B | C | D |
| 2. | A | B | C | D | 27. | A | B | C | D |
| 3. | A | B | C | D | 28. | A | B | C | D |
| 4. | A | B | C | D | 29. | A | B | C | D |
| 5. | A | B | C | D | 30. | A | B | C | D |
| 6. | A | B | C | D | 31. | A | B | C | D |
| 7. | A | B | C | D | 32. | A | B | C | D |
| 8. | A | B | C | D | 33. | A | B | C | D |
| 9. | A | B | C | D | 34. | A | B | C | D |
| 10. | A | B | C | D | 35. | A | B | C | D |
| 11. | A | B | C | D | 36. | A | B | C | D |
| 12. | A | B | C | D | 37. | A | B | C | D |
| 13. | A | B | C | D | 38. | A | B | C | D |
| 14. | A | B | C | D | 39. | A | B | C | D |
| 15. | A | B | C | D | 40. | A | B | C | D |
| 16. | A | B | C | D | 41. | A | B | C | D |
| 17. | A | B | C | D | 42. | A | B | C | D |
| 18. | A | B | C | D | 43. | A | B | C | D |
| 19. | A | B | C | D | 44. | A | B | C | D |
| 20. | A | B | C | D | 45. | A | B | C | D |
| 21. | A | B | C | D | 46. | A | B | C | D |
| 22. | A | B | C | D | 47. | A | B | C | D |
| 23. | A | B | C | D | 48. | A | B | C | D |
| 24. | A | B | C | D | 49. | A | B | C | D |
| 25. | A | B | C | D | 50. | A | B | C | D |

CHAPTER 8

## SAMPLE OMR ANSWER SHEET

***IMPORTANT:*** *PLEASE FILL IN NAME, SCHOOL CODE, CLASS, SECTION & ROLL NO. CORRECTLY*

### PERSONAL DETAILS

**1. STUDENT NAME (IN ENGLISH CAPITAL LETTERS ONLY)**

| | | | | | | | | | | | | | | |
|---|---|---|---|---|---|---|---|---|---|---|---|---|---|---|

**2. SCHOOL CODE**

| | | | | | |
|---|---|---|---|---|---|
| Ⓐ–Ⓩ | Ⓐ–Ⓩ | ⓪–⑨ | ⓪–⑨ | ⓪–⑨ | ⓪–⑨ |

**3. CLASS**

| | |
|---|---|
| ⓪ ① | ⓪–⑨ |

**4. SECTION**

| | | |
|---|---|---|
| Ⓐ Ⓑ Ⓒ Ⓓ Ⓔ Ⓕ Ⓖ Ⓗ Ⓘ | Ⓙ Ⓚ Ⓛ Ⓜ Ⓝ Ⓞ Ⓟ Ⓠ Ⓡ | Ⓢ Ⓣ Ⓤ Ⓥ Ⓦ Ⓧ Ⓨ Ⓩ |

**5. ROLL NO.**

| | | | | |
|---|---|---|---|---|
| ⓪–⑨ | ⓪–⑨ | ⓪–⑨ | ⓪–⑨ | ⓪–⑨ |

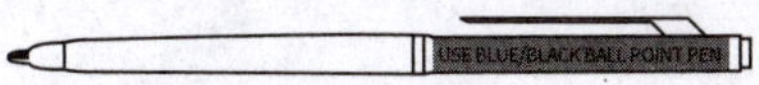


### MARK YOUR ANSWERS

| Q | | | | | Q | | | | |
|---|---|---|---|---|---|---|---|---|---|
| 1. | Ⓐ | Ⓑ | Ⓒ | Ⓓ | 26. | Ⓐ | Ⓑ | Ⓒ | Ⓓ |
| 2. | Ⓐ | Ⓑ | Ⓒ | Ⓓ | 27. | Ⓐ | Ⓑ | Ⓒ | Ⓓ |
| 3. | Ⓐ | Ⓑ | Ⓒ | Ⓓ | 28. | Ⓐ | Ⓑ | Ⓒ | Ⓓ |
| 4. | Ⓐ | Ⓑ | Ⓒ | Ⓓ | 29. | Ⓐ | Ⓑ | Ⓒ | Ⓓ |
| 5. | Ⓐ | Ⓑ | Ⓒ | Ⓓ | 30. | Ⓐ | Ⓑ | Ⓒ | Ⓓ |
| 6. | Ⓐ | Ⓑ | Ⓒ | Ⓓ | 31. | Ⓐ | Ⓑ | Ⓒ | Ⓓ |
| 7. | Ⓐ | Ⓑ | Ⓒ | Ⓓ | 32. | Ⓐ | Ⓑ | Ⓒ | Ⓓ |
| 8. | Ⓐ | Ⓑ | Ⓒ | Ⓓ | 33. | Ⓐ | Ⓑ | Ⓒ | Ⓓ |
| 9. | Ⓐ | Ⓑ | Ⓒ | Ⓓ | 34. | Ⓐ | Ⓑ | Ⓒ | Ⓓ |
| 10. | Ⓐ | Ⓑ | Ⓒ | Ⓓ | 35. | Ⓐ | Ⓑ | Ⓒ | Ⓓ |
| 11. | Ⓐ | Ⓑ | Ⓒ | Ⓓ | 36. | Ⓐ | Ⓑ | Ⓒ | Ⓓ |
| 12. | Ⓐ | Ⓑ | Ⓒ | Ⓓ | 37. | Ⓐ | Ⓑ | Ⓒ | Ⓓ |
| 13. | Ⓐ | Ⓑ | Ⓒ | Ⓓ | 38. | Ⓐ | Ⓑ | Ⓒ | Ⓓ |
| 14. | Ⓐ | Ⓑ | Ⓒ | Ⓓ | 39. | Ⓐ | Ⓑ | Ⓒ | Ⓓ |
| 15. | Ⓐ | Ⓑ | Ⓒ | Ⓓ | 40. | Ⓐ | Ⓑ | Ⓒ | Ⓓ |
| 16. | Ⓐ | Ⓑ | Ⓒ | Ⓓ | 41. | Ⓐ | Ⓑ | Ⓒ | Ⓓ |
| 17. | Ⓐ | Ⓑ | Ⓒ | Ⓓ | 42. | Ⓐ | Ⓑ | Ⓒ | Ⓓ |
| 18. | Ⓐ | Ⓑ | Ⓒ | Ⓓ | 43. | Ⓐ | Ⓑ | Ⓒ | Ⓓ |
| 19. | Ⓐ | Ⓑ | Ⓒ | Ⓓ | 44. | Ⓐ | Ⓑ | Ⓒ | Ⓓ |
| 20. | Ⓐ | Ⓑ | Ⓒ | Ⓓ | 45. | Ⓐ | Ⓑ | Ⓒ | Ⓓ |
| 21. | Ⓐ | Ⓑ | Ⓒ | Ⓓ | 46. | Ⓐ | Ⓑ | Ⓒ | Ⓓ |
| 22. | Ⓐ | Ⓑ | Ⓒ | Ⓓ | 47. | Ⓐ | Ⓑ | Ⓒ | Ⓓ |
| 23. | Ⓐ | Ⓑ | Ⓒ | Ⓓ | 48. | Ⓐ | Ⓑ | Ⓒ | Ⓓ |
| 24. | Ⓐ | Ⓑ | Ⓒ | Ⓓ | 49. | Ⓐ | Ⓑ | Ⓒ | Ⓓ |
| 25. | Ⓐ | Ⓑ | Ⓒ | Ⓓ | 50. | Ⓐ | Ⓑ | Ⓒ | Ⓓ |

# Collins Perfect Science Assessments 9

## CHAPTER 9

### SAMPLE OMR ANSWER SHEET

***IMPORTANT:*** *PLEASE FILL IN NAME, SCHOOL CODE, CLASS, SECTION & ROLL NO. CORRECTLY*

**PERSONAL DETAILS**

**1. STUDENT NAME (IN ENGLISH CAPITAL LETTERS ONLY)**

| | | | | | | | | | | | | | | |
|---|---|---|---|---|---|---|---|---|---|---|---|---|---|---|

**2. SCHOOL CODE**

| | | | | | |
|---|---|---|---|---|---|
| Ⓐ–Ⓩ | Ⓐ–Ⓩ | ⓪–⑨ | ⓪–⑨ | ⓪–⑨ | ⓪–⑨ |

**3. CLASS**

| | |
|---|---|
| ⓪ ① | ⓪–⑨ |

**4. SECTION**

| | | |
|---|---|---|
| Ⓐ Ⓑ Ⓒ Ⓓ Ⓔ Ⓕ Ⓖ Ⓗ Ⓘ | Ⓙ Ⓚ Ⓛ Ⓜ Ⓝ Ⓞ Ⓟ Ⓠ Ⓡ | Ⓢ Ⓣ Ⓤ Ⓥ Ⓦ Ⓧ Ⓨ Ⓩ |

**5. ROLL NO.**

| | | | | |
|---|---|---|---|---|
| ⓪–⑨ | ⓪–⑨ | ⓪–⑨ | ⓪–⑨ | ⓪–⑨ |

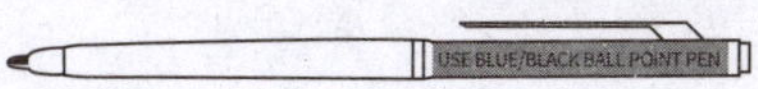


**MARK YOUR ANSWERS**

| | | | | | | | | | |
|---|---|---|---|---|---|---|---|---|---|
| **1.** | Ⓐ | Ⓑ | Ⓒ | Ⓓ | **26.** | Ⓐ | Ⓑ | Ⓒ | Ⓓ |
| **2.** | Ⓐ | Ⓑ | Ⓒ | Ⓓ | **27.** | Ⓐ | Ⓑ | Ⓒ | Ⓓ |
| **3.** | Ⓐ | Ⓑ | Ⓒ | Ⓓ | **28.** | Ⓐ | Ⓑ | Ⓒ | Ⓓ |
| **4.** | Ⓐ | Ⓑ | Ⓒ | Ⓓ | **29.** | Ⓐ | Ⓑ | Ⓒ | Ⓓ |
| **5.** | Ⓐ | Ⓑ | Ⓒ | Ⓓ | **30.** | Ⓐ | Ⓑ | Ⓒ | Ⓓ |
| **6.** | Ⓐ | Ⓑ | Ⓒ | Ⓓ | **31.** | Ⓐ | Ⓑ | Ⓒ | Ⓓ |
| **7.** | Ⓐ | Ⓑ | Ⓒ | Ⓓ | **32.** | Ⓐ | Ⓑ | Ⓒ | Ⓓ |
| **8.** | Ⓐ | Ⓑ | Ⓒ | Ⓓ | **33.** | Ⓐ | Ⓑ | Ⓒ | Ⓓ |
| **9.** | Ⓐ | Ⓑ | Ⓒ | Ⓓ | **34.** | Ⓐ | Ⓑ | Ⓒ | Ⓓ |
| **10.** | Ⓐ | Ⓑ | Ⓒ | Ⓓ | **35.** | Ⓐ | Ⓑ | Ⓒ | Ⓓ |
| **11.** | Ⓐ | Ⓑ | Ⓒ | Ⓓ | **36.** | Ⓐ | Ⓑ | Ⓒ | Ⓓ |
| **12.** | Ⓐ | Ⓑ | Ⓒ | Ⓓ | **37.** | Ⓐ | Ⓑ | Ⓒ | Ⓓ |
| **13.** | Ⓐ | Ⓑ | Ⓒ | Ⓓ | **38.** | Ⓐ | Ⓑ | Ⓒ | Ⓓ |
| **14.** | Ⓐ | Ⓑ | Ⓒ | Ⓓ | **39.** | Ⓐ | Ⓑ | Ⓒ | Ⓓ |
| **15.** | Ⓐ | Ⓑ | Ⓒ | Ⓓ | **40.** | Ⓐ | Ⓑ | Ⓒ | Ⓓ |
| **16.** | Ⓐ | Ⓑ | Ⓒ | Ⓓ | **41.** | Ⓐ | Ⓑ | Ⓒ | Ⓓ |
| **17.** | Ⓐ | Ⓑ | Ⓒ | Ⓓ | **42.** | Ⓐ | Ⓑ | Ⓒ | Ⓓ |
| **18.** | Ⓐ | Ⓑ | Ⓒ | Ⓓ | **43.** | Ⓐ | Ⓑ | Ⓒ | Ⓓ |
| **19.** | Ⓐ | Ⓑ | Ⓒ | Ⓓ | **44.** | Ⓐ | Ⓑ | Ⓒ | Ⓓ |
| **20.** | Ⓐ | Ⓑ | Ⓒ | Ⓓ | **45.** | Ⓐ | Ⓑ | Ⓒ | Ⓓ |
| **21.** | Ⓐ | Ⓑ | Ⓒ | Ⓓ | **46.** | Ⓐ | Ⓑ | Ⓒ | Ⓓ |
| **22.** | Ⓐ | Ⓑ | Ⓒ | Ⓓ | **47.** | Ⓐ | Ⓑ | Ⓒ | Ⓓ |
| **23.** | Ⓐ | Ⓑ | Ⓒ | Ⓓ | **48.** | Ⓐ | Ⓑ | Ⓒ | Ⓓ |
| **24.** | Ⓐ | Ⓑ | Ⓒ | Ⓓ | **49.** | Ⓐ | Ⓑ | Ⓒ | Ⓓ |
| **25.** | Ⓐ | Ⓑ | Ⓒ | Ⓓ | **50.** | Ⓐ | Ⓑ | Ⓒ | Ⓓ |

CHAPTER 10

## SAMPLE OMR ANSWER SHEET

***IMPORTANT:*** *PLEASE FILL IN NAME, SCHOOL CODE, CLASS, SECTION & ROLL NO. CORRECTLY*

### PERSONAL DETAILS

**1. STUDENT NAME (IN ENGLISH CAPITAL LETTERS ONLY)**

**2. SCHOOL CODE**

| | | | | | |
|---|---|---|---|---|---|
| Ⓐ–Ⓩ | Ⓐ–Ⓩ | ⓪–⑨ | ⓪–⑨ | ⓪–⑨ | ⓪–⑨ |

**3. CLASS**

| | |
|---|---|
| ⓪ ① | ⓪–⑨ |

**4. SECTION**

| | | |
|---|---|---|
| Ⓐ Ⓑ Ⓒ Ⓓ Ⓔ Ⓕ Ⓖ Ⓗ Ⓘ | Ⓙ Ⓚ Ⓛ Ⓜ Ⓝ Ⓞ Ⓟ Ⓠ Ⓡ | Ⓢ Ⓣ Ⓤ Ⓥ Ⓦ Ⓧ Ⓨ Ⓩ |

**5. ROLL NO.**

| | | | | |
|---|---|---|---|---|
| ⓪–⑨ | ⓪–⑨ | ⓪–⑨ | ⓪–⑨ | ⓪–⑨ |

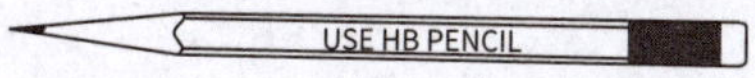


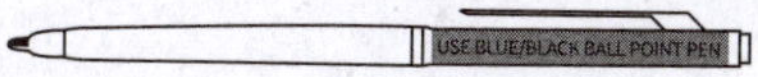


### MARK YOUR ANSWERS

| No. | | | | | No. | | | | |
|---|---|---|---|---|---|---|---|---|---|
| 1. | Ⓐ | Ⓑ | Ⓒ | Ⓓ | 26. | Ⓐ | Ⓑ | Ⓒ | Ⓓ |
| 2. | Ⓐ | Ⓑ | Ⓒ | Ⓓ | 27. | Ⓐ | Ⓑ | Ⓒ | Ⓓ |
| 3. | Ⓐ | Ⓑ | Ⓒ | Ⓓ | 28. | Ⓐ | Ⓑ | Ⓒ | Ⓓ |
| 4. | Ⓐ | Ⓑ | Ⓒ | Ⓓ | 29. | Ⓐ | Ⓑ | Ⓒ | Ⓓ |
| 5. | Ⓐ | Ⓑ | Ⓒ | Ⓓ | 30. | Ⓐ | Ⓑ | Ⓒ | Ⓓ |
| 6. | Ⓐ | Ⓑ | Ⓒ | Ⓓ | 31. | Ⓐ | Ⓑ | Ⓒ | Ⓓ |
| 7. | Ⓐ | Ⓑ | Ⓒ | Ⓓ | 32. | Ⓐ | Ⓑ | Ⓒ | Ⓓ |
| 8. | Ⓐ | Ⓑ | Ⓒ | Ⓓ | 33. | Ⓐ | Ⓑ | Ⓒ | Ⓓ |
| 9. | Ⓐ | Ⓑ | Ⓒ | Ⓓ | 34. | Ⓐ | Ⓑ | Ⓒ | Ⓓ |
| 10. | Ⓐ | Ⓑ | Ⓒ | Ⓓ | 35. | Ⓐ | Ⓑ | Ⓒ | Ⓓ |
| 11. | Ⓐ | Ⓑ | Ⓒ | Ⓓ | 36. | Ⓐ | Ⓑ | Ⓒ | Ⓓ |
| 12. | Ⓐ | Ⓑ | Ⓒ | Ⓓ | 37. | Ⓐ | Ⓑ | Ⓒ | Ⓓ |
| 13. | Ⓐ | Ⓑ | Ⓒ | Ⓓ | 38. | Ⓐ | Ⓑ | Ⓒ | Ⓓ |
| 14. | Ⓐ | Ⓑ | Ⓒ | Ⓓ | 39. | Ⓐ | Ⓑ | Ⓒ | Ⓓ |
| 15. | Ⓐ | Ⓑ | Ⓒ | Ⓓ | 40. | Ⓐ | Ⓑ | Ⓒ | Ⓓ |
| 16. | Ⓐ | Ⓑ | Ⓒ | Ⓓ | 41. | Ⓐ | Ⓑ | Ⓒ | Ⓓ |
| 17. | Ⓐ | Ⓑ | Ⓒ | Ⓓ | 42. | Ⓐ | Ⓑ | Ⓒ | Ⓓ |
| 18. | Ⓐ | Ⓑ | Ⓒ | Ⓓ | 43. | Ⓐ | Ⓑ | Ⓒ | Ⓓ |
| 19. | Ⓐ | Ⓑ | Ⓒ | Ⓓ | 44. | Ⓐ | Ⓑ | Ⓒ | Ⓓ |
| 20. | Ⓐ | Ⓑ | Ⓒ | Ⓓ | 45. | Ⓐ | Ⓑ | Ⓒ | Ⓓ |
| 21. | Ⓐ | Ⓑ | Ⓒ | Ⓓ | 46. | Ⓐ | Ⓑ | Ⓒ | Ⓓ |
| 22. | Ⓐ | Ⓑ | Ⓒ | Ⓓ | 47. | Ⓐ | Ⓑ | Ⓒ | Ⓓ |
| 23. | Ⓐ | Ⓑ | Ⓒ | Ⓓ | 48. | Ⓐ | Ⓑ | Ⓒ | Ⓓ |
| 24. | Ⓐ | Ⓑ | Ⓒ | Ⓓ | 49. | Ⓐ | Ⓑ | Ⓒ | Ⓓ |
| 25. | Ⓐ | Ⓑ | Ⓒ | Ⓓ | 50. | Ⓐ | Ⓑ | Ⓒ | Ⓓ |

CHAPTER 11

# SAMPLE OMR ANSWER SHEET

***IMPORTANT:*** *PLEASE FILL IN NAME, SCHOOL CODE, CLASS, SECTION & ROLL NO. CORRECTLY*

**PERSONAL DETAILS**

**1. STUDENT NAME (IN ENGLISH CAPITAL LETTERS ONLY)**

**2. SCHOOL CODE**

Columns 1–2: Ⓐ–Ⓩ; Columns 3–6: ⓪–⑨

**3. CLASS**

Column 1: ⓪ ①; Column 2: ⓪–⑨

**4. SECTION**

Ⓐ–Ⓘ, Ⓙ–Ⓡ, Ⓢ–Ⓩ

**5. ROLL NO.**

Columns 1–5: ⓪–⑨

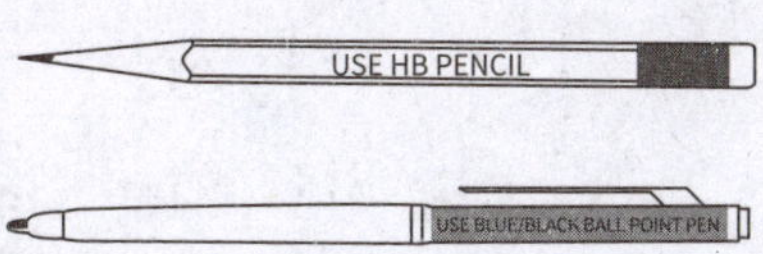


**MARK YOUR ANSWERS**

| | | | | |
|---|---|---|---|---|
| **1.** | Ⓐ | Ⓑ | Ⓒ | Ⓓ |
| **2.** | Ⓐ | Ⓑ | Ⓒ | Ⓓ |
| **3.** | Ⓐ | Ⓑ | Ⓒ | Ⓓ |
| **4.** | Ⓐ | Ⓑ | Ⓒ | Ⓓ |
| **5.** | Ⓐ | Ⓑ | Ⓒ | Ⓓ |
| **6.** | Ⓐ | Ⓑ | Ⓒ | Ⓓ |
| **7.** | Ⓐ | Ⓑ | Ⓒ | Ⓓ |
| **8.** | Ⓐ | Ⓑ | Ⓒ | Ⓓ |
| **9.** | Ⓐ | Ⓑ | Ⓒ | Ⓓ |
| **10.** | Ⓐ | Ⓑ | Ⓒ | Ⓓ |
| **11.** | Ⓐ | Ⓑ | Ⓒ | Ⓓ |
| **12.** | Ⓐ | Ⓑ | Ⓒ | Ⓓ |
| **13.** | Ⓐ | Ⓑ | Ⓒ | Ⓓ |
| **14.** | Ⓐ | Ⓑ | Ⓒ | Ⓓ |
| **15.** | Ⓐ | Ⓑ | Ⓒ | Ⓓ |
| **16.** | Ⓐ | Ⓑ | Ⓒ | Ⓓ |
| **17.** | Ⓐ | Ⓑ | Ⓒ | Ⓓ |
| **18.** | Ⓐ | Ⓑ | Ⓒ | Ⓓ |
| **19.** | Ⓐ | Ⓑ | Ⓒ | Ⓓ |
| **20.** | Ⓐ | Ⓑ | Ⓒ | Ⓓ |
| **21.** | Ⓐ | Ⓑ | Ⓒ | Ⓓ |
| **22.** | Ⓐ | Ⓑ | Ⓒ | Ⓓ |
| **23.** | Ⓐ | Ⓑ | Ⓒ | Ⓓ |
| **24.** | Ⓐ | Ⓑ | Ⓒ | Ⓓ |
| **25.** | Ⓐ | Ⓑ | Ⓒ | Ⓓ |

CHAPTER 12

## SAMPLE OMR ANSWER SHEET

***IMPORTANT:*** *PLEASE FILL IN NAME, SCHOOL CODE, CLASS, SECTION & ROLL NO. CORRECTLY*

### PERSONAL DETAILS

**1. STUDENT NAME (IN ENGLISH CAPITAL LETTERS ONLY)**

**2. SCHOOL CODE**

Columns 1–2: Ⓐ Ⓑ Ⓒ Ⓓ Ⓔ Ⓕ Ⓖ Ⓗ Ⓘ Ⓙ Ⓚ Ⓛ Ⓜ Ⓝ Ⓞ Ⓟ Ⓠ Ⓡ Ⓢ Ⓣ Ⓤ Ⓥ Ⓦ Ⓧ Ⓨ Ⓩ

Columns 3–6: ⓪ ① ② ③ ④ ⑤ ⑥ ⑦ ⑧ ⑨

**3. CLASS**

Column 1: ⓪ ①

Column 2: ⓪ ① ② ③ ④ ⑤ ⑥ ⑦ ⑧ ⑨

**4. SECTION**

Ⓐ Ⓑ Ⓒ Ⓓ Ⓔ Ⓕ Ⓖ Ⓗ Ⓘ Ⓙ Ⓚ Ⓛ Ⓜ Ⓝ Ⓞ Ⓟ Ⓠ Ⓡ Ⓢ Ⓣ Ⓤ Ⓥ Ⓦ Ⓧ Ⓨ Ⓩ

**5. ROLL NO.**

Columns 1–5: ⓪ ① ② ③ ④ ⑤ ⑥ ⑦ ⑧ ⑨

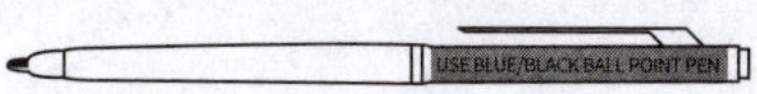


### MARK YOUR ANSWERS

| | | | | | | | | | |
|---|---|---|---|---|---|---|---|---|---|
| **1.** | Ⓐ | Ⓑ | Ⓒ | Ⓓ | **26.** | Ⓐ | Ⓑ | Ⓒ | Ⓓ |
| **2.** | Ⓐ | Ⓑ | Ⓒ | Ⓓ | **27.** | Ⓐ | Ⓑ | Ⓒ | Ⓓ |
| **3.** | Ⓐ | Ⓑ | Ⓒ | Ⓓ | **28.** | Ⓐ | Ⓑ | Ⓒ | Ⓓ |
| **4.** | Ⓐ | Ⓑ | Ⓒ | Ⓓ | **29.** | Ⓐ | Ⓑ | Ⓒ | Ⓓ |
| **5.** | Ⓐ | Ⓑ | Ⓒ | Ⓓ | **30.** | Ⓐ | Ⓑ | Ⓒ | Ⓓ |
| **6.** | Ⓐ | Ⓑ | Ⓒ | Ⓓ | **31.** | Ⓐ | Ⓑ | Ⓒ | Ⓓ |
| **7.** | Ⓐ | Ⓑ | Ⓒ | Ⓓ | **32.** | Ⓐ | Ⓑ | Ⓒ | Ⓓ |
| **8.** | Ⓐ | Ⓑ | Ⓒ | Ⓓ | **33.** | Ⓐ | Ⓑ | Ⓒ | Ⓓ |
| **9.** | Ⓐ | Ⓑ | Ⓒ | Ⓓ | **34.** | Ⓐ | Ⓑ | Ⓒ | Ⓓ |
| **10.** | Ⓐ | Ⓑ | Ⓒ | Ⓓ | **35.** | Ⓐ | Ⓑ | Ⓒ | Ⓓ |
| **11.** | Ⓐ | Ⓑ | Ⓒ | Ⓓ | **36.** | Ⓐ | Ⓑ | Ⓒ | Ⓓ |
| **12.** | Ⓐ | Ⓑ | Ⓒ | Ⓓ | **37.** | Ⓐ | Ⓑ | Ⓒ | Ⓓ |
| **13.** | Ⓐ | Ⓑ | Ⓒ | Ⓓ | **38.** | Ⓐ | Ⓑ | Ⓒ | Ⓓ |
| **14.** | Ⓐ | Ⓑ | Ⓒ | Ⓓ | **39.** | Ⓐ | Ⓑ | Ⓒ | Ⓓ |
| **15.** | Ⓐ | Ⓑ | Ⓒ | Ⓓ | **40.** | Ⓐ | Ⓑ | Ⓒ | Ⓓ |
| **16.** | Ⓐ | Ⓑ | Ⓒ | Ⓓ | **41.** | Ⓐ | Ⓑ | Ⓒ | Ⓓ |
| **17.** | Ⓐ | Ⓑ | Ⓒ | Ⓓ | **42.** | Ⓐ | Ⓑ | Ⓒ | Ⓓ |
| **18.** | Ⓐ | Ⓑ | Ⓒ | Ⓓ | **43.** | Ⓐ | Ⓑ | Ⓒ | Ⓓ |
| **19.** | Ⓐ | Ⓑ | Ⓒ | Ⓓ | **44.** | Ⓐ | Ⓑ | Ⓒ | Ⓓ |
| **20.** | Ⓐ | Ⓑ | Ⓒ | Ⓓ | **45.** | Ⓐ | Ⓑ | Ⓒ | Ⓓ |
| **21.** | Ⓐ | Ⓑ | Ⓒ | Ⓓ | **46.** | Ⓐ | Ⓑ | Ⓒ | Ⓓ |
| **22.** | Ⓐ | Ⓑ | Ⓒ | Ⓓ | **47.** | Ⓐ | Ⓑ | Ⓒ | Ⓓ |
| **23.** | Ⓐ | Ⓑ | Ⓒ | Ⓓ | **48.** | Ⓐ | Ⓑ | Ⓒ | Ⓓ |
| **24.** | Ⓐ | Ⓑ | Ⓒ | Ⓓ | **49.** | Ⓐ | Ⓑ | Ⓒ | Ⓓ |
| **25.** | Ⓐ | Ⓑ | Ⓒ | Ⓓ | **50.** | Ⓐ | Ⓑ | Ⓒ | Ⓓ |

# Collins Perfect Science Assessments 9

## CHAPTER 13

## SAMPLE OMR ANSWER SHEET

***IMPORTANT:*** *PLEASE FILL IN NAME, SCHOOL CODE, CLASS, SECTION & ROLL NO. CORRECTLY*

### PERSONAL DETAILS

**1. STUDENT NAME (IN ENGLISH CAPITAL LETTERS ONLY)**

| | | | | | | | | | | | | | | |
|---|---|---|---|---|---|---|---|---|---|---|---|---|---|---|

**2. SCHOOL CODE**

| | | | | | |
|---|---|---|---|---|---|
| Ⓐ–Ⓩ | Ⓐ–Ⓩ | ⓪–⑨ | ⓪–⑨ | ⓪–⑨ | ⓪–⑨ |

**3. CLASS**

| | |
|---|---|
| ⓪ ① | ⓪–⑨ |

**4. SECTION**

Ⓐ–Ⓘ, Ⓙ–Ⓡ, Ⓢ–Ⓩ

**5. ROLL NO.**

| | | | | |
|---|---|---|---|---|
| ⓪–⑨ | ⓪–⑨ | ⓪–⑨ | ⓪–⑨ | ⓪–⑨ |

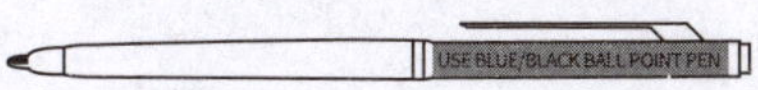


### MARK YOUR ANSWERS

| | | | | | | | | |
|---|---|---|---|---|---|---|---|---|
| **1.** | Ⓐ | Ⓑ | Ⓒ | Ⓓ | **26.** | Ⓐ | Ⓑ | Ⓒ | Ⓓ |
| **2.** | Ⓐ | Ⓑ | Ⓒ | Ⓓ | **27.** | Ⓐ | Ⓑ | Ⓒ | Ⓓ |
| **3.** | Ⓐ | Ⓑ | Ⓒ | Ⓓ | **28.** | Ⓐ | Ⓑ | Ⓒ | Ⓓ |
| **4.** | Ⓐ | Ⓑ | Ⓒ | Ⓓ | **29.** | Ⓐ | Ⓑ | Ⓒ | Ⓓ |
| **5.** | Ⓐ | Ⓑ | Ⓒ | Ⓓ | **30.** | Ⓐ | Ⓑ | Ⓒ | Ⓓ |
| **6.** | Ⓐ | Ⓑ | Ⓒ | Ⓓ | **31.** | Ⓐ | Ⓑ | Ⓒ | Ⓓ |
| **7.** | Ⓐ | Ⓑ | Ⓒ | Ⓓ | **32.** | Ⓐ | Ⓑ | Ⓒ | Ⓓ |
| **8.** | Ⓐ | Ⓑ | Ⓒ | Ⓓ | **33.** | Ⓐ | Ⓑ | Ⓒ | Ⓓ |
| **9.** | Ⓐ | Ⓑ | Ⓒ | Ⓓ | **34.** | Ⓐ | Ⓑ | Ⓒ | Ⓓ |
| **10.** | Ⓐ | Ⓑ | Ⓒ | Ⓓ | **35.** | Ⓐ | Ⓑ | Ⓒ | Ⓓ |
| **11.** | Ⓐ | Ⓑ | Ⓒ | Ⓓ | **36.** | Ⓐ | Ⓑ | Ⓒ | Ⓓ |
| **12.** | Ⓐ | Ⓑ | Ⓒ | Ⓓ | **37.** | Ⓐ | Ⓑ | Ⓒ | Ⓓ |
| **13.** | Ⓐ | Ⓑ | Ⓒ | Ⓓ | **38.** | Ⓐ | Ⓑ | Ⓒ | Ⓓ |
| **14.** | Ⓐ | Ⓑ | Ⓒ | Ⓓ | **39.** | Ⓐ | Ⓑ | Ⓒ | Ⓓ |
| **15.** | Ⓐ | Ⓑ | Ⓒ | Ⓓ | **40.** | Ⓐ | Ⓑ | Ⓒ | Ⓓ |
| **16.** | Ⓐ | Ⓑ | Ⓒ | Ⓓ | **41.** | Ⓐ | Ⓑ | Ⓒ | Ⓓ |
| **17.** | Ⓐ | Ⓑ | Ⓒ | Ⓓ | **42.** | Ⓐ | Ⓑ | Ⓒ | Ⓓ |
| **18.** | Ⓐ | Ⓑ | Ⓒ | Ⓓ | **43.** | Ⓐ | Ⓑ | Ⓒ | Ⓓ |
| **19.** | Ⓐ | Ⓑ | Ⓒ | Ⓓ | **44.** | Ⓐ | Ⓑ | Ⓒ | Ⓓ |
| **20.** | Ⓐ | Ⓑ | Ⓒ | Ⓓ | **45.** | Ⓐ | Ⓑ | Ⓒ | Ⓓ |
| **21.** | Ⓐ | Ⓑ | Ⓒ | Ⓓ | **46.** | Ⓐ | Ⓑ | Ⓒ | Ⓓ |
| **22.** | Ⓐ | Ⓑ | Ⓒ | Ⓓ | **47.** | Ⓐ | Ⓑ | Ⓒ | Ⓓ |
| **23.** | Ⓐ | Ⓑ | Ⓒ | Ⓓ | **48.** | Ⓐ | Ⓑ | Ⓒ | Ⓓ |
| **24.** | Ⓐ | Ⓑ | Ⓒ | Ⓓ | **49.** | Ⓐ | Ⓑ | Ⓒ | Ⓓ |
| **25.** | Ⓐ | Ⓑ | Ⓒ | Ⓓ | **50.** | Ⓐ | Ⓑ | Ⓒ | Ⓓ |

CHAPTER 14

## SAMPLE OMR ANSWER SHEET

***IMPORTANT:*** *PLEASE FILL IN NAME, SCHOOL CODE, CLASS, SECTION & ROLL NO. CORRECTLY*

### PERSONAL DETAILS

**1. STUDENT NAME (IN ENGLISH CAPITAL LETTERS ONLY)**

**2. SCHOOL CODE**

Ⓐ–Ⓩ | Ⓐ–Ⓩ | ⓪–⑨ | ⓪–⑨ | ⓪–⑨ | ⓪–⑨

**3. CLASS**

⓪–① | ⓪–⑨

**4. SECTION**

Ⓐ–Ⓘ | Ⓙ–Ⓡ | Ⓢ–Ⓩ

**5. ROLL NO.**

⓪–⑨ | ⓪–⑨ | ⓪–⑨ | ⓪–⑨ | ⓪–⑨

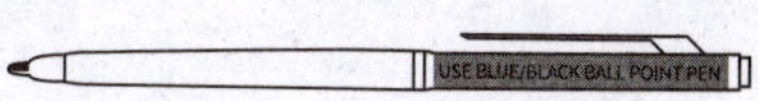


### MARK YOUR ANSWERS

| | | | | | | | | | |
|---|---|---|---|---|---|---|---|---|---|
| **1.** | Ⓐ | Ⓑ | Ⓒ | Ⓓ | **26.** | Ⓐ | Ⓑ | Ⓒ | Ⓓ |
| **2.** | Ⓐ | Ⓑ | Ⓒ | Ⓓ | **27.** | Ⓐ | Ⓑ | Ⓒ | Ⓓ |
| **3.** | Ⓐ | Ⓑ | Ⓒ | Ⓓ | **28.** | Ⓐ | Ⓑ | Ⓒ | Ⓓ |
| **4.** | Ⓐ | Ⓑ | Ⓒ | Ⓓ | **29.** | Ⓐ | Ⓑ | Ⓒ | Ⓓ |
| **5.** | Ⓐ | Ⓑ | Ⓒ | Ⓓ | **30.** | Ⓐ | Ⓑ | Ⓒ | Ⓓ |
| **6.** | Ⓐ | Ⓑ | Ⓒ | Ⓓ | **31.** | Ⓐ | Ⓑ | Ⓒ | Ⓓ |
| **7.** | Ⓐ | Ⓑ | Ⓒ | Ⓓ | **32.** | Ⓐ | Ⓑ | Ⓒ | Ⓓ |
| **8.** | Ⓐ | Ⓑ | Ⓒ | Ⓓ | **33.** | Ⓐ | Ⓑ | Ⓒ | Ⓓ |
| **9.** | Ⓐ | Ⓑ | Ⓒ | Ⓓ | **34.** | Ⓐ | Ⓑ | Ⓒ | Ⓓ |
| **10.** | Ⓐ | Ⓑ | Ⓒ | Ⓓ | **35.** | Ⓐ | Ⓑ | Ⓒ | Ⓓ |
| **11.** | Ⓐ | Ⓑ | Ⓒ | Ⓓ | **36.** | Ⓐ | Ⓑ | Ⓒ | Ⓓ |
| **12.** | Ⓐ | Ⓑ | Ⓒ | Ⓓ | **37.** | Ⓐ | Ⓑ | Ⓒ | Ⓓ |
| **13.** | Ⓐ | Ⓑ | Ⓒ | Ⓓ | **38.** | Ⓐ | Ⓑ | Ⓒ | Ⓓ |
| **14.** | Ⓐ | Ⓑ | Ⓒ | Ⓓ | **39.** | Ⓐ | Ⓑ | Ⓒ | Ⓓ |
| **15.** | Ⓐ | Ⓑ | Ⓒ | Ⓓ | **40.** | Ⓐ | Ⓑ | Ⓒ | Ⓓ |
| **16.** | Ⓐ | Ⓑ | Ⓒ | Ⓓ | **41.** | Ⓐ | Ⓑ | Ⓒ | Ⓓ |
| **17.** | Ⓐ | Ⓑ | Ⓒ | Ⓓ | **42.** | Ⓐ | Ⓑ | Ⓒ | Ⓓ |
| **18.** | Ⓐ | Ⓑ | Ⓒ | Ⓓ | **43.** | Ⓐ | Ⓑ | Ⓒ | Ⓓ |
| **19.** | Ⓐ | Ⓑ | Ⓒ | Ⓓ | **44.** | Ⓐ | Ⓑ | Ⓒ | Ⓓ |
| **20.** | Ⓐ | Ⓑ | Ⓒ | Ⓓ | **45.** | Ⓐ | Ⓑ | Ⓒ | Ⓓ |
| **21.** | Ⓐ | Ⓑ | Ⓒ | Ⓓ | **46.** | Ⓐ | Ⓑ | Ⓒ | Ⓓ |
| **22.** | Ⓐ | Ⓑ | Ⓒ | Ⓓ | **47.** | Ⓐ | Ⓑ | Ⓒ | Ⓓ |
| **23.** | Ⓐ | Ⓑ | Ⓒ | Ⓓ | **48.** | Ⓐ | Ⓑ | Ⓒ | Ⓓ |
| **24.** | Ⓐ | Ⓑ | Ⓒ | Ⓓ | **49.** | Ⓐ | Ⓑ | Ⓒ | Ⓓ |
| **25.** | Ⓐ | Ⓑ | Ⓒ | Ⓓ | **50.** | Ⓐ | Ⓑ | Ⓒ | Ⓓ |

# Collins Perfect Science Assessments 9

## CHAPTER 15

## SAMPLE OMR ANSWER SHEET

***IMPORTANT:*** *PLEASE FILL IN NAME, SCHOOL CODE, CLASS, SECTION & ROLL NO. CORRECTLY*

### PERSONAL DETAILS

**1. STUDENT NAME (IN ENGLISH CAPITAL LETTERS ONLY)**

**2. SCHOOL CODE**

| | | | | | |
|---|---|---|---|---|---|
| Ⓐ–Ⓩ | Ⓐ–Ⓩ | ⓪–⑨ | ⓪–⑨ | ⓪–⑨ | ⓪–⑨ |

**3. CLASS**

| | |
|---|---|
| ⓪–① | ⓪–⑨ |

**4. SECTION**

Ⓐ–Ⓩ

**5. ROLL NO.**

| | | | | |
|---|---|---|---|---|
| ⓪–⑨ | ⓪–⑨ | ⓪–⑨ | ⓪–⑨ | ⓪–⑨ |

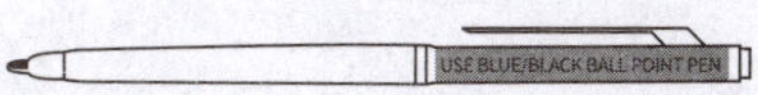


### MARK YOUR ANSWERS

| | | | | | | | | | |
|---|---|---|---|---|---|---|---|---|---|
| **1.** | Ⓐ | Ⓑ | Ⓒ | Ⓓ | **26.** | Ⓐ | Ⓑ | Ⓒ | Ⓓ |
| **2.** | Ⓐ | Ⓑ | Ⓒ | Ⓓ | **27.** | Ⓐ | Ⓑ | Ⓒ | Ⓓ |
| **3.** | Ⓐ | Ⓑ | Ⓒ | Ⓓ | **28.** | Ⓐ | Ⓑ | Ⓒ | Ⓓ |
| **4.** | Ⓐ | Ⓑ | Ⓒ | Ⓓ | **29.** | Ⓐ | Ⓑ | Ⓒ | Ⓓ |
| **5.** | Ⓐ | Ⓑ | Ⓒ | Ⓓ | **30.** | Ⓐ | Ⓑ | Ⓒ | Ⓓ |
| **6.** | Ⓐ | Ⓑ | Ⓒ | Ⓓ | **31.** | Ⓐ | Ⓑ | Ⓒ | Ⓓ |
| **7.** | Ⓐ | Ⓑ | Ⓒ | Ⓓ | **32.** | Ⓐ | Ⓑ | Ⓒ | Ⓓ |
| **8.** | Ⓐ | Ⓑ | Ⓒ | Ⓓ | **33.** | Ⓐ | Ⓑ | Ⓒ | Ⓓ |
| **9.** | Ⓐ | Ⓑ | Ⓒ | Ⓓ | **34.** | Ⓐ | Ⓑ | Ⓒ | Ⓓ |
| **10.** | Ⓐ | Ⓑ | Ⓒ | Ⓓ | **35.** | Ⓐ | Ⓑ | Ⓒ | Ⓓ |
| **11.** | Ⓐ | Ⓑ | Ⓒ | Ⓓ | **36.** | Ⓐ | Ⓑ | Ⓒ | Ⓓ |
| **12.** | Ⓐ | Ⓑ | Ⓒ | Ⓓ | **37.** | Ⓐ | Ⓑ | Ⓒ | Ⓓ |
| **13.** | Ⓐ | Ⓑ | Ⓒ | Ⓓ | **38.** | Ⓐ | Ⓑ | Ⓒ | Ⓓ |
| **14.** | Ⓐ | Ⓑ | Ⓒ | Ⓓ | **39.** | Ⓐ | Ⓑ | Ⓒ | Ⓓ |
| **15.** | Ⓐ | Ⓑ | Ⓒ | Ⓓ | **40.** | Ⓐ | Ⓑ | Ⓒ | Ⓓ |
| **16.** | Ⓐ | Ⓑ | Ⓒ | Ⓓ | **41.** | Ⓐ | Ⓑ | Ⓒ | Ⓓ |
| **17.** | Ⓐ | Ⓑ | Ⓒ | Ⓓ | **42.** | Ⓐ | Ⓑ | Ⓒ | Ⓓ |
| **18.** | Ⓐ | Ⓑ | Ⓒ | Ⓓ | **43.** | Ⓐ | Ⓑ | Ⓒ | Ⓓ |
| **19.** | Ⓐ | Ⓑ | Ⓒ | Ⓓ | **44.** | Ⓐ | Ⓑ | Ⓒ | Ⓓ |
| **20.** | Ⓐ | Ⓑ | Ⓒ | Ⓓ | **45.** | Ⓐ | Ⓑ | Ⓒ | Ⓓ |
| **21.** | Ⓐ | Ⓑ | Ⓒ | Ⓓ | **46.** | Ⓐ | Ⓑ | Ⓒ | Ⓓ |
| **22.** | Ⓐ | Ⓑ | Ⓒ | Ⓓ | **47.** | Ⓐ | Ⓑ | Ⓒ | Ⓓ |
| **23.** | Ⓐ | Ⓑ | Ⓒ | Ⓓ | **48.** | Ⓐ | Ⓑ | Ⓒ | Ⓓ |
| **24.** | Ⓐ | Ⓑ | Ⓒ | Ⓓ | **49.** | Ⓐ | Ⓑ | Ⓒ | Ⓓ |
| **25.** | Ⓐ | Ⓑ | Ⓒ | Ⓓ | **50.** | Ⓐ | Ⓑ | Ⓒ | Ⓓ |

## Space for Rough Work

## Space for Rough Work